THE
MARYKNOLL
GOLDEN
BOOK

Book Treasures, New York

THE
MARYKNOLL
GOLDEN
BOOK

an anthology
of mission literature

EDITED AND SELECTED BY

ALBERT J. NEVINS, M.M.

*Maryknoll's official symbol is the Chi Rho
(pronounced key row). It is composed
of a circle that represents the world
and the first two letters
of Christ's name in Greek. It signifies
"Christ over the world."*

TO THE MISSIONERS
OF ALL CENTURIES AND LANDS
WHO HAVE LABORED SO VALIANTLY
TO ESTABLISH THE KINGDOM OF GOD
ON OUR SUFFERING EARTH.

FOREWORD

The celebrated essayist, Thomas Carlyle, once remarked that the true university is a collection of books. Certainly, all the knowledge of the world, all the hope, all the excitement, can be found between the covers of literature's productive sowing. In our modern world where book collecting is not the art it once was, the anthology takes on greater importance. At regular intervals, someone or other comes along and gleans a field, gathering the best of fruits and flowers, presenting them in the form of an anthology. There are anthologies of science and sport and fiction and poetry and what-have-you, but as far as we can determine there has never been an anthology in English of mission literature.

The MARYKNOLL GOLDEN BOOK is an attempt to bring together in an anthology portions of some of the finer English literature on missions and mission peoples. The sources are almost as inexhaustible as the oceans, and far more uncharted. What most impressed the editor of this particular anthology was not alone the high quality and interest value of this book as finally determined but the vast amount of excellent material that had to be left out because of lack of room.

This is quite understandable. The Catholic missioner has been on the march since the first dawn of the Christian era, and Catholic mission literature is as old as the New Testament itself. In the preparation of this volume only material from the modern mission era was included, and all of this with but few exceptions was originally published in English. Because this anthology was prepared at Maryknoll, there is a generous serving of Maryknoll writings, but even here space restrictions imposed severe limitations.

The MARYKNOLL GOLDEN BOOK has been designed for general readership, and therefore the speculative and theoretical has been kept to a minimum. In this volume you will find stories and articles that touch the heart, that provide inspiration, that entertain; there are moments of drama and moments of humor. The authors are not all clergymen or missioners. You will find pieces by such well known names as Robert Louis Stevenson, W. Somerset Maugham, A. J. Cronin, James A. Michener and Alan Paton.

It is our hope that this is a book you will turn to often, that you will keep out where others can read it. It is our desire too that the material contained in this book will increase your love for the missions and mission peoples, that it will give you a little more understanding of our complex world, that it will inspire you to a greater appreciation of the principles for which Christ lived and died. If it does these things the hours of searching and selecting will be more than worth while.

The editor is deeply grateful to all the authors and publishers who cooperated to make this book possible, a number of whom broke long standing rules to allow us to include their writings. We were advised, for example, that Graham Greene never permitted selections to be taken from any of his longer works. Yet with Mr. Greene's permission you will find in this volume an excerpt from what this editor believes to be his finest novel. To all of these cooperators we wish God's choicest blessings.

And to our readers we extend the wish for profitable reading, coupled with the confidence that the selections in this volume will prove tasty samplings of the greater works from which they were taken. May these samplings induce many readers to go back to the sources and enjoy the entire original works. It is our final hope that within the covers of this book you will find something that will help you to know, love and serve God better, not only for your own salvation, but also for that of all the peoples of the world.

Albert J. Nevins, M.M.
Editor

CONTENTS

Poetry

Short Features

SELECTIONS BY AUTHOR:

THE
MARYKNOLL
GOLDEN
BOOK

GOOD-BY, MY WONDER HORSE

by J. Edmund McClear

> One of the most popular stories ever printed in *Mary-knoll—The Field Afar* was this account by a missioner in Guatemala of a mountain tragedy which cost him a trusted friend.

There will never be another Rosillo. Maybe it's a sign of weakness to cry over a dead animal, but the tears fell for he was a great horse, and he died because he trusted me.

This unique and rather foolish habit of mine of traveling alone over Guatemalan mountain trails nearly caught up with me the other day. If I had but wrapped the rope around my hand or if my foot had caught in it I should not be writing this account now; instead, I should be lying peacefully in the bottom of a ravine with my smashed-up horse.

I was returning from the city, anxious to get back to Soloma. On the mountaintop where I had left him, I found my old horse, Rosillo, waiting for me. I had a surprise for him and showed him his new saddle and bright, red-and-yellow saddle blanket. He was proud as a king for he liked flashy colors. He stood patiently while I adjusted the saddle. As I looked at him in the bright sunlight, I thrilled to think that he was mine. Instead of coming home by the old trail (how I wish I had!) I decided to have a look at the new road.

The Indians have been working on a new highway for twenty years. At the present time, they are encountering very rocky and very dangerous territory, with sheer drops of a thousand feet. Two Indians have been killed in plunges over the mountainside.

Down the new road Rosillo and I went galloping, with full power on every level spot. We passed the little crosses marking the spots where the Indians fell over; we sped by the big rock that juts up a hundred feet into the air. And then we came to the end of the finished section. I noticed a footpath leading off and concluded that it must connect with the other finished section, which descends to the little pueblo of San Juan Ixcoy.

I dismounted and began to lead Rosillo along this path. There were places he didn't want to go, and a big fallen tree he didn't want to jump, but always a gentle pull on the rope induced him to follow me. Soon the path became worse, narrower and steeper. I didn't wish to retrace my steps but decided it was the only thing to do.

And then it happened. It happened fast, but every instant is vividly mine. I can't forget a single detail. I was perhaps ten feet above Rosillo, with twenty steep and treacherous feet more to go to reach a ledge. The horse paused, sensing danger. Then the fact dawned on me: we couldn't turn back, because the trail was too narrow—and probably we couldn't get to the ledge.

Before I could decide what to attempt, Rosillo made a wild scramble up the bank, trying to reach me. He made it, but slipped in doing so and fell in the trail at my feet. I could see that he was scared, so I bent down and patted his nose and talked gently to him. There was terror in his eyes; he was slipping back; I was losing my beautiful Rosillo. I dug a place for my heels, and pulled on the rope with every ounce of strength I could muster. Rosillo made one mighty effort—rose nearly to his feet—and then plunged over backwards. I hung on to the rope; I never felt it tear the skin from my hands. I heard my horse crash in the underbrush; I saw him a hundred feet or so below, clear in the air; and I saw him hit rocks for the final time.

Half crying all the way, I scrambled down the mountainside. When I got to Rosillo he was still breathing. I removed the bit from his mouth, and took off the new saddle. I reached to pat him, but it was too late. He looked grand to me even as he lay dead. Carrying the saddle and blanket, I began to make my lonesome way up the mountain. I paused and looked back. Once I had thought only little boys cried at times like that, but I guess we're all little boys at heart.

ANTU CHRISTMAS

by James Keller and Meyer Berger

The perils and rigors of mission travel do not belong only to the days of Abbé Huc and other pioneers. Father James Keller, founder of The Christophers, and Meyer Berger, feature writer for the New York *Times*, recount an inspiring journey.

The wilderness trail to Antu is dangerous. It stretches through tremendous forests where wolves, bears, wild boars and wildcats have their lairs. It ranges up and down fabulous *Lao Pai San* or Old White Mountain. It winds around the *T'ien Che*, a great crater lake of which the Manchus speak, in awe, as Heaven's Pond. This lake is supposed to be the dwelling place of the grandfather of all dragons. The fish in its icy blue waters, a strange variety with spikelike scales, are, according to local superstition, poisonous to humans. The Manchus seldom go near it, even though the region yields valuable falcon feathers and ginseng, both highly prized as native medicines.

Father Joseph Sweeney and Father Francis Bridge were not bothered by local superstitions, but they knew the trail might

* From *Men of Maryknoll*. Copyright, Charles Scribner's Sons.

well be a Winter death trap. Just one year before, in December, 1929, Father Sweeney had covered only 200 miles of the journey from Fushun to Lin Kiang, a somewhat less formidable trail, when Doctor Hoh, his native assistant, had died in the bitter cold. Father Sweeney bore Dr. Hoh on their sled to the next inn, had a coffin made, and took him back, alone. There had been no heroics about it. Father Sweeney's report to the home Knoll barely mentioned it in passing.

Antu lies just under the Siberian border, some 450 miles up-country from the mission center at Fushun. Father Sweeney had heard vague native rumors of a handful of Christians at Antu who had long before lost contact with the world outside. His idea was to bring Christmas to them. He estimated that a six weeks' start might give him some margin. He prepared for the trip as Commander Peary prepared for the polar dash, and looked pretty much as Peary did on the trail. He chose as companion Dr. Wong, who had replaced Dr. Hoh.

Father Sweeney had not counted on Father Bridge making the journey. Bridge had spent his childhood in the coal mines in Pennsylvania's Westmoreland Fields. He had been an A.E.F. sergeant in the first world war. Now fighting inevitable death from a painful disease, he stubbornly kept on at Fushun Mission. "I don't want to go home," he'd say. "I'd rather work and die in Manchuria." His superiors, who knew the spirit, allowed him to remain.

Just before Father Sweeney and Dr. Wong left their mission for Antu, Father Bridge showed up. He was muffled, as they were, in coat, trousers and cap of wolf-skin. Under this layer of fur he had sheep-wool secondary garments. Only his eyes and the top of his nose were visible in the frosty air. His feet were enormous in over-size boots and several strata of wool stockings. He was jubilant at the prospect of adventure. He had sent Barney Google, as he called his house-boy, back to the mission with Spark and Plug, his ponies, "I'm with you for Antu and a Merry Christmas and a Happy New Year," he exulted. There was nothing Father Sweeney could do about it.

To awed natives Father Sweeney and Father Bridge looked—

as indeed physically they were—like supermen. Father Sweeney was six feet, three inches high, Father Bridge six feet, two. In their furs they had monstrous proportions. Their mission kits were stowed on a native *kali*, a rather large wooden sled with box-like chassis. They got the *kali* aboard the train at Fushun and made the first leg of their journey by rail to Tun-hua, the end of the line. This took them through dark, interminable Kirin Forest, haunt of Manchurian Robin Hoods and all manner of other predatory wild life.

At Tun-hua, they heard a German Benedictine monk maintained a mission on the forest's rim, some distance from the station. They started for it at noon. Screaming gales searched out open places in the parkas and blinded them with powdery snow. At intervals they stumbled, chest high, through enormous drifts that all but buried Dr. Wong. The glare off the snow, while the sun was high, created little islands of dark in their vision. When this became unbearable they held one hand on the sled ropes and covered their eyes with the fur mitts. There were, of necessity, frequent rests. Father Bridge's breath came hard. He'd turn his head away, so the others might not see him fight for air.

At ten o'clock that night, all limbs acreak, Father Bridge made out a cross against the brilliant low-hung stars. The party floundered toward it. It was dark. Wind tried to tear the low mud shack free from the drifts. Half-frozen, Father Bridge pounded stiffly at the gate. He and Father Sweeney called hoarsely to the inmates. For ten minutes there was no answer. The wind snatched the cries from their numbed lips and tore them into insignificant syllables. The gate-thumping was barely audible above the gale.

Finally, though, the mission door opened. A startled Manchu boy gaped sleepily from behind a guttering lantern at the towering, snow-covered visitors. He slammed the door shut hastily and bolted it from inside. Father Bridge broke into sudden laughter and for a moment Father Sweeney thought hysteria crouched behind the outburst. "No use," Father Bridge bellowed, "to every wise house-boy we can only be highwaymen. I'll try to reach the padre with Latin." He edged closer to the mission door. He roared in Latin, "Please open that gate before Christmas. We're American missioners from Fushun."

The door opened again. Behind the lantern, this time, stood the Benedictine monk, a little man with a great beard. The light shone on his pink, bald head. Blue eyes, somewhat myopic, stared at the Maryknoll men from behind thick lenses. The little man had a big voice. He threw the door wide and the travellers pushed through, shaking the snow from their parkas and shoulders. The room was pleasantly warm. The *k'ang*—the native stove bed—was heated and the visitors, rid of outer garments, stretched on it to bake the stiffness from their bones.

In the lantern's light, the priests saw a low native table cluttered with books and papers. Father Liborius Morgenschweis, the Benedictine, apologized for the scholarly disorder. "I am writing a Chinese-Korean dictionary for the missions," he explained in Latin. He seemed fascinated by the idea of a journey to carry Christmas to Antu, but, like the native trail policemen, he doubted if the party would get through. He stirred the frightened house-boy into making hot tea. The priests talked long past midnight, curled up on the re-stoked *k'angs* and plunged into subregions of slumber.

While the expedition rested two days with Father Morgenschweis, Father Bridge bought Mongolian ponies to pull the *kalis*. Antu, at this stage, lay more than 100 miles to the southeast, Fushun 550 miles southwest. Lin Kiang, nearest Maryknoll post, was at the Korean-Manchurian border, 300 miles south. The little Benedictine went a little way with the expedition, trying to the last moment to persuade the American padres to celebrate Christmas with him and his handful of parishioners. They thanked him, but pushed on. The goal was Christmas in Antu.

They walked, because even with fur covers in the *kali* box, limbs soon numbed in the intense cold. And they walked briskly. To stop was to invite frostbite and complete numbness. Twenty-five miles took them out of open country again and into tremendous forest. They moved like pygmies through the snow under trees that soared, in some cases, more than a hundred feet. Father

Bridge seemed in excellent health after the rest. Sight of the great trees reminded him of schooldays back in the coal country and he recited, so the forest echoed and re-echoed the words: "This is the forest primeval . . ."

Beyond the Kirin boundary line, the expedition to Antu struck eastward. As the sun went down the second night out, they saw a tiny cluster of mud dwellings through the twilight. Snarling dogs, much like wolves, barked at their approach and little fur-bundled men came outdoors to stare at them. Their size excited lively communal debate. The little men and the village children circled Father Sweeney and Father Bridge to observe their height from different angles. This was like the Barnum and Bailey come to town. They had never seen white men before. They were especially fascinated by the missioners' noses. Their own were mere buttons. The priests' noses, normal enough where white men dwell, were monstrosities to them.

That night the Antu Christmas expeditionary force slept at the primitive inn in the wilderness. The one room that was the entire establishment had rush lighting. It was heavy and thick with smoke that seeped through cracks in the *k'angs* that stretched along either wall. The natives were conditioned to the smoke and their eyes remained wide in undiminished wonder at the size of these strangers. Each newcomer, brought by eager messengers from outside, boldly approached the missioners to study their incredible proportions at close range. A few ventured to feel the noses. Father Bridge and Father Sweeney didn't mind, particularly. This experience was not altogether new.

Father Bridge took sick through the night. Father Sweeney, staring up through the smoke-filled dark, heard him stifle sounds of pain. He nudged the soldier priest. He whispered, "Frank, we'll start back tomorrow. We'll pass Christmas in that German mission." Father Bridge lay quiet. Finally he said, "I don't want to seem tough about it, Joe, but tomorrow we'll do no such thing." He fished for his medical kit in the dark and fumbled for a little bottle of pain-killing pellets. He swallowed them. "Be okay in the morning, Joe," he assured Father Sweeney. "Goodnight."

Oddly enough he did seem improved when the inn stirred to life in half-dark before the wintry sunrise. He said, "I feel like the whole Notre Dame backfield. Don't get in my way, or try to stop me. It's on to Antu."

They were five days on the trail from the Benedictine's mission to Antu. On the third, they came out of the woods again into great areas cleared, quite obviously, both by the woodsman's axe and by great forest fires that had brought thousands of the towering pines and elms to charred stumps and ashes. Eventually they crossed a vast, snowy plain where the only trees that seemed to flourish were occasional clumps of deciduous pines. They encountered a few wayfarers but these, after their initial fright and astonishment, knew of no Catholics in, or near Antu. Worse than that, they had never heard of Christians, let alone Catholics. The expedition pushed on, nevertheless.

Early in the afternoon of the fourth day, the party topped a ridge and from this crest stared in breathless wonder at *Lao Pai San*, the Old White Mountain of Manchu legends. It had been a hard day. For the second time since they had put out of Tun-hua, their *kali* had torn from its ropes and had dropped in splinters, into a yawning, snow-filled gorge so deep that its bottom was merely a black pit. This time, as on the first, their precious mission kits and their medicines had, fortunately, spilled in the snow on the trail and the Mongolian ponies had managed to save themselves from the death plunge.

Yet the expedition had been lucky. In spite of predictions they had somehow kept clear of the robber bands in Chapei Forest though the woods swarmed with them. These latter-day blood-brothers of Robin of Nottinghamshire, are mostly descendants— or so the local stories go—of the great Nurhachu, founder of the Manchu Dynasty, who assembled the primitive hunters and woodsmen of upper Manchuria for the incredible trek that ended in Peking, with Nurhachu's kin on the Emperor's throne in the Middle Kingdom.

Anyway, a Divine hand seemed to be gently steering the Antu expedition clear of major harm and mischief. Dr. Wong, riding somewhat ahead of the *kali* the night before they approached

Antu, suddenly came tearing back through the deep snow with his pony in a lather. He seemed agitated. "We must turn off from this next settlement," he babbled to the two priests. "The inn there is infested with highwaymen." Wong had stumbled into the inn, it turned out, but the armed band hadn't noticed. Guards and all were whirling giddily in top heaven, sodden with opium. The priests were fatigued but they worked their way wearily around the settlement. They slept that night off the trail.

The sun was gone and the air crackled and snapped with cold well under 50 degrees below zero when Antu showed up in their sight the next night. It was December 23, 1930. Again they had floundered and gasped their way all day through man-high drifts and wind-blasted snow had picked their faces raw. They were on the verge of utter snow-blindness. They crossed the upper Sungari River on solid ice and drove under Antu's West Gate. Antu is a walled town and lookouts are perched along the walls to sight possible enemies—local hoop-de-doos break out in this region occasionally when the lads get bored—but it seems there were no guards this night.

The West Gate was locked, but scouting around the outer wall the expedition found a crude inn still open. Their stomping entry, as they shook the snow from their furs, stopped local inn gossips mid-phrase, so to speak. Here, as in earlier stops among primitives, the Americans' extraordinary height left the home-town talent agape. "It must have been the same when the Indians first saw Christopher Columbus," Father Sweeney's apt to say when he recounts it. When the inn's customers had had an eyeful, they rushed into the open to spread the word about the gigantic freaks who had materialized out of the night. The inn owner suddenly found his place packed to the doors.

Those who couldn't squeeze into the inn did the next best thing. They punched through the inn's parchment windows and stared over the heads of their fellow-townsmen for a peek, shrilly calling the Antu term for "Holy Smoke!" From within the wall came a fussy little man, sharp-eyed and keen, and a bit on the pompous side. He was some kind of official. He shouldered his way through the excitedly chattering common people and stared at the priests a long time. At last he thought he had it figured out. "Russians," he told the neighbors confidently. "Long noses from Siberia. I have seen others like these."

Father Bridge politely corrected him. "Americans," he told the fussy little man in Mandarin. "We come from the Beautiful Land." The United States, it seems, is always the "Beautiful Land" to people on the steppes. Fact is, the appellation originated in the East through the accident that the Chinese character officially chosen to approximate the sound of its first syllable happens to mean "beautiful."

The fussy gentleman made a kind of stump speech about the Beautiful Land. "Americans," he said, in effect, "they are a great people. No flies on Americans." This is not a true translation, Father Sweeney would hasten to explain, but it carries the germ of the speech. It was much longer and pretty flowery, and that's typical of Oriental speeches. You talk your way around a block to cross a conversational crack one foot away.

Next morning, after a night on the inn's k'ang, the expedition entered the West Gate. The fussy little man, his confidence bolstered by further information from the Americans, proudly led them along narrow gutters through swarms of fellow-citizens and shrieking children. These, he declaimed, were Catholic priests, representatives of the Catholic Church. This didn't seem to mean much, so he tried to get the idea over in a simpler way. He said, "These foreigners walk the good road. Their church is the good road gate." The populace nodded, as if all got it, and crowded closer.

Father Sweeney and Father Bridge were bearded when they reached the inn, but they had washed and shaved when they got off the k'angs in the morning. They had been careful to scour the wooden wash basin with ashes and to use carbolic soap for lathers. The basin was community property. Now, hemmed in by the hordes, the priests were clear-cheeked and ruddy. Antu, they noted, was a square city within square walls. It was protected by a medieval moat and its two main streets crossed in the town's center, each street end stopping dead at a gate.

The missioners recognized in drawn features and heavy-lidded eyes, all about them, the marks of opium smokers. They learned later that poppies are extensively cultivated outside Antu in the brief Summer, and that the seeds are made into the sticky gum that is Asia's curse. The local chief of police was eager to help. He begged the visitors to have dinner in his humble home—a mud-walled, grass thatched little place like most of the others in Antu—but they had to beg off. They explained they had come over difficult roads to celebrate an important holy day. He tried to be helpful anyway, but like the rest of the townsfolk, knew of none of the Catholic immigrants from Shantung in Antu.

Father Sweeney looked at Father Bridge and Father Bridge looked back at Father Sweeney. It was heart-breaking, after the journey to bring Christmas to Antu, to find that the reports of forgotten Antu Christians were apparently myths, after all. Anyway, they decided to celebrate the Mass on their own. The inn wasn't a likely place for it. No privacy. Besides, it was not decent atmosphere for the Holy Sacrifice. At last they found an old couple in a one-room mud hut near the inn who seemed willing to rent their place for the service. This couple, pagans, moved into the noisy inn.

The rented room was about ten feet wide, fifteen feet long. The thatch ceiling was low. In one corner stood a mud stove that was weak on heat but generous with smoke. In a farther corner were two forty-gallon jugs of pickled Chinese cabbage, somewhat on the high side, and along one wall the traditional *k'ang*. An old hen had the run of the place and kept getting underfoot, grumpily uttering a sort of running commentary on the poor pickings. There was an aged, long-haired tom-cat, too, which slept most of the time on the *k'ang*. Oddly enough, it made no passes at the grumpy hen, which astonished the Americans.

Father Bridge set the rickety table in place as an altar. Father Sweeney helped him. Still weary from their travels and not a little sore at heart over their failure to find the forgotten Christians to whom they had meant to bring Christmas, they finally dropped onto the *k'ang*. Joe Sweeney was a long way from Clark Street in New Britain, Conn.; Frank Bridge was a far cry from the little mine shack in the Westmoreland Fields, and the surroundings weren't the least bit like home on Christmas Eve, but they fell into deep sleep, just the same, with the decrepit tom-cat purring a lullaby.

Father Bridge was first up, Christmas morning. He awakened Father Sweeney with a deep-throated version of "Adeste Fideles." He sang "The Star Spangled Banner," and Father Sweeney stood up and sleepily came to salute. When the anthem ended, Father Sweeney said, "The same to you, Sir, and many of them." The tom-cat yawned. The gossipy old hen fluffed her feathers and started moving around, still complaining.

Father Sweeney served the first Mass ever celebrated in far-off Antu. Before he had quite finished, Dr. Wong pushed open the creaky cottage door. Four Catholics who had lived a full decade in Antu—they were some of the sought-for immigrants from south of the Great Wall—stood behind him. Tears ran down their withered cheeks at sight of the little altar and the vested giant priests towering in the candlelight. During the second Mass another Chinese Christian slipped into the room. He had heard of the missioners from the Beautiful Land as he passed by the inn. The room glowed in the candles' weak beams. Father Bridge cupped his hands around the chalice to prevent the Sacred Species from freezing. When the Mass was ended he sang again, in sheer exultation, and his voice was vibrant and rich:

"O, Little Child of Bethlehem . . ."

The simple hymn faded, and died in Antu's frozen air. Antu's little knot of Christians came to press the Shen Fu's hands in gratitude. One old woman murmured, "Father, come back to us again. Do not discard our souls."

Frank Bridge died in St. Mary's Hospital in San Francisco, three years later, in April, when Spring was at the windows. He was then thirty-eight. He had worked in the mines as a boy, in the Pittsburgh steel mills and with the A.E.F. in his youth, and had been ten years in the missions. He never forgot the first Christmas in frozen Antu. In brief respite from pain in the hospital he liked to tell about that day. He'd say: "I always thought the little room in Antu that morning was like the stable

in Bethlehem, and that the worshippers were like the shepherds.
I never knew a happier Christmas."

THE CHINA INCIDENT

by A. J. Cronin

> When we asked this distinguished author of innumer-
> able best sellers for permission to include this revealing
> selection from *The Keys of the Kingdom,* his gracious
> consent came from Switzerland with the "hope that this'
> contribution may help in furthering your magnificent
> work."

It was Joseph, the prize gossip, who first told Father Chisholm
that Mr. Chia's son was sick. The cold season was late in breaking, the Kwang Mountains were still deep in snow; and the
cheerful Joseph blew upon his nipped fingers as he chattered
away after mass, assisting the priest to put away his vestments.
"Tch! My hand is as useless as that of the little Chia-Yu."

Chia-Yu had scratched his thumb upon no one knew what;
but in consequence, his five elements had been disturbed and the
lower humours had gained ascendency, flowing entirely into one
arm, distending it, leaving the boy's body burning and wasted.
The three highest physicians of the city were in attendance and
the most costly remedies had been applied. Now a messenger
had been despatched to Sen-siang for the *elixir vitae*: a priceless

* From *The Keys of the Kingdom.* Little, Brown and Co. Copyright, A. J.
Cronin.

extract of frog's eyes, obtained only in the circle of the Dragon's moon.

"He will recover," Joseph concluded, showing his white teeth in a sanguine smile. "This *hao kao* never fails . . . which is important for Mr. Chia, since Yu is his only son."

Four days later, at the same hour, two closed chairs, one of which was empty, drew up outside the chapel shop in the Street of the Netmakers, and a moment later the tall figure of Mr. Pao's cousin, wrapped in a cotton-padded tunic, gravely confronted Father Chisholm. He apologized for his unseemly intrusion. He asked the priest to accompany him to Mr. Chia's house.

Stunned by the implication of the invitation, Francis hesitated. Close relationship, through business and marriage ties, existed between the Paos and Chias, both were highly influential families. Since his return from the Liu village he had not infrequently encountered the lean, aloof, and pleasantly cynical cousin of Mr. Pao, who was, indeed, also first cousin to Mr. Chia. He had some evidence of the tall mandarin's regard. But this abrupt call, this sponsorship, was different. As he turned silently to get his hat and coat, he felt a sudden hollow fear.

The Chia house was very quiet, the trellised verandahs empty, the fish pond brittle with a film of ice. Their steps rang softly, but with a momentous air, upon the paved, deserted courtyards. Two flanking jasmine trees, swathed in sacking, lolled like sleeping giants, against the tented, red-gold gateway. From the women's quarters across the terraces came the strangled sound of weeping.

It was darkish in the sick-chamber, where Chia-Yu lay upon a heated *kang*, watched by the three bearded physicians in long full robes seated upon fresh rush matting. From time to time one of the physicians bent forward and placed a charcoal lump beneath the boxlike *kang*. In the corner of the room, a Taoist priest in a slate-coloured robe was mumbling, exorcising, to the accompaniment of flutes behind the bamboo partition.

Yu had been a pretty child of six, with soft cream colouring and sloe-black eyes, reared in the strictest traditions of parental respect, idolized, yet unspoiled. Now, consumed by remorseless fever and the terrible novelty of pain, he was stretched upon his back, his bones sticking through his skin, his dry lips twisting, his gaze upon the ceiling, motionless. His right arm, livid, swollen out of recognition, was encased in a horrible plaster of dirt mixed with little printed paper scraps.

When Mr. Pao's cousin entered with Father Chisholm there was a tiny stillness; then the Taoist mumbling was resumed, while the three physicians, more strictly immobilized, maintained their vigil by the *kang*.

Bent over the unconscious child, his hand upon the burning brow, Father Chisholm knew the full import of that limpid and passionless restraint. His present troubles would be as nothing to the persecution which must follow a futile intervention. But the desperate sickness of the boy and this noxious pretence of treatment whipped his blood. He began, quickly yet gently, to remove from the infected arm the *hao kao*, that filthy dressing he had so often met with in his little dispensary.

At last the arm was free, washed in warm water. It floated almost, a bladder of corruption, with a shiny greenish skin. Though now his heart was thudding in his side Francis went on steadfastly, drew from his pocket the little leather case which Tulloch had given him, took from that case the single lancet. He knew his inexperience. He knew also that if he did not incise the arm the child, already moribund, would die. He felt every unwatching eye upon him, sensed the terrible anxiety, the growing doubt gripping Mr. Pao's cousin as he stood motionless behind him. He made an ejaculation to Saint Andrew. He steeled himself to cut, to cut deep, deep and long.

A great gush of putrid matter came heaving through the wound, flowing and bubbling into the earthenware bowl beneath. The stench was dreadful, evil. In all his life Francis had never savoured anything so gratefully. As he pressed, with both his hands, on either side of the wound, encouraging the exudation, seeing the limb collapse to half its size, a great relief surged through him, leaving him weak.

When, at last, he straightened up, having packed the wound with clean wet linen, he heard himself murmur, foolishly, in

English: "I think he'll do now, with a little luck!" It was old Dr. Tulloch's famous phrase: it demonstrated the tension of his nerves. Yet on his way out he strove to maintain an attitude of cheerful unconcern, declaring to the completely silent cousin of Mr. Pao, who accompanied him to his chair: "Give him nourishing soup if he wakes up. And no more *hao kao*. I will come tomorrow."

On the next day little Yu was greatly better. His fever was almost gone, he had slept naturally and drunk several cups of chicken broth. Without the miracle of the shining lancet he would almost certainly have been dead.

"Continue to nourish him," Father Chisholm genuinely smiled as he took his departure. "I shall call again tomorrow!"

"Thank you." Mr. Pao's cousin cleared his throat. "It is not necessary." There was an awkward pause. "We are deeply grateful. Mr. Chia has been prostrate with grief. Now that his son is recovering he also is recovering. Soon he may be able to present himself in public!" The mandarin bowed, hands discreetly in his sleeves, and was gone.

Father Chisholm strode down the street—he had angrily refused the chair—fighting a dark and bitter indignation. This was gratitude. To be thrown out, without a word, when he had saved the child's life, at the risk, perhaps, of his own . . . From first to last he had not even seen the wretched Mr. Chia, who, even on the junk, that day of his arrival, had not deigned to glance at him. He clenched his fists, fighting his familiar demon: "O God, let me be calm! Don't let this cursed sin of anger master me again. Let me be meek and patient of heart. Give me humility, dear Lord. After all it was Thy merciful goodness, Thy divine providence, which saved the little boy. Do with me what Thou wilt, dear Lord. You see, I am resigned. But, O God!"—with sudden heat: "You must admit it was such damned ingratitude after all!"

During the next few days Francis rigorously shunned the merchant's quarter of the city. More than his pride had been hurt. He listened in silence while Joseph gossiped of the remarkable progress of little Yu, of the largesse distributed by Mr. Chia to the wise physicians, the donation to the Temple of Lao-tzu, for the exorcising of the demon which had troubled his beloved son. "Is it not truly remarkable, dear Father, how many sources have benefited by the mandarin's noble generosity?"

"Truly remarkable," said Father Chisholm dryly, but wincing.

A week later, when about to close his dispensary after a stale and profitless afternoon, he suddenly observed, across the flask of permanganate he had been mixing, the discreet apparition of Mr. Chia.

He started hotly, but said nothing. The merchant wore his finest clothes: a rich black satin robe with yellow jacket, embroidered velvet boots in one of which was thrust the ceremonial fan, a fine flat satin cap, and an expression both formal and dignified. His too-long fingernails were protected by gold metal cases. He had an air of culture and intelligence, his manners expressed perfect breeding. There was a gentle, enlightened melancholy on his brow.

"I have come," he said.

"Indeed!" Francis' tone was not encouraging. He went on stirring with his glass rod, mixing the mauve solution.

"There have been many matters to attend to, much business to settle. But now,"—a resigned bow,—"I am here."

"Why?" Shortly, from Francis.

Mr. Chia's face indicated mild surprise. "Naturally . . . to become a Christian."

There was a moment of dead silence—a moment which, traditionally, should have marked the climax of these meagre toiling months, the thrilling first fruits of the missionary's achievement: here, the leading savage, bowing the head for baptism. But there was little exultation in Father Chisholm's face. He chewed his lip crossly, then he said slowly: "Do you believe?"

"No!" Sadly.

"Are you prepared to be instructed?"

"I have not time to be instructed." A subdued bow. "I am only eager to become a Christian."

"Eager? You mean you want to?"

Mr. Chia smiled wanly. "It is not apparent—my wish to profess your faith?"

"No, it is not apparent. And you have not the slightest wish to profess my faith. Why are you doing this?" The priest's colour was high.

"To repay you," Mr. Chia said simply. "You have done the greatest good to me. I must do the greatest good for you."

Father Chisholm moved irritably. Because the temptation was so alluring, because he wished to yield and could not, his temper flared. "It is not good. It is bad. You have neither inclination nor belief. My acceptance of you would be a forgery for God. You owe me nothing. Now please go!"

At first Mr. Chia did not believe his ears.

"You mean you reject me?"

"That is putting it politely," growled Father Chisholm.

The change in the merchant was seraphic. His eyes brightened, glistened, his melancholy dropped from him like a shroud. He had to struggle to contain himself; but although he had the semblance of desiring to leap into the air he did contain himself. Formally, he made the kowtow three times. He succeeded in mastering his voice.

"I regret that I am not acceptable. I am of course most unworthy. Nevertheless, perhaps in some slight manner . . ." He broke off, again he made the kowtow three times and, moving backwards, went out.

That evening, as Father Chisholm sat by the brazier with a sternness of countenance which caused Joseph, who was cooking tasty river mussels in his rice, to gaze at him timidly, there came the sudden sound of firecrackers. Six of Mr. Chia's servants were exploding them, ceremoniously, in the road outside. Then Mr. Pao's cousin advanced, bowed, handed Father Chisholm a parchment wrapped in vermilion paper.

"Mr. Chia begs that you will honour him by accepting this most unworthy gift—the deeds of the Brilliant Green Jade property with all land and water rights and the rights to the crimson claypit. The property is yours, without restraint, forever. Mr. Chia further begs that you accept the help of twenty of his workmen till any building you may wish to carry out is fully accomplished."

So completely taken aback was Francis he could not speak a word. He watched the retreating figure of the cousin of Mr. Pao, and of Mr. Chia, with a strange still tensity. Then he wildly scanned the title deeds and cried out joyfully, "Joseph! Joseph!"

Joseph came hurrying, fearing another misfortune had befallen them. His master's expression reassured him. They went together to the Hill of Brilliant Green Jade and there, standing under the moon amidst the tall cedars, they sang aloud the Magnificat.

Francis remained bare-headed, seeing in a vision what he would create on this noble brow of land. He had prayed with faith, and his prayer had been answered.

Joseph, made hungry by the keen wind, waited uncomplainingly, finding his own vision in the priest's rapt face, glad he had shown the presence of mind to take his rice-pot from the fire.

THE LITTLE CART

Ch'en Tzu-lung was a Chinese patriot and poet of the seventeenth century. He died, as millions of his countrymen have died, fleeing war and hunger. The following is a translation of one of his poems:

The little cart jolting and banging through the yellow haze of dusk.
The man pushing behind: the woman pulling in front.
They have left the city and do not know where to go.
"Green, green those elm-tree leaves: they will cure my hunger."
The wind has flattened the yellow mother-wort:
Above it in the distance they see the walls of a house.
"There, surely, must be people living who'll give you something to
        eat."
They tap at the door, but no one comes: they look in, but the kitchen
        is empty.
They stand hesitating in the lonely road, and their tears fall like rain.

WHY I REMAIN A NEGRO

by Walter White

> When the Supreme Court handed down its historic decision on desegregation, the man most responsible for this triumph of racial justice was Walter White, whose whole life was spent in behalf of the people of his race. Unfortunately, Mr. White died just before victory came.

I am a Negro. My skin is white, my eyes are blue, my hair is blond. The traits of my race are nowhere visible upon me. Not long ago I stood one morning on a subway platform in Harlem. As the train came in I stepped back for safety. My heel came down upon the toe of the man behind me. I turned to apologize to him. He was a Negro, and his face as he stared at me was hard and full of the piled-up bitterness of a thousand lynchings and a million nights in shacks and tenements and "nigger towns." "Why don't you look where you're going?" he said sullenly. "You white folks are always trampling on colored people." Just then one of my friends came up and asked how the fight had gone in Washington—there was a filibuster against legislation for a permanent Fair Employment Practices Commission. The Negro on whose toes I had stepped listened, then spoke to me penitently.

"Are you Walter White of the NAACP? I'm sorry I spoke to you that way. I thought you were white."

* *Why I Remain a Negro* appeared originally in *The Saturday Review*. Copyright, The Saturday Review Associates.

I am not white. There is nothing within my mind and heart which tempts me to think I am. Yet I realize acutely that the only characteristic which matters to either the white or the colored race—the appearance of whiteness—is mine. White is the rejection of all color; black is the absorption of every shade. There is magic in a white skin; there is tragedy, loneliness, exile, in a black skin. Why then do I insist that I am a Negro, when nothing compels me to do so but myself?

I have seen Negroes, male and female, killed by mobs in the streets of Atlanta. I stood with my father, who was a mail carrier, and watched them die. The next night they came to the Negro section, perhaps five thousand of them. Our house was just outside the section, above it, on Houston Street. It was a neat, modest home, in which my father and mother raised a family of seven children. The whites resented our prosperity; so at times, did the Negroes. The Negroes resented our white skin, and the ethical standards which my parents maintained themselves and required of their children.

In the darkened house that night there were my mother and father, four of my sisters and myself. Never before had there been guns in our house, but that night, at the insistence of friends, we were armed. My father was a deeply religious man, opposed to physical violence. As we watched the mob go by, their faces weird in the light of the torches they carried—faces made grotesque and ugly by the hate which was twisting and distorting them—my father said, "Don't shoot until the first man puts his foot on the lawn; and then don't miss."

I heard a voice cry out, a voice which I knew belonged to the son of our neighborhood grocer. "Let's burn the house of the nigger mail carrier! It's too nice a house for a nigger to live in!"

In the flickering light the mob swayed, paused, and began to flow toward us. In that instant there opened up within me a great awareness; I knew then who I was. I was colored, a human being with an invisible pigmentation which marked me a person to be hunted, hanged, abused, discriminated against, kept in poverty and ignorance, in order that those whose skin was white would have readily at hand a proof of their superiority, a proof patent and inclusive, accessible to the moron and the idiot as well as to the wise man and the genius. No matter how low a white man fell, he could always be certain that he was superior to two-thirds of the world's population, for those two-thirds were not white.

It made no difference how intelligent or talented I and my millions of brothers were, or how virtuously we lived. A curse like that of Judas was upon us, a mark of degradation fashioned with heavenly authority. There were white men who said Negroes had no souls, and who proved it by the Bible. Some of these now were approaching us, intent upon burning our house. My father had told us to kill them.

It was a violence which could not be avoided. The white men insisted upon it. War was with them a business; war and pillage, conquest and exploitation, colonization and Christianization. Later, when I was older, I thought about this and I began to see why. Theirs was a world of contrasts in values: superior and inferior, profit and loss, cooperative and non-cooperative, civilized and aboriginal, white and black. If you were on the wrong end of the comparison, if you were inferior, if you were non-cooperative, if you were aboriginal, if you were black, then you were marked for excision, expulsion or extinction. I was a Negro; I was therefore that part of history which opposed the good, the just, and the enlightened. I was a Persian, falling before the hordes of Alexander. I was a Carthaginian, extinguished by the legions of Rome. I was a Frenchman at Waterloo, an Anglo-Saxon at Hastings, a Confederate at Vicksburg, a Pole at Warsaw. I was the defeated, wherever and whenever there was a defeat.

Yet as a boy there in the darkness amid the tightening fright, I knew the inexplicable thing—that my skin was as white as the skin of those who were coming at me.

The mob moved toward the lawn. I tried to aim my gun, wondering what it would feel like to kill a man. Suddenly there was a volley of shots. The mob hesitated, stopped. Some friends of my father's had barricaded themselves in a two-story brick building just below our house. It was they who had fired. Some of the mobsmen, still bloodthirsty, shouted, "Let's go get the nigger."

Others, afraid now for their safety, held back. Our friends, noting the hesitation, fired another volley. The mob broke and retreated up Houston Street.

In the quiet that followed I put my gun aside and tried to relax. But a tension different from anything I had ever known possessed me. I was gripped by the knowledge of my identity, and in the depths of my soul I was vaguely aware that I was glad of it. I was sick with loathing for the hatred which had flared before me that night and come so close to making me a killer; but I was glad I was not one of those who hated; I was glad I was not one of those made sick and murderous by pride. I was glad I was not one of those whose story is in the history of the world, a record of bloodshed, rapine, and pillage. I was glad my mind and spirit were part of the races that had not fully awakened, and who therefore had still before them the opportunity to write a record of virtue as a memorandum to Armageddon.

It was all just a feeling then, inarticulate and melancholy, yet reassuring in the way that death and sleep are reassuring. Years later, when my father lay in a dingy, cockroach-infested Jim Crow ward in an Atlanta hospital, he put it into words for me and my brother.

"Human kindness, decency, love, whatever you wish to call it," he said, "is the only real thing in the world. It is a dynamic, not a passive, emotion. It's up to you two, and others like you, to use your education and talents in an effort to make love as positive an emotion in the world as are prejudice and hate. That's the only way the world can save itself. Don't forget that. No matter what happens, you must love, not hate." Then he died. He had been struck by an automobile driven by a reckless driver—one of the hospital doctors.

I have remembered that. I have remembered that when, sitting in the gallery of the House or the Senate, I have heard members of our Congress rise and spill diatribe and vilification on the Negroes. I have remembered it when the Negroes were condemned as utter failures in soldiering. I remembered it when, in the Pacific, where I went as a war correspondent, a white officer from the South told me that the 93rd Division, a Negro unit, had been given an easy beachhead to take at Bougainville, and had broken and run under fire. I collected the facts and presented them to him. Bougainville was invaded in November 1943. The 93rd was ordered there in April 1944. The first night it bivouacked on the beach, and motion pictures were shown.

I remembered it when I talked with my nephew for the last time, as he lay in a bitterly cold, rain-drenched tent on the edge of the Capodichina airfield near Naples. He was a Georgia boy, the youngest of four children. His father, like mine, was a mail carrier. He, like me, could have passed for a white man. By sacrifice and labor his parents provided him with a college education. He won a master's degree in economics, and the next day enlisted in the Army Air Corps, as a Negro. He went to the segregated field at Tuskegee, Alabama.

He hated war, he loathed killing. But he believed that Hitler and Mussolini represented the kind of hate he had seen exhibited in Georgia by the Ku Klux Klan and the degenerate political demagogues. He believed that the war would bring all of that hate to an end. He was a fighter pilot. He fought well. Over the Anzio beachhead he was shot down, bailing out and escaping with his right leg broken in two places. He was offered an opportunity to return home but he refused it. "I'll stick it out until the war is finished or I am," he told a friend. Later, returning from a bomber escort mission to Germany, his plane lost altitude over Hungary, was fired upon by anti-aircraft batteries, and was seen striking a tree and bursting into flames. That was the end of one of the men Senator Eastland of Mississippi described as "utter and dismal failures in combat in Europe."

It would be easy to grow bitter over such things, but in remembering my nephew and our last conversation, in which he asked me whether the war would really bring an end to prejudice and race hatred. I remember also the Negro corporal of an engineers' unit, who said to me, "This is the only work they would give me, but I don't mind. We learn a trade; we do constructive work. The combat soldiers are taught how to kill. It will bother them. It will stick with them. It will have no effect on us. We will not have to unlearn it."

I could be sophisticated about the advantages of being a Negro. I am amused, for instance, at the fact that because it is considered remarkable that a Negro can write a book at all, a passing fair volume by one of my brothers is frequently hailed as a masterpiece. Everyone with the slightest sense is aware that genius has no color line. Everyone knows also that people generally choose friends and companions for their taste, manners, intelligence, and personality. Yet it does not occur to him that Negroes do likewise. Therefore he often mourns that we colored people cannot freely associate with whites, when it should be obvious that if we did have this privilege we would like no more of them for friends than he does. It is beyond the imagination of a white man to think that to a Negro he is dull.

Negro athletes and singers do not benefit from their color as do Negro scientists and intellectuals, for whereas the latter are considered wonderful if they attain mediocrity, the former are expected to surpass anything the whites can do. In the main, however, I have found it advantageous to be a Negro. My sense of humor is never without material, and I am easily able to judge the worth of white people by their reaction when they discover that I am not white. I am also able to add to my knowledge by pondering the fact that the people who turn away from me when they are told my identity are the most superior of all the peoples, for they look down upon those who are not afraid to be seen with me, and call them "nigger lovers."

Sometimes it is more enlightening not to insist that I am a Negro. Once on a subway going to Harlem I fell into conversation with a man who spoke with a marked German accent. "This used to be a pleasant line to ride on," he said. "But now there are too many Negroes. They have a distinctive smell." He wrinkled his nose.

"Suppose you and I had to do the same kind of work they do on the docks or over hot kitchen stoves," I said. "That is the kind of work Negroes are forced to do because they are Negroes. Would we be odorless—particularly if we lived in antiquated, crowded, segregated tenements, which we were forced to inhabit also because we were Negroes? Would we reek of lilies of the valley?"

He looked at me with amazement. "But Negroes do smell," he insisted.

I was tempted to paraphrase Dr. Samuel Johnson and tell him that "It is you who smell; they stink." But instead I quoted from the late James Weldon Johnson, who said, "Do you imagine the manufacture of deodorants is exclusively for a Negro market? I notice that the advertisements invariably feature a young and beautiful girl—a white girl."

The man shook his head, "I've lived in this country for thirty years," he said. "You're the first white man I've ever heard talk like that."

Looking at him I recalled an incident in Brooklyn during the early part of the war. A plant was manufacturing the famous and secret Norden bombsight. The plant refused to hire Negroes, but did hire persons of German descent. Most of these were loyal Americans, but a few were arrested by the F.B.I. for stealing the secret of the bombsight, and convicted. But it was too late. Germany got the information and passed it on to Japan. One of the officials of the company told a friend that, "I'd close down the plant rather than hire niggers."

Negro soldiers made a good record in this recent war. They have in previous ones. Yet I recall with uneasiness the grimness on a Negro soldier's face when he told me, one day in the Pacific, "Our fight for freedom will start the day we arrive in San Francisco."

It has indeed, and there are times when I have felt with a sweep of fear that the patience of the colored man is close to its end. I remember the clamoring stillness and the blood heat of a day in Georgia. A lynching was prevented when a band of colored women walked with cans of kerosene toward the village store, a terrible calm upon their faces, an awful quiet in their silent stride. I remember how I felt when I stood beside my father and knew that the whites would not let me live, that I must kill them first and then be killed.

Yet I know, I know, I know that there is no reason for this

killing, this hatred, this demarcation. There is no difference between them. Black is white and white is black. When one shoots
the other he kills his reflection. Only hate, the negative force, can
separate them; only love, the positive force, can bind them
together.

I am one of the two in the color of my skin; I am the other
in my spirit and my heart. It is only a love of both which binds
the two together in me, and it is only love for each other which
will join them in the common aims of civilization that lie before
us. I love one for the sins she has committed and the fight she
had made to conquer them—and conquer them, in great degree,
she has. I love the other for her patience and her sorrows, for
the soft sound of her singing, and for the great dawn which is
coming upon her, in which her vigor and her faith will serve
the world.

Some of the members of the black race are passing over to the
white race. It may be that I am one of these; that I am a member
of a vanguard that in the millennium to come will transmute the
great potentialities of the colored races into the civilizations
which are to follow. I pray that those civilizations will be better
and more virtuous than ours, and that the bridge which I and
others are building will grow strong and be a highway for good.

I have a feeling that life is a rushing force, certain of its course
and destination. Our bodies are its medium, and it shapes them
to its use. As the social pattern of the Negro evolves, will his
color change? Is it changing now? We do not know, and I, for
one, am sure that it does not matter. I am white and I am black,
and know that there is no difference. Each one casts a shadow,
and all shadows are dark.

A little Boy of heavenly birth,
  But far from home today,
Come down to find His ball—the earth—
  That sin has cast away.
O comrades, let us one and all
  Join in to get Him back His ball.

—FR. TABB

CHRIST IN THE SIERRA

by John M. Martin

A reminder of the importance of things we take for granted is given by a veteran Maryknoller, along with a tribute to stanch Mexican faith.

It was the third day of our trip in the high mountains of north-western Mexico. We had slept on the ground for the past two nights, and hoped to get to the village of San Miguel by sundown. We two Maryknoll Fathers were riding on mules and were accompanied by four villagers, also mounted, a committee of honor to escort us.

The heat of the third day was almost unbearable; but after the ascent over the last ridge of mountains started, cool air moved in, and jackets were donned. Darkness came, and still San Miguel was almost two hours away. Lightning flashed, and thunder rumbled, but no rain fell; it was too early in the year for the wet season. Then a burro, overloaded and tired, lay down in the path and refused to move despite innumerable proddings. The poor animal was completely exhausted, and we decided to leave it behind in the custody of a man named Pancho. Finally the flickering lights of San Miguel flashed in view. After twelve hours in the saddle, we arrived at the little village.

The church bell was rung violently and a handful of villagers gathered to greet the priests. The newcomers were shown into a two-room, adobe rectory. The dirt floor had been swept, but there was no furniture. We spread our sleeping bags on the floor and partially disrobed, so that we could proceed by the light of a flashlight to extract biting insects that had bored beneath the skin—pests like those called chiggers in the United States. Finally we fell into a deep sleep—only to be awakened at three in the morning by Pancho, who announced joyfully that the burro on the mountain path had recovered and had just arrived with the cargo. Exasperation was stifled and thanks offered as politely as possible under the circumstances.

At six o'clock, the noise of chickens, mules, ducks and turkeys aroused us, and we awoke to discover a group of bright-eyed boys watching us from a doorway. The lads were completely mystified by the safety razor that one priest was using, and by the mirror through which he could tell the boys what they were doing behind his back. As we stood at our sleeping bags, a smiling grandmother dashed in unabashed, to kiss the priestly hands and extend a hearty welcome. Apparently other feminine eyes were watching the Padres, for another elderly voice was heard from a nearby hedge, calling to one of the boys to receive a jar of water for the priests' ablutions. When the Padres emerged from the rectory, about one hundred persons were standing outside the church door. We learned that about two hundred more lived in the surrounding territory, and would add to the attendance every Sunday. All of them stayed for two Masses and afterwards gathered at the front door to meet the priests.

"Father," one of the elders of the village said, "we have been praying for you for a long time. Every day at sunset, all of us— men, women and children—have gathered here to say the rosary, asking Our Lady of Guadalupe to send us a priest. And now you are here!"

In our ignorance we asked them, "How many months did you pray before we came?"

"Months, Father!" the old man exclaimed. "Why, we prayed for you for thirty-six years."

We could not help but think of the folks at home in the big cities, with Mass every hour, confession at convenient times, and a telephone to bring the priest quickly with the saving oil of

Extreme Unction, while these mountain folk had been without the Eucharist for almost a generation.

We shall never forget the Sunday on which we re-established Christ in His mountain home. The altar was rebuilt, and the tabernacle, which had been brought in on muleback, was safely anchored in readiness for the great moment when the Word would dwell among them. There had been weeks of instructions concerning the Eucharist, and rehearsals in genuflecting, for these poor people had never been in a church where the Sacred Host had been reserved. They also had to be taught about the Sacrament of Penance, that confession was not necessary for every Communion.

These confessions provided a real problem. At first it was difficult to get the men to confess.

"What? Go to confession before all those women in the church!" they exclaimed. So the Padres tried reserving Saturday mornings and afternoons for the women's confessions, and set aside nighttime for the men. At first, the men responded to the idea, but the women went on strike. Finally the problem seemed solved by having one priest hear the men's confessions in the sanctuary while the other attended to the women in the main part of the church.

To make it easier, the priest in the sanctuary rigged a sheet as a screen. However, many of the men, in their simplicity, came before the priest and said, "Father, I am very embarrassed to kneel before you. Would it be all right if I made my confession to you from the other side of the curtain?" It never occurred to them they had already revealed their identities to the confessor before telling their sins through the protecting screen.

The moment on that Sunday when the Hosts were consecrated for reservation in the tabernacle, was a memorable one. Suddenly the people realized that Emmanuel (God-with-us) had finally come to stay. One man dashed out of doors to ring the church bell. Another set off a long string of firecrackers, while many others sobbed audibly as they knelt on the tile floor of the church. At the *Domine, non sum dignus*, all of the parishioners thumped their breasts strenuously, producing the effect of muffled drums in the distance. There was no doubt that they felt unworthy to have the Master enter under their roof.

When finally the sanctuary lamp had been lighted, and the people had genuflected carefully, they gathered outside in small groups. One old lady came to the priest and asked that the Padre type a list of names of the women; she wished to post it on the church door.

"Father," the old lady said, "we women are so grateful for Christ's coming that we have resolved to assign hours of watch, so that, as long as there is daylight, there will be at least one woman in the church adoring Our Lord, *lest we lose Him!*"

WE OF NAGASAKI

The following two accounts of the atom-bombing of Nagasaki were collected by Dr. Takashi Nagai, a famed Catholic scientist, who later died of radiation poisoning. His many books written while he agonizingly wasted away are masterpieces of Christian resignation.

Fujie Urata Matsumoto's Story

Fujie Urata was about thirty-five at the time of the bombing. When the explosion occurred she was working in a millet patch in Koba, and was thus spared. She was first cousin of Midori Nagai, Dr. Nagai's wife.

I was pulling up weeds in the rows of millet on the hillside at Koba, at a place three and a half miles from Urakami; Mount

* From *We of Nagasaki* by Takashi Nagai. Copyright, Duell, Sloan and Pearce.

Kawabira stands in between. In Urakami we were neighbors of Dr. Nagai's, and if I had been at home at the time I certainly would have died. My old mother, Take Urata, who had stayed home to watch the house, was burned to death.

Suddenly I heard a loud roar overhead. It sounded as though a plane had just dropped its bombs and was flying away.

Here it comes, I thought.

There was a sudden flash of red light.

Then a flash of blue.

The red was bright enough to stun a person, but the blue!—it was so bright that not even the worst liar could have found the words to describe it.

That was all. There was a wind which blew away the weeds I had pulled up, but nothing else happened.

What could these flashes be? . . .

I scanned the sky. Rising higher than high Kawabira, in the sky over Urakami, a puffy black smoke began boiling up and up, filling that whole part of the sky. Kawabira seemed to divide the world in two, one part looking normal as ever and the other strange and terrible. I couldn't attend to my work. I sat down at the edge of the field. It was almost noon, so I ate some of the food I had brought. After about fifteen minutes a bawling, stark-naked child passed by along the road at the foot of the hill. He looked as though he had been swimming in the river and had had an accident.

Five minutes after a girl of about twenty came struggling along the road uphill from Urakami. Her clothes were in shreds and her hair in disorder. She seemed barely able to stay on her feet. I could hear her loud sobbing from where I sat on the side of the hill. Next a weeping schoolboy came along, his clothes in tatters also, and his face and hands black and swollen. I suddenly became anxious about my mother. I scrambled down the hillside and ran down the road toward Urakami.

As I came nearer to Urakami, I began to meet many injured people. They must have been workers from the arsenal, young men and women, all of them naked, except that some still had their leather belts around their waists and on some the strings of their *mompe* still circled their ankles. They were stumbling along unsteadily, trying to escape behind Mount Kawabira, weeping crazily, forgetting even to be ashamed of their nakedness. Their faces, necks, and hands were blistered and on some of them I could see sheets of skin that had peeled right off and hung down flapping, all black with dust. The hair of the women was singed and frizzled. Many of these people had been wounded and were smeared with blood.

I tried to find out what had happened to them, and cried, "For heaven's sake, what is it? What's happened?" Always the same answer—"I don't know, all I saw was a sudden flash, then everything went to pieces!" Some just stared with blank expressions, unable to answer at all.

Sometimes one of them would stumble in the road and sprawl on his face, lying there without trying to get up.

I was carrying my jug of tea, so I ran from one to another making them drink a little. At the spring in Topposui I stopped to fill the jug with water. I was still about two miles from Urakami but already I could see many houses afire.

When I finally reached Urakami, about two hours after the big flash, I found everything in flames. I managed to get to a spot overlooking the Yamazato Elementary School. From here I could see that my own part of town was completely gutted. Everywhere, smoke rose from the embers. I tried to find the path to my house but the ground was covered with hot ashes and even if I had found it I couldn't have used it.

What had happened to my mother! I kept shouting and calling toward the house. There was no answer. I walked all around the neighborhood, wherever walking was possible. Finally I came to the school playground. There I found my cousin, Sadako Moriyama, who was fetching water, and her sister Sayoko and the two little ones, Takeo and Ritsuko, who were inside the shelter. Sadako had a dazed expression. The four children were just sitting there helpless, waiting for someone to come and take care of them.

What about my mother? . . . And my sister Tatsue? . . . And my cousin Midori, Dr. Nagai's wife? . . . And Sadako's family the Moriyamas? . . . They were all on my mind. How could they have lived through this! Takeo and Ritsuko were shaking with sobs and Ritsuko had cuts and bruises all over her body. I saw that they must be moved quickly. The whole sky was covered by a terrible cloud. It hid the sun completely and made the day like twilight.

We set out for Dr. Nagai's summer cottage on the hillside at Koba. I took Ritsuko on my back, and with Sadako pulling Takeo along we began to climb the road I had come down a while before.

As we walked Takeo kept doubling up and complaining, "My tummy hurts." He was getting weaker all the time. Sadako and Ritsuko were both feeling faint. It was a strange kind of weakness. I thought they must have been exposed to some sort of poisonous fumes.

When we finally reached the cottage, Makoto and Kayano, Dr. Nagai's children, were standing under the shaddock tree in the garden, looking as if they expected someone. They were overjoyed when they saw us and came running up.

"Where's Mummy?" Kayano asked immediately.

"What! Isn't she here yet?" I had taken it for granted.

Makoto shook his head. He looked so lonely.

None of our relatives and neighbors from Urakami were here yet. Could they all have died? I was half out of my mind. This time I was going to find my mother and bring her back. I hurried off to Urakami again.

But when I came alongside the spring in Topposui I found my cousin Sojiro Urata slumped in a heap on the ground, motionless as something carved. At first I did not recognize him. His face was burned and covered with black blisters and blood was trickling from his head. But there was something familiar about the shape of his mouth so I said to him, "Aren't you Cousin Sojiro?" He opened his eyes, narrow slits between swollen lids, as though he were awakening from sleep.

"Ah! Fujie? Take me to the church. Is it far? I want to confess to the father. I want the sacrament."

It was clear that death was crowding in on him. His right forearm was broken and horribly bent. It was gruesome. His shirt and trousers were in rags. He must have kept falling on the road. His whole body was caked with mud.

I had to find my mother but here was my cousin on the brink of death right before my eyes, craving pardon for his sins. I could not desert him. I decided I would first get him to the church in Koba, a mile and a half uphill, then return and find Mother.

He nibbled a little of the *mugimeshi* I was carrying and drank from the spring. Then he said, "Get me some salt." I found some in a store near the spring and poured it in the palm of his hand. He licked it up hungrily.

I put a splint on his broken arm and hung it from his neck with a bandage. He was getting back a little of his spirit. Then I put my neck under his left arm, and with my right arm around his waist we began walking slowly. He was without strength. His legs wobbled so that I had to drag him while he hung on to me around the shoulders. As we struggled on he kept feeling faint and had to lie down in the road and rest. I spoke to him several times but he could only gasp. Each time we stopped to rest he would say, "I can't see. . . . Aren't we there yet? Is it far?"

Sojiro was a decent fellow, but in the army he had been a medical corps non-com and had also been a policeman in Shanghai, so in the past he had often swaggered around acting important. But now that he knew death's visit was near he had become very humble, earnestly clinging to the hand of God as he climbed the sloping road to the church.

"Is it still far?"

How many times did I hear that question!

"Not very far. Keep your courage up!" How many times did I have to encourage him!

He looked as though his heart would collapse any minute. I was at my wit's end. On the road, here and there, sprawled the dead bodies of people who had struggled this far before they dropped. The road here ran along the stream and there were few houses. In two hours we covered about a mile, from Topposui to the little village of Kawabira. By a piece of luck I found a bicycle trailer in a store here, and I piled Sojiro into it. It was a great relief for him too, and he was overjoyed. The road now became a steep slope. It took more than my strength to get the trailer up the hill, and I had to ask help part of the way.

When we finally reached Koba it was on toward evening. I called from the foot of the stone steps leading up to the church and Father Shimizu came out, followed by Maruo, the cook, and others. They carried Sojiro inside.

Sojiro immediately asked for the last rites. Father Shimizu put on a short surplice and, with a stole about his shoulders, knelt at Sojiro's head and solemnly made the sign of the cross. . . . So Sojiro had received the last sacrament. I had seen to it. I felt as if a load had been lifted from my shoulders.

Once again I hurried back down the road, pulling the empty trailer. At the shop I stopped to return it, but when I tried to continue toward Urakami the people there held me back. It was too dark to go looking for my mother now, they said. I would only be running into danger. In the sky over Urakami the horrible cloud was bright-red with the reflection of the burning town. As I stood there complete exhaustion suddenly came over my whole body. I suppose that my tension relaxed. Slowly I started back for the cottage in Koba.

How frightened and lonely the children were! The cottage was so still that I held my breath. With the power lines down outside, there was no light and the radio was dead. A red fire glowed in the *irori*. Little Takeo Moriyama had fallen asleep, exhausted. Ritsuko was in pain from her injuries—she had been buried under mounds of earth—and she could not sleep.

"Mama! Mama!" she was racked with sobs. Her mother Shizuko Miwa, was my cousin. Was she alive? I wondered. With the child calling for her so, surely she must be alive somewhere. Yet if she were safe and sound she would certainly have come looking for them here long before now.

Makoto and Kayano made none of their usual noise and rumpus. They sat staring at the *irori*. "It's late," I said to them, "time to go to sleep," but they would not go. They kept their ears pricked up for the sound of footsteps outside . . . their father's or their mother's. Around the house the air was filled with the chirping of Suzumushi. The sound of footsteps would have stilled their noise, but when the night lifted and turned to day they had not stopped once.

The morning sky was clear. The cloud which had filled the sky over Urakami had drifted eastward. Somehow I felt a kind of hope; I had the feeling that it was over. I started out to look for my mother and sister.

Urakami was a hill of ashes. It had never been so hushed. It reminded me of the way deserts look in pictures, except that it was even more quiet than a desert. A desert is always bare of people, animals, and anything that grows but here, up to only yesterday, there had been houses and living creatures. In a single day these had disappeared.

In the ashes I could make out nothing moving or motionless. Up on one slope the cathedral was completely in flames, sending up a great red blaze. How still and solemn the whole scene looked under the morning sun! This was the only fire still burning in ancient Urakami. All the others had gone out.

My mother's bones were among the ashes of our house. I found her at the mouth of the air-raid shelter under the floor, consumed to such a little heap of bones. She must have heard the explosion and rushed to the shelter, where she was crushed. Since she was sixty-seven and had not been very well, she often had to lie down. She spent most of her time telling her beads and praying. That was her main business, but see how she departed this life! I decided I must find my sister Tatsue, and together we would gather her bones.

In the ruins of Ichitaro Yamada's house, next door to ours, I could see the bodies of four or five children alongside the body of an adult. Ichitaro himself had been drafted and was away in the army, and here was his family, wiped out. I would not want to see the look on his face when he came back.

My younger brother Masaichi was also away in the army. If he came back . . . he would say I had neglected Mother, he would blame me for having let her die alone. I dreaded his anger, but my mother's ashes were more accusing still.

When I left the house yesterday my mother was asleep. The air-raid sirens had sounded during the night, and we had had to go to the community air-raid shelter. She was exhausted, so I let her sleep. Whenever I left the house I always said goodbye to her, but yesterday of all days I didn't want to wake her! . . . I left quietly without a word. Now I could hardly stand the pain of regret.

The pumpkin field in front of the house was blown clean. Nothing was left of the whole thick crop, except that in place of the pumpkins there was a woman's head. I looked at the face to see if I knew her. It was a woman of about forty. She must have been from another part of town—I had never seen her around here. A gold tooth gleamed in the wide-open mouth. A handful of singed hair hung down from the left temple over her cheek, dangling in her mouth. Her eyelids were drawn up, showing black holes where the eyes had been burned out. The head had come right off at the neck. There was not much blood. She had probably looked square into the flash and gotten her eyeballs burned, then the blast must have taken her head off at the neck and sent it flying with the blood gushing out behind.

There was a big persimmon tree in the field, too big for one person to get his arms around. It had been snapped off at eye-level and blown through the air. From its position I guessed that the blast must have come from the direction of the Matsuyama section. Beside the stump lay the body of old lady Maruo. Her daughter Sami was squatting on the ground, in a trance, holding her child. Sami was Sojio's wife.

"Sami!"

"What! Is it Fujie! You're alive? . . ."

"Come on! Pull yourself together! Don't you know Sojiro is at the church in Koba?"

"Is he alive?"

"I'm not sure. . . ."

"Is he dead, then? Tell me, Fujie! Or is he alive! Is he?"

"Go on, hurry over and find out. The father gave him the sacrament last night. I don't know what happened afterward."

"All right, I'm going. . . . I was pinned under the house but

I got out all right, with the baby, but Takeyoshi, my eldest, was out chasing dragonflies and he hasn't come back yet . . . I was just waiting . . . But how can I go to Sojiro? What about my mother's body? And maybe Takeyoshi is alive, wandering around some place! . . ."

Holding the baby, she stood up and sat down several times, unable to make up her mind.

"Don't wait around thinking it over! There's no sense in that. While you're thinking it over Sojiro may be dying! Go on, hurry! Then come right back and we'll attend to your mother. Anyway, there aren't any coffins. We'll have to have one made in Koba and bring it back. Come on, now; hurry up! If Takeyoshi is alive he can get to Koba by himself. He's not an infant, he's ten years old."

So together we offered prayers for her mother and all the neighbors. Then she hurried off to the church in Koba carrying the baby.

In the wreck of Reiko Urata's house nearby I could see a charred skeleton, sandwiched between the sink and the stove. Could it be Reiko's mother? I wondered.

Next door to Reiko lived the Shibatas. The young couple had been blown out onto the path behind the house. Young Shibata had recently graduated from medical school. They were good people and the wife had been working in a school for the blind, paying her husband's expenses with what she earned. Finally he had gotten his degree and been appointed to Saga Hospital. They must have died together in happiness—right in the midst of packing to go to his new post in Saga.

Midori's bones were still in her kitchen, so I knew that Dr. Nagai had not come home yet. Because I knew that if he were alive he would want to bury her with his own hands, I let the bones lie where they were.

Everybody was dead, everybody I had come looking for. And I had expected I would be coming back to Koba today with all of them—I had been so keyed up, looking forward to the excitement. . . .

Enemy planes roared by overhead, one after another. I was

tense, dreading still another great flash. I knew that there was supposed to be danger in an air raid only while the planes were directly overhead; if you were careful, you could avoid the bombs. But now I didn't know when or where another big flash might come.

If a war like this lasted very long we would go out of our minds if we survived at all. I suddenly felt terrified. I could not stay here in Urakami a minute longer. I just left my mother's body and the bodies of so many of my relatives and scurried off to Koba.

Satoru Fukabori's Story

Ten-year-old Satoru Fukabori was staying with his aunt in No-naka, a short distance from Urakami up on Mount Kawabira. When the house collapsed he was pulled from the wreckage by his uncle.

I was staying with my aunt in Nonaka. That's a little village a mile and a half from Urakami, up on Mount Kawabira past the Sei Furanshisuko Hospital. I was still in grade school then. That was why my mother had sent me away from Urakami.

My brother Suzushi was staying at my aunt's too. He'd got himself a broken leg while we were down at the piers fetching salt water; he slipped carrying a bucket. The reason we were fetching salt water was the salt shortage. We kids were supposed to get water from the ocean and boil it for the salt. But after Suzushi got his leg broken my mother sent him to Nonaka because he couldn't run when there were air raids.

Our house in Urakami was right in front of Dr. Nagai's. My mother was there. So were my sister Hatsuko and my brother Masaru—he and Suzushi were older than me—and also my little brother Masanori and the baby. I have still another brother, Mitsunori. He was the oldest. He had worked in the shipyards to support the family, but then he was drafted so my sister and my brother Masaru had to go to work, and they got factory jobs.

We raised our own wheat and potatoes and all the vegetables we needed. We had a garden my mother had planted.

I was in my aunt's garden when the bomb exploded. I was standing right next to the persimmon tree. I heard a plane go ZAA-aaoooo, like they always did when they let go their bombs, then there was a flash, a bright-red-and-blue flash! Then there was a noise like WHEE-eesh! . . . like a steam engine when it's coming toward you, only it was falling straight down and I thought it was going to land right on top of me.

I made a rush and jumped onto the *engawa*, and right after that came a hot wind that blew me into the house, and the next thing I knew, before I could even get up, the house caved in on me.

I got a nail in my head under the skin. A lot of boards and sticks and things landed on top of me. I couldn't move my head; it was caught. One beam was on top of it—the one the nail was sticking out of—and the other one was under my chin. I couldn't move my head up and down, and I could barely turn it to the side. I remember the squeaky noise from the nail when I tried to turn my head.

I was collecting butterflies as summer homework, and I used to pin them to boards through their heads. I thought God must be punishing me now, for there I was just like a butterfly.

I kept trying to get the top beam off me, but I couldn't budge it. Then I heard my uncle outside, calling to me. He shouted, "Don't worry, Satoru, I'll get you out!" I heard him grunting, and I could tell he was trying to pry up the beam on top of my head. It worked. The beam came up all right, but it took me with it, on account of the nail. Uncle shouted, "Come on!"—of course, he couldn't see the nail—"Hurry up! Out, quick!"; but I couldn't get free. I shouted back, "I can't, Uncle! There's a nail from the beam sticking in my head!"

Then he came in after me. He lifted me off the nail and carried me outside. It was a five-incher.

I wasn't feeling so good. I had to sit down on the ground a while. All around, everything was wrecked, the fences and the trees and the houses. When I looked down at Urakami, I thought it must be the blood in my eyes that made it look like that. The big persimmon tree was down, too, and it was a big tree.

I said, "Uncle, where did the red ocean come from?"

Uncle said, "What are you talking about? The whole town is burning!"

I said, "How did it get that way?" I was still pretty mixed up.

Uncle said he didn't know, nobody knew. He said, "There was that bright light. Didn't you see it?" He said something invisible came and ran wild over the town and left it burning. Then he said, "Come on, let's get out of here and get into the shelter!" Just then we heard a plane and Uncle shouted, "Listen! Hear that? More planes! Come on!" We ran to the shelter. Suzushi was already there. He said, "Hey, Satoru, what's the matter with your face?"

I touched it, and the skin came off like the skin of a peach.

After a while some people from the other houses came running into the shelter. Just like me, they had pieces of skin coming off, only it was coming off all over their bodies.

Every now and then planes came over, and every time there was almost a panic in the shelter. The ones near the entrance started pushing to get inside more. They shouted, "Get inside! Move back farther! Let us in, there'll be another flash!" They were so scared! And the ones inside yelled when they got squeezed, because their burns hurt.

The whole night was like that. Some people died before morning. When somebody died it was hard to get the body outside, because we were packed in so tight. That was the way it was until morning. Then we went outside to look around. I went over to the front of our yard to look down at Urakami, but it was all gone. The red ocean was gone—it was turned into a white ocean bottom. That was the first time I thought of my folks.

My mother and the baby were burned to death in the house and my little brother Masanori died later. My aunt found him crying in the school shelter and she got him to Nonaka, but he died five days after. My sister died about the same time as Masanori, in Nonaka too. I was only a little boy then—anyway, I was only thinking about my own burns.

About my brother Masaru, we never saw him again. Mr. Tanaka, who lived near us in Urakami, said to me a few days after the bomb, "Satoru, I saw your brother Masaru sitting along the side of the road near Mori. I heard somebody calling for help but I couldn't stop for him—you understand, don't you, sonny? I had to get home to my own family."

My uncle and my aunt went over to Mori, but they couldn't find a trace of Masaru. It was worse not finding his body now that we knew Mr. Tanaka had seen him alive.

Whenever I run into Mr. Tanaka I always think of Masaru. Then I remember that I didn't think of him myself.

THE KID DOWN THE BLOCK

by Bob Considine

> Every day millions of Americans read Bob Considine's syndicated column. Here he tells some little known facts about himself, and gives a few observations on the priesthood and missioners.

One of our children, for reasons too involved to mention, was baptized at the somewhat worldly age of three years by Monsignor (now Bishop) Michael J. Ready. The child accepted his redemption from original sin with a stoic speculative mien. The orisons of the priest, the use of holy water, and other details of the sacrament were, to him, one more example of the incomprehensible tactics of the adult world.

* From *The Maryknoll Story*. Copyright, Robert Considine. Published by Doubleday and Company.

"You're getting me wet," the child remarked with weary impatience at one stage of ablution. Again, when the bit of salt was placed on the tip of his tongue, he remarked, "Bitter, isn't it?"

The good monsignor was patient. He plodded on through the ceremony, and as he prayed, and the corsages of the mother and godmother began to droop, the child's interest in the priest quickened. He followed his every move, scrutinized his vestments, searched his own meager experience for a possible clue to the mysteries being revealed to him. Then his eyes brightened, and he believed he had solved everything—had found the reason why this man with the water, salt, unfamiliar costume, and whispered prayers was so kind and gentle with him.

"You're a cowboy, aren't you?" the child asked, with brimming enthusiasm. It was the finest compliment he could bestow.

It was his first brush with a man of God, and his reaction followed a familiar pattern for Catholic children: first awe, consternation, or fear, then an inexplicable feeling of warmth that is a blend of that which one feels for a parent who deserves trust, or for a quiet friend who has demonstrated his loyalty in some intrinsic way.

It was something like that in my own case. The first priests I knew seemed as remote from the life around me and as alien and impersonal as the penguins in the Washington zoo. Then an old and careworn one showed up at our house in Swamp Poodle, a section of Washington known for its saloons, soot from the railroad, the sobriety of the Sodality ladies, and St. Aloysius Church. My father had died on this Christmas Eve of long ago, leaving a thunderstruck wife and five children. I remember being doused by a shower of tears from the good, lachrymose ladies of the neighborhood. But then the old priest came in, one of the parish Jesuits, saying something like "Tsk, tsk," and in a little time he seemed to have things in hand: the matter of a little money from here and there, food and a half barrel of beer for the wake ("the arrangements," as a professional pallbearing friend of the family called them piously), and he saw to it, too, that my younger brother and I received a few Christmas presents under a make-shift tree in the house of Tom Campbell next door.

I then looked upon the priesthood with the baffled manner of a child seeing a magician, a magician who somehow spotted him in the audience or let him feed the trained seal. The warmth and the trust were beginning to take root. What remaining misgivings I had were washed away on my first terrified day in the robes of altar boy. An indulgent older altar boy had dressed some of us in the outfits on hand and ordered us to kneel to one side of the altar, as a sort of window dressing. We didn't know the difference between a surplice and a sacristy. But at Communion time on this first day there was a heavy flow of the congregation to the rail. A second priest, a fat and busy little man named Kelly, came out of the sacristy, picked up an extra ciborium, stared about him a little critically, and finally fastened his eyes on me, staring at him dimly.

"You," he whispered.

I knelt there petrified until someone jabbed me in the short ribs, handed me the Communion plate to hold beneath the chins of the faithful at the rail, and shoved me after the priest.

Father Kelly was a fast man with a *Corpus Domini nostri*. Holding the golden tray in a palsied paw, I began to back up in terror, to keep from being trampled by him. I held my own for four or five communicants, but it was short-lived glory. The last user of my cassock apparently had been Primo Carnera. Yards of it were now irrevocably underfoot. I was more or less walking up the back of it in my effort to avoid being run down by the on-rushing priest. When I fell over backward, as I did, I hit the lightly carpeted flooring like a load of rivets, shattering the bliss-ful composure of a good twenty yards of thoughtful communi-cants. I lay there, waiting for the swift kick from Father Kelly which would properly express what should have been his deep indignation. Instead he put on the brakes, reached down to me with a smile, and pulled me gently to my feet. He adjusted the evil cassock around me and showed me how to hold it to keep from tripping. He waited until I was ready, a crinkled kindness about his eyes. Then, when I was set, he began again slowly: "*Corpus Domini nostri. . . .*"

There came a long period after that when the priest, to me, was a mentor of infinite patience, a person of imposing learning, and an imbiber of great draughts of personal sacrifice, a strong brew for which I had no great thirst. Ostensibly he had been put in my path by God, to serve as elderly guide and counsel in the absence of a father; to forgive such sins as I could commit; to arrange such things as a summer in camp when there wasn't enough money to pay as others did. The priest was a friend and no longer an object of wonder or terror. But when classes or Masses were done for the day, he was not of my world.

It went that way (as it must for so many others) until one day at Gonzaga High a fellow said to me, "Lanahan's going away to be a priest."

Lanahan! It seemed impossible. Sure, he was a good egg . . . smart . . . and helpful to the rest of us in the class who loafed or were not too bright. But he was just a kid down the block, just another one of us. He got in his share of trouble, made his allotted amount of noise, played baseball about as well as the rest of the mob, and talked of going on to Georgetown.

It is indeed hard, at first, to comprehend that priests are people.

A boy grows older, develops a cantaloupe at his waistline, and gets short of wind. And he learns, at first to his embarrassment, that a priest can be younger than he is, as well as stronger and wiser, and infinitely more at peace with his soul. World War II was a vivid eye opener to a lot of us, and forgive me if this is too personal. As a war correspondent I saw something of the priest in the field afar: the unshaven and dirty chaplain who was as much a part of the mud and the muck and the mayhem as GI Joe, and God. I saw him uncomplainingly at work in seemingly God-deprived places ranging from Burma to Greenland; from dreary continental training camps to Berlin; from North Africa to that preview of the ultimate war, the test of the A-bombs at Bikini. He was still the kid down the block, quietly possessed of the fire and fortitude and selfless courage of Christ.

Saw something else, too, in those tempestuous years: the missionary who was on hand when the liberators and their chaplains arrived . . . the missionary who had never been told (or who had never wanted) to leave the places that became the battlegrounds of the great war. The storming and consolidation of beaches was old hat to him. His war had begun the day a Man said, "Go ye and teach all nations." It would not end with his life span. He measured his gains not in sand and ruptured city but in souls that would outlive all matter. If the transitory liberator had an extra pair of shoes for him to give to some wretch who needed them, well and good. The missionary dealt in such logistics. If the liberator had a can of Spam to put what amounted to meat on the missionary's bones as he was led out of his concentration or internment camp, well and good. It meant that he, the missionary, could carry on with new assurance against the enemy which can know no border or comprehend no peace: the anti-Christ.

I sought for some time to express in words the feeling of many who, because of the war, saw the American priest at work in alien lands. It is a great and ennobling sight to witness a good American shedding both the light of God and that of the country he loves in works of charity and carrying truth abroad. Such men are the intimacy of our foreign relations, far from the tinsel and glitter of our diplomatic and money-changing agencies abroad. They are of the people of the distant lands, just as they are of the people of this stupendously great nation. It is a miraculous meld.

There are many fine mission groups overseas. But, to me, the men of Maryknoll, or the Catholic Foreign Mission Society of America—to give them their full handle—epitomize all the vigor, earthiness, and godliness of this country in its spiritual and physical relations abroad. One does not have to be a Catholic to say, "These are real American men. We've never had finer."

The products of Maryknoll are men who might have been Presidents, plumbers or professors, diplomats, doctors or dramatists, bankers, bartenders or barristers, contractors, concertists, or cardinals. The paths that lead them to hostile lands that may never have known Christ or a white face begin in New York City and Walla Walla, Chicago and Keokuk, San Francisco and What

Cheer, Iowa. These are men from the teeming canyons of great population centers, and men from the bleak prairie lands. These are Americans. Nobody pushed them to Maryknoll.

"Why?" is a questioning word that pursues the man of Maryknoll from young manhood to his mortal death at the limit of his dedicated life. It is a word spoken, not without hurt and confusion, by some of the parents of the candidates—perhaps especially by those parents who took for granted the young man's ascent into the profession and world of his father. It is a word that must be spoken by the boys who grew up around the priest-to-be, and perhaps by the girl who saw in him the husband she would one day want. But the answers to "Why?" probably are no more complicated than those given by a recent class of Maryknoll students busily and happily at work at that fabulous fountainhead of the Society, the oriental-thatched buildings which rise like an oddly foreign dream above the Hudson River at Ossining, New York.

"When I was in Korea with the Army I met a Maryknoll priest," one explained. "I saw how missioners were needed."

Another said, "During the war I served in China. There I obtained a firsthand view of the great work of the missions, and the still greater tasks that lie ahead."

"St. Francis Xavier's life influenced me to be a missioner," another answered. "And Father Jerry Donovan's life drew me to Maryknoll."

"I saw the movie *The Keys of the Kingdom*. Then I read an article about a tribe of uncivilized Indians in South America. I want to take the word of God to them." . . . "I first heard of Maryknoll from a fellow at Notre Dame." . . . "I love the 'little guy,' and from what I saw of service in the Pacific, Maryknoll helps him." . . . "I read the story of Maryknoll in the *Catholic Digest*." . . . "When I was in Japan with the Navy I saw how much the Japanese people needed Christ."

One of the lads said it especially well and clearly. It will, I hope, reveal to the reader the core of why so many gifted Americans, capable of making the world and its favors their oyster, embraced instead the drudgeries and dangers of God's work in the field afar. The young man said it all in one sentence:

"I joined Maryknoll in order to be be closer to God and because by being a Maryknoll priest I should have the opportunity to bring other people into the Faith."

GIFTS FOR A SEMINARIAN'S MOTHER

You must smile I know
At what I gave you long ago;
Mother, you recall
When I was very small,
The milk-white "lucky" stones
I found and carried home—
And the bottled bumble bee
I brought for you to see.
And you never gave a sign
That your delight was less than mine
The day I brought into the house
A bright eyed, wooly mouse!
When at school I won for you
A dozen marbles—O, so blue;
I stole roses from some yard
And in church, a "holy card."
Now I think of you at night
And in the morning when I pray.
Accept these sincere lines
Of this poor verse of mine;
Those former things were worthless
And these are—O, so small!
But the future still holds all—
If Our God is kind
In the future I shall find
That which brightest beams
Among my boyhood dreams . . .
When vested in the priestly white,
Underneath the altar light,
I can give—our God—to you!

—GEORGE KROCK

MOVING DAY FOR BABIES

by Daniel McShane

Father McShane spent his apostolate in China in rescuing abandoned babies. Baby 2483 on his baptismal register was the last one he saved. From it he caught smallpox and died.

I was not long home from Hong Kong when I learned that the head of the pagan orphanage had expressed a desire to send his little infants to the Sisters' orphanage at Canton. After two days I went to him and inquired whether the report were true. His answer was that he had been quoted correctly, and of course the reason was that he hadn't enough money to keep them. He stated, moreover, that if I would assume responsibility for the transfer, it would no doubt win added respect and appreciation for the Loting Catholic Church. I told him I would consider his offer, and in a day or two would give him my answer.

I then began to make inquiries as to what effect such a move would have on the pagan population of this vicinity.

At best, it is no easy matter to get from a Chinese his real opinion on a given subject. The Chinese are so polite that, for fear of offending, they will often evade until they feel pretty sure what kind of answer is wanted. However, the answers I received on this subject were so spontaneous and uniform that I felt convinced I should make no mistake in getting the little ones

* From *The Man on Joss Stick Alley* by James Edward Walsh. Longmans Green and Company.

into the hands of the Sisters. I decided also to engage two or three pagan nurses to take care of the ten or twelve infants as far as Hong Kong. This would have the advantage of bringing these pagan women in close touch with the Sisters' orphanage; they would see just how the Sisters conduct their work, and they would also learn that the Sisters are not selling or destroying the babies as the Chinese do.

In two days, I went back to the orphanage and told the superintendent that I was willing to take ten or twelve babies to Hong Kong. The Sisters there had only recently offered to relieve me of all the infants that I couldn't manage. I told the old gentleman that, since his orphanage was in such financial straits, and especially since I was so interested in the welfare of the little ones, I would defray the cost of the trip. We then settled on the following Thursday for the departure to Hong Kong. I at once engaged a small boat to take us down to the West River, where we would have to transfer to the big boats that ply between Wuchow and Hong Kong.

When I went to the reception room Thursday morning, to make the selection of babies, what was my surprise to find exactly thirty-three little urchins—all, with the exception of about six, in the very best of health! Both the superintendent and matron of the orphanage were there, and they told me to make my selection and to take as many as I wanted. When we had twenty-nine picked out, I thought it best to call a halt! Having made the necessary preparation for the trip, the signal was given, and in less than twenty minutes, we were on our boat and were moving down towards the West River.

We had pretty good sailing the remainder of the day. Of course the youngsters were noisy and restless, but considering the circumstances, they were not too bad. Before leaving Loting, I suggested buying baskets to put the little ones in, but my suggestion was not considered. As a result, the babies were planked right down on the floor, with nothing between them and the hard boards but a page from *The Baltimore Sun*. I brought along a supply of milk, but was surprised to learn how indifferent the nurses were in preparing it; in fact, it was only when I insisted that they gave it to the children at all. They preferred to feed them rice and rice gruel. And this is the way the food was administered: the gruel was simply poured down the little one's throat as fast as it would swallow it, while the rice was first chewed by the nurse for a minute or so and then stuffed into the baby's mouth. I must admit that this was a revelation to me, especially since the ages of the infants were from five to forty days old.

That night we passed through the section of the country most thickly infested with pirates and robbers, but I hadn't the slightest fear that any of them would wish to relieve me of my charges.

The next day, at two p.m., we reached the West River, and shortly after we anchored at Namkonghau. It did not take long for the sampan dwellers to learn our mission, and the news of our arrival soon spread through the place. Within an hour the dozen or so sampans were crowding around, while the villagers were actually boarding the boat to get a look at the passengers. Baby after baby was picked up, examined, and given a favorable or unfavorable comment. A certain number asked outright for a baby; and one woman even offered to pay a few cents for one. I suppose their object was to re-sell the babies and thus make a few cents. Then there were a few whose actions were so suspicious that even my pagan nurses suspected they were planning to steal a baby, so within a few minutes my three faithful helpers had gathered the little ones from the other end of the boat and placed them on the floor directly in front of me. I then saw that they wanted my help, so, laying aside my breviary, I assumed the role of watchman for the next three hours.

At exactly five we heard the whistle of the approaching Hong Kong steamer. I didn't know when I ever heard a sound so consoling, for immediately I had visions of boarding the boat, getting the babies settled in a quiet corner, and then retiring for a bit of rest. But wait—! the river at this point is probably two miles wide, and only the middle of it is navigable for large steamers; consequently, local passengers must be ferried in a long, open flat-bottomed boat. Before getting on this ferry, I engaged four women from the village, to help the nurses transfer the youngsters from our boat to the ferry, and from the ferry to the steamer.

As we approached the steamer, the "rail-hangers" caught sight of the infants, and within a minute or so, it looked as if their boat might capsize, so many of the passengers rushed to the rail to get a peep at the babies. I got on the steamer, elbowed my way through the crowd, and finally reached the comprador, on the second deck. I asked him where he would place the little ones, but imagine my feelings when he told me that he could not make room for even one new passenger! He encouraged me, however, by saying that another big boat was following and that I could easily get accommodations on it. By this time at least half of the babies had been transferred from the ferry to the boat, but there was nothing to do but shift them right back again and row back to the dock to await the next steamer.

Fifteen minutes later we were being ferried out to the next and last steamer for Hong Kong that day. As soon as the comprador, who was watching our approach, saw the infants, he motioned for us to go back, but I was too anxious to get on his boat to heed his gestures. When the boat came to a stop, I got on and started to mount the stairs that led to the second deck. The comprador himself met me and told me that they were crowded and could not take on any more. I made an effort to reach the captain on the third deck, but before I could advance far, the boat started, and I was forced to get off. We returned a second time to our little boat at the dock, and I must admit that it was not pleasant to do so, since it would be twenty-four hours before the next steamer would arrive. The nurses sensed the difficulties and insisted on returning at once to Loting. But I knew that within an hour I could reach Father Chan's mission, and could then telegraph Father Walsh at Wuchow to reserve a cabin on tomorrow's Hong Kong boat.

Before forwarding the message, the operator handed me a bill for five dollars and eighty-two cents. This seemed very expensive, and when I considered that I could actually go to Wuchow for sixty cents, and be able to return on the same boat on which I was now trying to make reservation, I decided not to send the telegram but to go directly.

As it was then ten p.m. and the boat to Wuchow was due to leave about two a.m., it was hardly worth while returning to the babies. Then, too, Father Chan's boy promised to go down early the next morning and remain with them until I should return from Wuchow.

At one a.m. I got up, dressed, and waited till one-thirty. At two we hurried to the dock, and I was considerably cheered by the news that our boat had not yet arrived. We waited just three hours before it came.

The boat anchored at Wuchow at noon. I hastened immediately to the steamer that was to leave at two p.m. for Hong Kong, secured a cabin for this trip, and then started to find Father Walsh's mission. There was just about enough time with him to explain my visit and eat dinner, when I had to leave to catch the boat.

Once started on this steamer and moving down the river, I felt as though our troubles were over. For would it not be an easy matter to pick up the babies at Namkonghau, place them in the nice cabin reserved for them, and then let the nurses do the rest?

As we neared Namkonghau, I could plainly see our little boat at the dock, and concluded that the babies were on the ferry that was coming out to the steamer. I then went to the lower deck, elbowed my way through the steerage passengers, and finally arrived at the gangway where the new passengers would enter.

It did not take me long to see that there were no babies on the ferry, and I shouted to the ferryman to tell me where they were. "Over there," answered he, pointing to the direction of our ship. I took this to mean that they had come out in another ferry on the other side. I hurried up to the first deck and scanned the whole water line of the vessel on that side, but could see no boats. Then I asked one of the crew if any babies had been brought aboard, and he replied that he didn't see any. Down again I went to the ferryman and asked him if the babies were still on the dock, and he told me they were!

By this time the steamer had started to move, and before I realized it, we were fast approaching the ship's full speed. I hurried to the captain and asked him to please stop the boat for a few minutes. I'll remember that captain to my dying day, for he had the ship almost at a standstill before he heard the full reason for my request. I then sent a message to the owner of our small boat and requested him to row down to the steamer. At the same time the captain gave orders to have his steamer pull in towards the shore. In this way our little boat, when it arrived, was able to push right next to the gangplank that was let down, and the transfer of the babies was effected without much trouble and in a remarkably short time.

This was when I felt like "saying something"—but to what effect? The Chinese passengers were enjoying the affair as much, perhaps, as they would their evening chow; and any indication on my part that I did not agree with them would but lower me in their estimation. I simply retired to my own cabin and congratulated myself that my entire party was together again.

The rest of the journey was uneventful. It was about three p.m. the next day when we docked at the Hong Kong pier. In response to a telegram sent by Father Walsh to our procure, to "have automobiles meet Father McShane and party," I found the procurator himself and two clerical visitors at the pier to welcome us.

I doubt if Hong Kong ever had in its midst more innocent "greenhorns" than those nurses of mine. Previous to landing, the leader of the three suggested that I buy a couple of big baskets to carry the babies to the Sisters' orphanage. I told her I would get something better than baskets. So when the little ones were all placed in the automobiles, I told the nurses to get in, also. I noticed they were very reluctant to do so. And why shouldn't they be? They had never in their lives, except at marriage, been carried by coolies, and it never entered their minds that they were now to have such a privilege repeated. They were willing enough to have their baggage carried, but they insisted on placing themselves behind the automobiles, expecting, of course, that the automobiles would be carried by coolies, and they could follow on foot. We finally got them into the cars, and just what passed through their minds when the machines began to move, and more rapidly, too, would be interesting, indeed, to learn.

It did not take long to reach the Sisters' orphanage, where the infants were received with open arms. When they were finally bunked in little, clean, white beds, I could not but think how fortunate they were to be placed in the hands of the good Sisters. And I thought, too, how fortunate I was in being able, through the generosity of American friends, to finance such an undertaking, for I know there are hundreds of other missioners who, for lack of money, would have been helpless to rescue these infants. It was well worth the money and trouble, and I was glad to have shared in it.

THE MARTYRDOM OF ST. JOHN
DE BREBEUF

by Christopher Regnaut

Few works of history can compare with the monumental and priceless Jesuit Relations—the diaries, reports and accounts of the early missioners to North America. From these records we have extracted this account of one of our American martyrs, written by one of the heroic laymen who assisted the Jesuits in their work.

Father John de Brebeuf and Father Gabriel L'Alemant had set out from our cabin, to go to a small Village, called St. Ignace, distant from our cabin about a short quarter of a League, to instruct the Savages and the new Christians of that Village. It was on the 16th Day of March, in the morning, that we perceived a great fire at the place to which these two good Fathers had gone. This fire made us very uneasy; we did not know whether it were enemies, or if the fire had caught in some of the huts of the village. The Reverend Father Paul Raguenau, our Superior, immediately Resolved to send some one to learn what might be the cause. But no sooner had we formed the design of going there to see, than we perceived several savages on the road, coming straight toward us. We all thought it was the Iroquois who were coming to attack us; but, having considered them more closely, we perceived that they were Hurons who were fleeing from the fight, and who had escaped from the combat. These poor savages caused great pity in us. They were all covered with wounds. One had his head fractured; another his arm broken; another had an arrow in his eye; another had his hand cut off by a blow from a hatchet. In fine, the day was passed in receiving into our cabins all these poor wounded people, and in looking with compassion toward the fire, and the place where were those two good Fathers. We saw the fire and the barbarians, but we could not see anything of the two Fathers.

This is what these Savages told us of the taking of the Village of St. Ignace, and about Fathers John de Brebeuf and Gabriel L'Alemant:

"The Iroquois came, to the number of twelve hundred men; took our village, and seized Father Brebeuf and his companion; and set fire to all the huts. They proceeded to vent their rage on those two Fathers; for they took them both and stripped them entirely naked, and fastened each to a post. They tied both of their hands together. They tore the nails from their fingers. They beat them with a shower of blows from cudgels, on the shoulders, the loins, the belly, the legs, and the face,—there being no part of their body which did not endure this torment."

The savages told us further, that, although Father de Brebeuf was overwhelmed under the weight of these blows, he did not cease continually to speak of God, and to encourage all the new Christians who were captives like himself to suffer well, that they might die well, in order to go in company with him to Paradise. While the good Father was thus encouraging these good people, a wretched Huron renegade,—who had remained a captive with the Iroquois, and whom Father de Brebeuf had formerly instructed and baptized,—hearing him speak of Paradise and Holy Baptism, was irritated, and said to him, "Echon," that is Father de Brebeuf's name in Huron, "thou sayest that Baptism and the sufferings of this life lead straight to Paradise; thou wilt go soon, for I am going to baptize thee, and to make thee suffer well, in order to go the sooner to thy Paradise." The barbarian, having said that, took a kettle full of boiling water, which he poured over his body three different times, in derision of Holy baptism. And, each time that he baptized him in this manner, the barbarian said to him with bitter sarcasm, "Go to Heaven, for thou art well baptized."

After that, they made him suffer several other torments. The first was to make hatchets red-hot, and to apply them to the loins and under the armpits. They made a collar of these red-hot hatchets, and put it on the neck of this good Father. This is the fashion in which I have seen the collar made for other prisoners: They make six hatchets red-hot, take a large withe of green wood, pass the six hatchets over the large end of the withe, take the two ends together, and then put it over the neck of the sufferer. I have seen no torment which more moved me to compassion than that. For you see a man, bound naked to a post, who, having this collar on his neck, cannot tell what posture to take. For, if he lean forward, those above his shoulders weigh the more on him; if he lean back, those on his stomach make him suffer the same torment; if he keep erect, without leaning to one side or other, the burning hatchets, applied equally on both sides, give him a double torture.

After that they put on him a belt of bark, full of pitch and resin, and set afire to it, which roasted his whole body. During all these torments, Father de Brebeuf endured like a rock, insensible to fire and flames, which astonished all the bloodthirsty wretches who tormented him. His zeal was so great that he preached continually to these infidels, to try to convert them. His executioners were enraged against him for constantly speaking to them of God and of their conversion. To prevent him from speaking more, they cut off his tongue, and both his upper and lower lips. After that, they set themselves to strip the flesh from his legs, thighs, and arms, to the very bone; and then put it to roast before his eyes, in order to eat it.

While they tormented him in this manner, those wretches derided him, saying: "Thou seest plainly that we treat thee as a friend, since we shall be the cause of thy Eternal happiness; thank us, then, for these good offices which we render thee,— for, the more thou shalt suffer, the more will thy God reward thee."

Those butchers, seeing that the good Father began to grow weak, made him sit down on the ground; and, one of them, taking a knife, cut off the skin covering his skull. Another one of those barbarians, seeing that the good Father would soon die, made an opening in the upper part of his chest, and tore out his heart, which he roasted and ate. Others came to drink his blood, still warm, which they drank with both hands,—saying that Father de Brebeuf had been very courageous to endure so much pain as they had given him, and that, by drinking his blood, they would become courageous like him.

This is what we learned of the Martyrdom and blessed death of Father John de Brebeuf, by several Christian savages worthy of belief, who had been constantly present from the time the good Father was taken until his death. These good Christians were prisoners to the Iroquois, who were taking them into their country to be put to death. But our good God granted them the favor of enabling them to escape by the way; and they came to us to recount all that I have set down in writing.

Father de Brebeuf was captured on the 16th day of March, in the morning, with Father L'Alemant, in the year 1649. Father de Brebeuf died the same day as his capture, about 4 o'clock in the afternoon. Those barbarians threw the remains of his body into the fire; but the fat which still remained on his body extinguished the fire, and he was not consumed.

I do not doubt that all which I have just related is true, and I would seal it with my blood; for I have seen the same treatment given to Iroquois prisoners whom the Huron savages had taken in war, with the exception of the boiling water, which I have not seen poured on any one.

I am about to describe to you truly what I saw of the Martyrdom and of the Blessed deaths of Father John de Brebeuf and of Father Gabriel L'Alemant. On the next morning, when we had assurance of the departure of the enemy, we went to the spot to seek for the remains of their bodies, to the place where their lives had been taken. We found them both, but a little apart from each other. They were brought to our cabin, and laid uncovered upon the bark of trees,—where I examined them at leisure, for more than two hours, to see if what the savages had told us of their martyrdom and death were true. I examined first the Body of Father de Brebeuf, which was pitiful to see, as well as that of Father L'Alemant. Father de Brebeuf had his legs, thighs, and arms stripped of flesh to the very bone; I saw and touched a large number of great blisters, which he had on several places on his body, from the boiling water which these barbarians had poured over him in mockery of Holy Baptism. I saw and touched the wound from a belt of bark, full of pitch and resin, which roasted his whole body. I saw and touched the marks of burns from the Collar of hatchets placed on his shoulders and stomach. I saw and touched his two lips, which they had cut off because he constantly spoke of God while they made him suffer.

I saw and touched all parts of his body, which had received more than two hundred blows from a stick. I saw and touched the top of his scalped head; I saw and touched the opening which these barbarians had made to tear out his heart.

In fine, I saw and touched all the wounds of his body, as the savages had told and declared to us; we buried these precious Relics on Sunday, the 21st day of March, 1649, with much Consolation.

It is not a Doctor of the Sorbonne who has composed this, as you may easily see; it is a relic from the Iroquois, and a person who has lived more than thought.

NOT A THING FOR HIMSELF

by Sister Maria del Rey

> As a Pittsburgh newspaper reporter, she was the girl who
> always got her story. Now as a Maryknoller, Sister Maria
> del Rey keeps her talent busy. Here she reproduces a
> story she heard in Chile about the late Father Thomas
> R. Wellinghoff.

Know Padre Tomas? Of course, I did! He was my best friend.
Absolutely, my best friend. Though, come to think of it, you'd
be hard put to find anybody here in Curepto he wasn't the best
friend of.

I was here when he came, a fresh young padre straight from
the States, with the gringo accent heavy on his tongue. We
weren't too happy then to have a foreign priest. He might change
our old easy-going ways. I was here also on that sad Sunday
morning when they announced in Church before the Mass,
"Padre Tomas died suddenly of a heart attack half an hour ago.
Please pray for his soul." I still hear the gasp that followed—the
silence before we sank to our knees. It wasn't that the parish
had lost a pastor. Each of us had lost his dear son. And yet,
though it seems strange to say it, as we looked on that young
face in the white stillness of the coffin, we knew we had lost a
father too.

It's only on looking back that you can see how he was a father

* From *In and Out the Andes* by Sister Maria del Rey. Copyright, Maryknoll
Sisters. Publisher, Charles Scribner's Sons.

to us—correcting us, guiding us, pushing us firmly into the right path. You wouldn't think, to see him riding down the main street with his cape flying out behind, with a hand lifted in greeting to everybody, from the smallest *chico* playing in the mud to the the rich old mayor himself—you wouldn't think that he took his job as spiritual father seriously. He had the nicest way of doing it.

"You're just like my own mother," he told my senora, on his very first visit to our home. "Let me call you Mama!" I don't remember now that he even waited for her answer. We're not the priesting kind of a family. Don't know of any priest on either side, at all, at all. But from then on it was "Mama" every time he crossed the threshold.

My old lady's not so well. She takes medicine for her liver right along. I remember well that Padre Tomas got to questioning her about it. It was pretty plain, I guess, that we didn't have too much money and he probably knew (as everybody in town knew) that most of my pay went to the tavern. Heaven help me, that's the way it was! Well, Padre Tomas said to my old wife, "Mama, I'm going to Santiago next week. I'll get you some of that medicine there."

My back began to stiffen and so did Luisa's. We're poor and I have my faults, I know, but still we're not letting strangers. . . .

"Padre," says Luisa slowly, "my senor can buy what I need."

Padre Tomas laughed aloud. He came over and gave my senora a big hug. "Of course, he can!" he said. "Of course! But you're Mama to me here in Curepto, so let me have the happiness of getting medicine for my Mama."

Claro! It was so plain. A man has the right to get medicine for his Mama, hasn't he? You couldn't get insulted at that, could you? All the same, it stung me that my wife's medicine came from another pocket than mine. I thought of it the next time I went into the tavern. I thought of it—and marched right out the door with my pay squeezed tight in my pocket.

But that's the way he was. Never any sour looks. Smiling and laughing that big all-over laugh all the time, but firm and steady underneath. A number of fellows used to hang around outside the bar. When they saw Padre Tomas hurrying down the street, they'd call.

"Come over and have a drink, Padre!"

He'd wave and laugh. "I'm in a hurry now, boys. Can't do it. But I'll be seeing you later."

Everywhere he went people loaded him down with gifts. His pockets were always bulging. Then he'd go into Old Magdalena's home next door to ours and say, "Look what I found on the bush outside your door. You've got a wonderful plant there, Magdalena. It grows buns and oranges and meat loaf all on the same bush!" and Magdalena would say, "Now Padre, the people give you those things for yourself!"

"They gave it to the wrong fellow, then," he'd reply, filling up her cupboard as if he lived there and had a right to go to her cupboard at any time.

And so he had! He was in and out of our houses like he owned every one of them. No one ever thought to invite him in any more than you'd tell your brother he was free to come in. He knew it without anybody's word.

He knew us so well, he never stood on ceremony. Said just what he thought and never tried to act like a guest when we all knew he was one of the family. That's how he cured Maria Lopez of her quick temper.

Maria's a wonderful woman; don't let anybody tell you different. She's been a school teacher here for twenty years and supports her mother by it. What's more, her sister Josefina isn't quite right in the head, so Maria does sewing on the side to pay for Josefina's staying in an asylum up in Curico. Maria gets to know about many poor children in school. In a quiet way she gives them things they need; two of them she took into her house and brings them up as her own. So you see Maria's a fine woman. But she does get mad at people, and stays mad for a long, long time.

Well, Maria was real good to Padre Tomas. He liked to go over there for dinner and jolly up her old mother who's always complaining about her aches and pains. Then one day, Maria killed her pig and she sent Padre Tomas the head as a present. That's the custom in our town. When you kill a pig you divide it among your friends and they do the same for you.

Padre Tomas sent the head back to Maria with a note. "Why don't you cook it for me, too, Maria? I'm coming over tomorrow night and we'll enjoy it."

Now Maria's a good cook. She does things in the Chilean way. This head she was going to make extra-special so she put in a lot of *ahi*. *Ahi* is a small plant, but is it hot! Padre Tomas took one bite and all but spit it out.

"What are you trying to do, Maria? Poison me?" Then he started joking with her mother, "How I pity you, Senora! To live with Maria, the worst cook in Curepto!" and lots more of the same.

Maria started to boil inside. Poor thing, you can see her side of it. Working all day over a special treat and then being called the worst cook in Curepto. She flounced out of the room in a rage.

Padre Tomas thought she'd get over it, but things began to look serious when she did not go to Communion for three days. She, who was a daily communicant for years. So the Padre sailed right into the battle. That was his way when he saw things go amiss.

"I've missed you these mornings, Maria. You're in church but you don't receive Our Lord."

"I can't." Maria was stiff as a board.

"Why not? Come on, out with it, Maria."

"If you must know, Padre," she said, "I'm mad at you. Terribly, terribly mad. So mad, that it's a big sin."

Padre Tomas laughed again. "I'm not that important, Maria. Being mad at me is no big sin."

"I'd have to go to confession, Padre. And I won't go."

"Well, if being mad at me is all you've got on your conscience, don't bother to confess it. Lots of good holy people get mad at me. Go on to Communion, Maria."

She did, but she was still pretty stiff. A couple days later he went to visit her mother. Maria opened the door for him but disappeared right away. Padre Tomas gave her mother a crucifix.

"This is for you, Mamita," he said in a loud voice. "And there's another for Maria when she learns not to get mad over nothing."

It was that night Maria sent him a big dish of pig's head—without *ahi*.

I don't think the man ever rested. He seemed to be going all day around Curepto or up in the hill district of this big parish. You'd see him in the morning after Mass visiting the school, giving out report cards or seeing about some rapscallion who was causing trouble. Then he'd be out meeting a funeral and walking down the village street in black stole. Next you'd see him chatting with the market women and going away with his pockets stuffed. (Poor fellow, he gave it all away; he ate like a sparrow when he was by himself, his housekeeper said.) His cassock was out at the elbows and his shoes were only uppers. "I like a man with his feet on the ground," he used to answer when we joked him about it.

Then you'd see him in the middle of a bunch of boys. He took them down to the seaside for two days, once, and spent 600 pesos for ice cream cones. The boys will never forget it.

At night, often, he'd thunder through town on his big white horse flying out to a hut 25 or 30 kilometers away, where some poor fellow was giving his soul back to God. Before he came to Curepto, we never called the Padre at night nor did we ask him to come long distances. But Padre Tomas let it be known that he wanted to be called. "Just let me know," he said. "Any time, any place, for anybody. We all need help when we're dying."

I went with him on a week-end trip, once. That's how I know he was a man of iron. I'm no softie myself, but I couldn't go at his speed. We left Saturday after he was through hearing confessions in the afternoon. We rode 40 kilometers through bad mud to *La Hornilla* (The Little Oven), arriving around midnight. I turned in, but Padre Tomas sat up awhile saying his prayers by the light of a candle dip. In the morning when I woke, he was busy hearing confessions before the Mass!

After breakfast, he started around visiting the sick who couldn't come. He knew all their names and all their symptoms.

"Let's go up to see the L-Shaped Lady," he said when I was all for getting back to have dinner and a bit of rest.

So we went. And went. And went. Climbing up a steep hill to the last house in La Hornilla. There was Old Juana bent, just like he said, to the letter L. Padre Tomas started emptying his pockets. "I know who has a sweet tooth!" he exulted. "I got a package of candy from my folks in the States."

She was delighted. Padre Tomas was on his knees before her because the old lady was so bent over she could not see his face otherwise.

"Ay, Padre!" she cackled over toothless gums. "Sugar and spice and all things nice. That's me. But I'm not always so sweet, sorry to say. Oh, I knew you wouldn't come to La Hornilla and not be up to hear my confession."

That's the way he was. He heard her confession and we went back to get our mounts. We were due at Conception, 10 kilometers away, to hear confessions and say Mass the next morning.

It was dusk when we came into town. It was "Hello!" here and "Buenos noches!" there all along the street. "How's your baby?" to one and "Mass is at 7," to another. He was hardly down from his horse when he started off again to visit the sick and arrange to bring Holy Communion to them. Me? I was all in! I saw to the horses, ate a bit of supper and went to bed. I remember waking up during the night and hearing Padre Tomas and our host, Don Ramon, playing cards.

Does that shock you? Oh, Padre Tomas was a whizz at any card game. Don Ramon wasn't very much of a Catholic. In fact, hadn't been to church for years even when the Padre brought Mass right to his front door. But he loved cards and Padre could play them. He got him, too, over the card table. It wasn't a year before Don Ramon renounced his Masonry and came back to the Church.

The best trick Padre Tomas ever played came just about a month before that fearful announcement in church on Sunday, November 20, 1949. It was right that the Good Lord let him have that last fling, seeing as how He was going to take him so soon.

Each year in Curepto we elect a Queen of the Carnival—sort of a Queen of the May. For us, down south of the Equator, November is the month of Our Lady. Everything's springtime then. It's our loveliest month.

The Queen of the Carnival contest is run by the township to make a little money for the public works. Whichever girl can sell the most votes wins. With a system like that, it's plain that the richest girl will win. It's always been that way in Curepto and we common folk didn't mind it too much. We're used to it.

But Padre Tomas was different. He determined that a poor girl would be Queen. He chose a policeman's daughter, Teresa, a nice girl and pretty as a picture. For a time, in the early days of the contest, he let her work hard selling votes to her friends. But soon, she was running a very bad second to old Don Carlos' girl, because Don Carlos could hang a sword over many a man's head if he didn't buy votes from his daughter.

Padre Tomas went to the police chief then. "Look here," he said. "It's up to you *carabinieros* to put Teresa on top. But let's not let Don Carlos know. You get votes from every man on the police force for Teresa and I'll get them from the parish school. But we won't reveal them until the last minute. That way, Don Carlos won't have time to throw in more votes for his girl."

The last night of the contest everybody was in the town plaza. The mayor was getting in late votes and reading out the score. Don Carlos was away out in front; so far out, he felt mighty sure of himself. It was just like every other year. The contest was closing in another minute, when Padre Tomas stepped over to the rostrum and handed a packet of votes to the mayor. You should have seen his face!

"But . . . but . . . but . . ." he sputtered.

"No buts about it, Your Honor," the Padre said. "These votes are for Teresa and they're in before the deadline."

The mayor in a trembling voice read out the score, afraid to look at Don Carlos. Teresa's score made everybody else's look like a dead fish

The town went mad with delight. We never knew before how much we really wanted a Queen from one of ourselves. Teresa and her court were everybody's darlings. There never, never was such a fiesta in Curepto. People came from a long way off to sit in our plaza and watch the happy faces of us all. It was a poor man's fiesta. As they say, God must love poor people because He made so many of them. That fiesta was the best Curepto had ever known.

Padre Tomas was tired, I guess, although he kept going the same as always. Every evening he had devotions in Church for *La Mes de Maria*—like the May devotions you have up North. He had funerals, weddings, baptisms, sick calls, and mission trips. Then on Saturday, the 19th, he carefully prepared his sermon for the next day. It was on the Last Judgment. He went to bed late, as usual. Around 5:00 next morning Padre Martin heard him call. It was almost too late to get the oils and administer Extreme Unction. In half an hour, Padre Tomas was dead. Dead, at thirty-two years! Padre Tomas was dead.

Can you imagine how we felt? Can you picture us in church as we came to Mass that Sunday morning and heard Padre Martin say, "Padre Tomas died half an hour ago. Let us now pray for the repose of his soul."

They kept his body four days in church, dressed in the Holy Mass vestments. People came in and went out, came in and went out all day long. Me? I stayed there. In a corner of the church I watched them come and go. *Huasos* from the *fundos* far away rode up to the church door and left their dusty sweating horses tied to a pole while they knelt beside his bier. Children wandered in after school hours and said the rosary on their fingers for him.

"He gave me a haircut," one boy boasted as a group went out. "He pulled out this front tooth!" said another. Old and young women were there all the time looking at his clean strong features and thinking of his mother so far away. "He said I was just like his sister," I heard them say. "And I was like his aunt." I smiled to myself. Padre Tomas' relatives sure looked like a lot of different people!

Don Carlos came in, too. And the mayor. The two of them

forgot all about the contest. Nobody was ever mad at Padre Tomas long. Not even Maria.

Wednesday we buried him in the little cemetery outside of town. The crowd filled our main street, and surged along the road up the hill. I thought of the hundreds of times Padre Tomas had climbed that hill to consign one of us in Curepto to his last resting place. And now we were trudging after his coffin. The Bishop of Talca was there and twenty-five of his fellow priests from Maryknoll. The Mayor and city treasurer, the *fundo* owners, the store-keepers, the school teachers and their children. *Huasos* and country people, farmers in their ox carts, and of course everybody who lived in Curepto. There were thousands in our town that day. It was the biggest affair Curepto had ever seen.

The band was out, too. Now we are mighty proud of our band. It has won more than one medal in the provincial contests. But when it was time to play while the body was being lowered into the grave, Pablo the clarinetist couldn't find his reed mouthpiece, and the band had to play on without him.

This was serious for Pablo. The mouthpiece is small and you can't get them anywhere but in Santiago. Poor Pablo turned his pockets inside out and searched the tall grass on the cemetery long after the crowd had gone. Juan the bandleader helped him search. A band without a clarinet isn't much good. But it was no use. Then a sudden inspiration seized Juan.

"Let's ask Padre Tomas to help us find it, Pablo," he said. "Surely, even up there above he can't forget us in Curepto."

Down the two of them went on their knees in the freshly turned earth. Then they turned to go home.

"There isn't much use looking," Pablo said as they plodded home in the thick dust which thousands had trampled that morning. "And yet I can't help hoping . . ." And there it was, as plain as day, sitting on top of a rut in the road!

That's why, here in Curepto, when a child loses his school pencil the Mama will say, "Pray to Padre Tomas. He helps careless boys to find their lost things."

That's why, too, you will find in any hut in this wide parish a little picture of Padre Tomas tacked to the wall and sometimes there's a candle in front of it.

Padre Tomas lives with us still even though four years have gone by since he died so suddenly. His spirit is part of us. He never kept anything for himself. Not even the love we gave him. That, he gave to God. It was not because we loved him for himself that we went to Mass oftener and tried to live better lives. That's proved because we are still going to Mass and still trying, even though another priest has taken his place. No, Padre Tomas took nothing for himself. Not even our love.

BIG BABY

by Albert J. Nevins

Africa's prehistoric "water horse" is far from extinct. When angry, he moves his 8,000 pounds with express train speed, bites with a four foot mouth. Here in a few paragraphs is his life story.

The story is told in Nairobi of a certain Hollywood actor who turned up in the city late one night, white and shaken. The actor had left Nairobi late that afternoon to drive north towards Mount Kenya, where his company was on location, and acquaintances were surprised when he reappeared so soon after leaving.

After a doctor arrived and gave the screen hero an injection of vitamin B to quiet his nerves, the actor told an incoherent story. Shortly after dusk, driving along a lonely road, he had noticed a large shadow coming towards his jeep. Suddenly his headlights picked out a huge monster "as large as a house," with fire coming out of its eyes and its whole body glistening. The beast let out a roar that shook the earth. Without waiting to see more, the actor whirled his jeep around and sped back to the safety of Nairobi.

The next morning some friends accompanied the actor to the spot, and there the mystery became revealed. From tracks in the dirt, the monster was identified as an ordinary hippopotamus. The fiery eyes and glistening body were probably caused by headlight reflection. The rest was imagination.

Even for an African veteran, a chance meeting with a hippo can be a startling experience. The hippo is the second largest animal in the world, exceeded only by the elephant. A full-grown hippo weighs about 8,000 pounds; stands 4 feet tall and about 14 feet long; it is built close to the ground, and has short legs. To find this relic of prehistoric days suddenly lumbering towards one is a very disconcerting experience.

The hippo has a thick grayish-brown skin, sometimes several inches deep. A reddish sweat usually covers the beast's body. This sweat is an oily substance that serves to keep the skin moist when the animal is out of water, and also acts as a water-repellent when the hippo is swimming or bathing. The red color comes from flecks of blood.

The hippo is a very timid animal and has learned to shun man. By day the beast usually hides in rivers and lakes with only its eyes and nostrils protruding. At night it comes on land in quest of food. Sometimes in the day, the huge animals, which live in herds, play with one another, rising up and down in the water, splashing about, and having a gay time.

The hippo's body is nearly all stomach, and naturally the beast must consume mountains of food. Its ordinary diet consists of plants growing in shallow water, but at night it feeds along the banks and often goes in search of cultivated fields. With its four-foot-wide mouth and long teeth, the huge beast makes short work of a cornfield. What it doesn't eat is destroyed by being trampled underfoot. It is his destructive powers while eating that makes the hippo so unpopular among farmers.

Whenever a hippo makes its appearance, the natives try to kill it before they are eaten out of house and home. The usual method is to capture it by strategy rather than by bold attack. Once wounded or frightened, it becomes a charging means of death.

The natives have many stories that illustrate the ferocity of the hippo when it is in danger. Once in Lake Victoria a hippo charged a canoe, upset it, and bit its occupants almost in half. There are many cases of unwary natives being trampled to death at night or while swimming. Hippos have attacked steamboats.

Many a missioner in Africa is called, when a hippo is on a crop-pillaging foray, to do with a gun what native spears have failed to accomplish. If the missioner is successful, a big feast is ensured the natives.

Brother Fidelis, of Maryknoll's Musoma mission, shot a hippo in Lake Victoria one day. The natives towed the monster to shallow water, and then scores of men waded in and rolled the hippo over and over until dry land was reached. As soon as the huge beast was high and dry, it seemed as if every native in the region descended upon it. Knives rose and fell, the skin was ripped away, and soon excited feasting was going on all along the shore. The hide was saved. The huge teeth were kept as ivory.

A hippo mother has one baby a year. The baby is born in the water. Because the infant cannot swim, it clings to its mother's neck. The mother hippo has to protect her young from crocodiles and other enemies, as well as from male hippos, which seem to resent infant intrusion into the herd. The hippo reaches adulthood in about five years, and will live for about twenty-five years more.

The largest concentration of hippos is to be found in Uganda, across Lake Victoria from the Maryknoll mission. The beasts are becoming rare sights in the populated areas, but still flourish in the remote and swampy districts. But even in the Musoma section, bands of hippos are often seen sporting in the lake by day, and at night the roars and cries of fighting males can be frequently heard.

The hippo serves one good purpose. Because of his enormous appetite, he keeps shore lines free of tangled tropical growth.

HOW TO BE A WITCH

by Francis X. Lyons

> The shortage of priests has allowed the Andean Indian
> to drift into a mixture of paganism and Catholicism.
> Father Lyons describes the beliefs of some of the people
> among whom he works.

If you have a sick cow or a lazy wife, Mr. Yatiri is the man to
see. This medicine man will slip the bundle off his back, peer
inside it, and bring out a smelly salve, made of pig's fat, for the
sick cow. Or he will chant a special incantation to drive out the
laziness and the other undesirable qualities of your spouse. Mr.
Yatiri is proud of his profession; it is an ancient one.

Before the Spanish Padres came to Bolivia, bringing the Catholic Faith with them, the mountain Indians had a highly developed
religion. They believed in an all-powerful god, whom they called
Viracocha. This god delegated most of his work to a whole galaxy
of minor gods, such as the Sun, the Moon, the stars, and the
various other heavenly bodies.

These Indians thought of Thunder as the weather god. He was
clad in brilliant garments, and held a war club in one hand, a sling
in the other. The lightning was the flash of his garments as he
strode through the heavens; the bolt of lightning was the boulder
from his sling. Thunder kept the rain in a huge jug he borrowed
from his sister. Rain fell to the earth when Thunder broke the
jug with his slingshot.

They believed the Moon to be the wife of the Sun. To the
Indians an eclipse of the moon meant that a mountain lion was

trying to devour the moon. Hence their custom of making a great deal of noise during an eclipse. They were attempting to scare off the attacker.

Centuries ago medicine men traveled among the Indians. Even today men like Mr. Yatiri make a pretty good living for themselves by playing on the superstitious beliefs of these unlettered, mountain people.

When an Indian has a complaint, he looks up Mr. Yatiri. The conversation is likely to be as follows:

"Senor Yatiri, I don't know what is the matter with me. I've been like this for three months now, and I thought maybe you—"

Mr. Yatiri frowns, pulls at his beard, and asks: "How do you stand financially? Do you perhaps own a home, a farm, or some cattle?" The medicine man smiles with relief at the affirmative reply, and goes into his diagnosis:

"Now the trouble with you is that your heirs are bewitching you. They are hoping that you will die, so that they can inherit your property. Take this holy dust, and mix it in a glass of water. Be sure to take a dose of this each morning. And here is some salve; you must rub your whole body with it at least once a day. Tonight I'll come to your house to chase away the evil spirit. Mind that you have some good liquor on hand. My fee is one hundred pesos, please."

It's as simple as that, this business of being a medicine man. But it has its occupational hazards, too. If the Indian thinks that Mr. Yatiri is not giving him his money's worth, all the Indian has to do is rub oil over his head and body—and the evil that afflicts him will transfer itself to the medicine man.

If you would like to be a witch, the Indians say, you must start a collection of ropes that have been used for hanging criminals. Other helpful things are skulls; fistfuls of hair from a man who died in horrible pain. You can add the finishing touches to your collection if you obtain a few teeth of a woman who died from a snake bite.

If you become a witch, you mustn't sleep in uninhabited places, for these are where the ghostmen will get you. They look like little, old men who are forever smiling. It is their kindly aspect that will lead you to destruction. Ghostmen live in abandoned caves, in houses set far out in the wilderness, and in rivers. They lie in wait for the unwary.

If you should manage to escape the ghostmen, you are liable to bump into the *mekhala*. This type of evil spirit has the aspect of a skinny woman with greasy, disheveled hair. Her eyes are mean and deep-set, and throw off frightful sparks. Her work is to steal the brains, and sometimes the souls, of the children whom she finds sleeping. The only way you can ward off her attack is by devotion to *Pacha-Mamma* (which translated, means Earth Mother).

But be careful how you celebrate Earth Mother's feast day! On the night before Pentecost, you must call all your friends and neighbors to the house. On a table in your back yard, pile up all the money you made during the year, and all the jewels you own. Then get hold of the best liquor and sprinkle it in all the dark corners. This procedure, plus a short prayer to Earth Mother, should do the trick. All the evil spirits will then leave you alone. At least until they get over being drunk!

The Indians believe that a rainbow appears in the sky for only one reason, and that is to announce bad luck. Whatever you do, don't point to the rainbow, or your finger will drop off. Do not let your children look at the rainbow, or they will die. If you have the bad luck to see it, close your mouth quickly, so that your teeth won't fall out.

These are a few of the superstitions that have endured from ancient times. The mountain Indians believe in them. In general, an Indian sees no difficulty in being a Catholic and practicing these superstitions on the side. If he has any scruples, Mr. Yatiri will remove them for a fee.

Inadvertently, I have been giving the medicine man a lot of business. I just discovered that, if the priest visits an Indian's house, the Indian will surely die of hunger, with his stomach plastered to his spine! I'm sure this is a modern notion, invented by Mr. Yatiri.

I can just see Mr. Yatiri following me from house to house, casting out the evil spirits that he says I left behind.

THE MAN WHO MAPPED

THE AMAZON

by Marion Lansing

> As in North America, many of the great pioneers and
> explorers of South America were Jesuit missioners.
> Among these, the name of Father Samuel Fritz ranks
> high. This biography tells why.

On the streets of the luxury-loving Spanish city of Lima, Peru,
there appeared one day in the year 1692 a strange figure: a priest,
tall, thin, with ruddy countenance and long, curly beard. He was
wearing a short cassock of palm fiber instead of the usual cloth
robe, with hempen sandals on his feet and a cross of chonta
wood in his hand. With him walked several Indians, tall, fine-
looking men, but of strange face and dress, different from the
natives of the Peruvian capital.

It was as if in the days of the New Testament John the Baptist had suddenly appeared from the wilderness in his garment of
camel's hair on the fashionable streets of Rome or Alexandria.
The people ran together from all parts of the city to see the sight,
but while they gazed curiously, there was no one who did not
know from the mere sight of Father Fritz that he was a holy man.
They conducted him to the establishment of the Jesuits, and
there the members of his own order received him warmly, and

* From *Against All Odds*. Copyright, Doubleday, Doran & Co.

his Indians with him. There he waited until an audience with the viceroy could be arranged.

Until our own century Father Samuel Fritz, Jesuit missionary in South America at the end of the seventeenth century and the beginning of the eighteenth, was known chiefly by his map of the Amazon River. During the forty years of his service as "Apostle to the Indians," he drew and redrew this map of the Amazon region which was to be used by explorers who followed him. It is no such map as used to appear in the old school geographies and in medieval wonder books, with wild beasts and picturesque Indians drawn in to fill spaces which would otherwise have been marked unknown. This is an amazing, detailed, intricate drawing, which looks like a picture of the blood stream of the human body, with hundreds of arteries and veins running out from a central trunk. Most of these lines, and the spaces between them, are labeled with names—strange, unfamiliar Indian names—and each of these wavy lines, so carefully sketched in, stands for a river or stream which Father Fritz saw with his own eyes. The distances between the rivers and streams that are shown as flowing into the main current of the Upper Amazon are measured or calculated. The heights of the falls have been taken and the levels of the waters recorded. Father Fritz was not given to extolling his own work. His hardships during his long missionary work are passed over lightly in his journal. But on the map is written in his own hand the statement that he has made it "with no little toil and exertion, having navigated the river in the greater part of its course as far as it is navigable."

Samuel Fritz was a native of Bohemia, born in 1654, a student who showed such intellectual brilliance during his years in the Jesuit college that his superiors in the order had marked him as one who would advance to high positions. But after a few years of university life he turned his back on these tempting prospects and chose the vocation of missionary, coming in 1686 to faraway Quito, now the capital of Ecuador, then a part of Peru, on the west coast of South America.

If he had stayed in Quito or gone south to Lima, where there were several Jesuit establishments, his life would not have differed very greatly from that which he had left behind. In Lima there were a university, a cathedral, and many churches. But it was to be six years before Father Fritz was to make his dramatic entry into Lima, and in the year of his arrival he did not expect ever to visit that city. The young missionary put behind him the opportunity for a comfortable life of teaching and elected to go out into the wilderness. He chose to make the difficult journey across the great mountain wall of the Andes and search out the wild Indian tribes of the river forests.

Father Fritz went alone and carried on most of his early work alone, save for the company of the "dear children," his natives whom he soon gathered around him. To them this tall, red-headed, kindly man was a miracle, sent straight from that heaven of which he told, to deliver them from their fears of evil spirits and nature gods and from their many misfortunes and diseases.

"I went without pause by day or night up and down the great river," he said of himself.

He carried in his canoe only his wooden cross, his small portable altar, and his bell to give the call to worship. The people came in crowds to listen to his preaching and were persuaded to gather in villages and learn the civilizing ways of the new faith. They brought their sick to him, and he did what he could for them, drawing on such medical knowledge as he possessed and a kindly wisdom about the laws of health.

It was not an easy miracle that he performed. There were those in every tribe who worked against him. He knew well that at any moment these "children of the forest," who looked on him as almost a divine being, might turn against him for some unknown cause or in anger at some simple word of reproof and put him out in the wilderness alone to die.

In the third year of his ministry he was taken desperately ill, with a swelling of the limbs and a fever, so that he was in constant pain and too weak to move himself. He was at the village of the Jurimaguas when this heavy sickness came upon him, and in that month the annual flood of the river brought the waters to such an extraordinary height that the whole village was almost covered. Most of the people fled to the forests, but the few who remained cared for him. He was moved to a shelter on the roof of one of the houses and lay there for three months, "only a handbreadth," as he wrote, "above the rushing flood." There he lay, sleepless from pain, although he might not have been able to sleep otherwise with the gruntings of the alligators and crocodiles and lizards beneath him. His devoted Indians brought him such small supplies of food as they could get, but the rats came and fed on it, becoming so bold that they gnawed his spoon and plate and the handle of his knife.

There came a day when he knew that he could stay no longer, unless it were to meet his death. He must get down the river to some place where he could receive medical aid. "More dead than alive," as he says, he was carried down the river in a canoe, into Portuguese territory, stopping first at a Christian mission station where he was kindly cared for and then being taken, because of the seriousness of his illness, to the city of Para, just inland from the Atlantic Ocean. Though he was so ill, he gathered much information on the way down the river for his map. He was always observing, recording, and sketching for his future use.

At Para, Father Fritz recovered his health but met other trouble. The governments of Spain and Portugal were disputing over the possession of the Upper Amazon basin. In the region where he had been laboring there were said to be markers, set up by a Portuguese explorer a half century earlier. Since Father Fritz came from the Spanish city of Quito, he was considered a Spanish disturber of the peace, who might make trouble among the Indians for the Portuguese traders as they came up the river claiming these villages.

Suspected of being a spy, he was detained in Para for twenty-two months, until finally orders came directly from the king in Portugal ordering his release and instructing the Brazilian officials to conduct him up the river to his mission. On this return journey he made great progress with his map, laying out the river's course and marking the streams which entered it.

It was a sad journey, however, and a sad return. Portuguese traders were entering all the villages, exchanging implements of iron, glass beads, and cheap manufactured articles for the sarsaparilla, balsam, gums, resins, and wax which the Indians had to offer. But such trading was only a beginning. The Portuguese carried off men, women and children to be sold on the coast as slaves. They were planning to do so in his own regime as soon as they had delivered him to his forest home. But when he came to that home other traders had been there before them. The villages were emptied or destroyed and the mission houses gone. The natives had fled before the white men's raids and the destruction caused by a severe earthquake.

When the news of the holy father's safe return spread, his people came out from their jungle homes to greet him with rejoicing. If he had been there, they told him, the earthquake would not have happened. It was a punishment sent by his God because of the wickedness of the Portuguese in imprisoning him. They carried him ashore from his canoe to the center of their new village, celebrating the event with feasting and dancing to the music of drums, fifes, and wood flutes. It is one of the happy pictures, of the good father's life, this finding of his people in their forests, after he had thought them all dead or enslaved, and being welcomed by them as one returned from the dead.

Father Fritz stayed for a year on the rivers, but the raids continued. He made up his mind that the Spanish authorities in Peru must know what was being done. This boundary dispute was a matter between two nations. He left his mission station and set out for Lima, going by a new, unexplored river route and marking its course on his precious map as he went.

One wonders if this simple priest, who had come to Quito from Bohemia and never set foot in Spain, had any notion of the place to which he was coming. Lima, Pizarro's "City of Kings," rivaled in gaiety and luxury the finest cities in Europe. A new viceroy had come recently, Melchor Portocarrero, Count of Montclova, a distinguished military officer who had held a like position in Mexico. The city had been recovering, when he arrived, from the destructive earthquake of 1687. The first task of the new viceroy had been to help the citizens, by grants of government money, in the rebuilding of their beautiful city.

Here, on that day in 1692, appeared Father Fritz in his fiber

cassock, with hempen sandals on his feet and Indians of an unfamiliar tribe escorting him. It was as if he came from another
world, as indeed he did, a world of savage life within the jungle.
The members of the Jesuit Order who took him in arranged an
audience with the viceroy, and he declared that he was going to
it just as he was, in his own ragged fiber cassock. Only when they
represented to him that he must wear a cloth cassock for the
honor of the order, and to show proper respect at court, did he
reluctantly yield.

So the two worlds came together, the world of Father Fritz
and the world of the viceroy, a man who enjoyed the pomp and
luxury that went with his office and seldom went outside his
palace except in his carriage with its six horses and an escort of
outriders.

To the eternal honor of the Count of Montclova be it remembered that he received the holy man with the utmost love
and veneration. There were many interviews after that first one.
The viceroy sent almost daily for Father Fritz and sat with him
for hours, questioning him and listening while he told of the
customs of the jungle and river people, of the conversions he had
made to Christianity, and of the strange country on either side
of the river. The father told, too, of the way the Portuguese were
claiming territory which he thought belonged to Spain and of
their cruel treatment of his "children." The traders had so many
gifts for them, things which the simple folk coveted, the gay-
colored clothes, and the beads, and other trifles; and he, the missionary, had none. That, at least, could be remedied, the viceroy
said. He himself would see that the holy man was well supplied
with such articles to carry back as gifts and for barter.

The viceroy would have kept Father Fritz in Lima, but as soon
as he felt that his errand was done he declared that he must return to his work. Before he left he drew maps of the region such
as no one else could have drawn, maps which showed what lands
belonged to Spain and were being taken away from her. The
viceroy had the whole story written down and promised to send
it to the king. When Father Fritz and his Indians started on the
long journey back, he had all the gold and silver which the vice-

roy could make him take, money drawn from his own private store, not from the government treasury. As the holy father and his six Indians made their way back they took the heights of the rivers and waterfalls at every stopping place along the new route. Father Fritz never forgot the map he was drawing.

During the next twenty years the missionary founded at least forty villages among the Amazon River tribes, bringing the people together out of their wild, wandering life. He helped the people to build churches in them, for he could be a good carpenter when the need arose. He was an artist, too, and made sacred paintings for their altars, pictures which were found many years after his death. Sharing the people's daily life, he did not hesitate to share their dangers. There is a record in his journal of an attack made upon the tribe with which he was living by a heathen people from a distance. Hearing the disturbance, he hurried to the scene.

"I ran up with my Cross," he writes, "to die with or for my converts."

The trouble which he foretold came upon his people. What he was building, other white men tore down. His "children" had to leave their villages and move farther and farther away from the river in order to escape the traders and slave catchers. For the last ten years of his life he had to leave them and go to work among another Indian people, a warlike nation dwelling safely on streams farther from the Amazon. There he lived until his death in 1724, when he was within a month of his seventieth birthday.

He stands as a conspicuous example of the double work done by devoted church fathers, that of civilizing the people and of opening up unknown regions. But the place to look for Father Samuel Fritz's name is not in church records, though it might be found there. It is in the list of South America's early scientists. The map which he made with "no little toil and exertion" admits him to that company as a geographer of no mean skill and learning.

MY LIFE WITH THE RUSSIANS

by Raymond A. Lane

> Bishop Lane meets an unforgettable character in Alex
> ander who had a penchant for trouble and a desire to
> be back on his farm with his puppy. It happened in
> Manchuria at the end of World War II.

The Feast of the Assumption of Our Lady, August 15th, 1945,
lives forever in our memory. We had a secret radio which brought
news of what was happening. Russia had been let into the war
against Japan. There were some long night hours that we spent
in damp, mosquito-infested bomb shelters. The Japanese guards
disappeared. On the morning of the 15th, a Manchu guard came
into our dining hall. He was not a Christian but, having lived
with us for two or three years, he had come to know our Church
calendar. He wrote on the blackboard a series of Chinese characters signifying something like this: "On this day of Holy
Mother Going-up-to-Heaven Festival, you are free men again."

The frightful mass withdrawal of the Japanese from Manchuria, or rather their attempted withdrawal, was beginning.
Trucks, trains, and strings of open coal cars were jammed with
fleeing Japanese. Several successive days of torrential downpour
soaked the roads and the families en route. A feeling of catastrophe was in the air. Women and children and old folk died by
the tens of thousands, some from exposure, some from under-
nourishment, and the rest from spotted typhus. Japanese escape

* From *The Early Days of Maryknoll*, David McKay Company.

in those days was hopeless. Russians were coming in to take over the towns and run the railways.

We left our place of internment at Szepingkai (pronounced "Sipping Guy"), and started for our mission at Fushun. We were under Russian escort. Ordinarily, it is a two-hour ride to Mukden. It took us a day and a half. We reached Mukden at midnight and walked into a nightmare. The city was ablaze with bonfires made by the Russians and Chinese, who had been looting the Japanese department stores. There was machine gun fire that would strike terror to the stoutest heart. Nearly all the lights in the railway station had been destroyed, and in the darkness Russian soldiers were robbing, not only the Japanese, but also the Chinese and Korean refugees returning from labor camps. It was a sickening sight.

We waited in the station for daylight to come, and by the craziest of contrasts a group of Russian boys carrying Tommy guns gathered around us to sing American songs in Russian. One of them was from the Ukraine and he did a native dance, in his battle boots. Another had discovered a guitar in one of the Mukden stores. He had it with him and played it marvelously well; he whistled and danced at the same time. He had been with an orchestra in Prague before the war. We sang Kate Smith's favorite song, "God Bless America!" to which they generously applauded. We added a few of Stephen Foster's. A big lad, whose parents died in the siege of Leningrad, leaned on his machine gun and sang "Rose Marie" in Russian.

The war ended in August, 1945. I was in Manchuria for almost a year after that, at Fushun until Christmas, and then at Dairen. That was during the Russian occupation. Never to be forgotten are those days with the Russians.

We had hour-long discussions with Captain Sogolov, an electrical technician with the Subaikal Motorized Army. This army was sent to Fushun to dismantle the giant electric power plant built by the Japanese. Captain Sogolov, a strict adherent of the Soviet code of etiquette, invited himself to live with us. He talked by the hour, in Russian, and was determined to make himself understood, and equally determined to understand our replies to his one hundred and one questions. Our contributions were expressed in a new sort of Esperanto, made up of newly acquired Russian words, bits of German, French, American slang, and plenty of pantomime. Whenever his wordy descriptions brought blank looks to our faces, he acted them out and at times did everything but stand on his head to put across his idea. He was a gentleman, through and through, when he was sober.

With Captain Sogolov was Alexander, his aide-de-camp, likewise invited by the captain to live with us. Alexander was a good boy, because all of God's children are good. But Alexander was also a bad boy, because, taken from his home when only a youngster, he had been brought up in a barracks on the Soviet principle of mass education. For Alexander, you know, belonged to the state, not to his family, and apparently the only rule of right and wrong that Alexander learned was, "Don't get caught at it!"

I couldn't help liking Alexander, with all his roughness. He was eighteen years old. He carried a Russian submachine gun, the magazine of which looked like the film box of a movie camera. He wore heavy cleated campaign boots, and he would come pounding in on our clean floors calling, "Papa! Papa!" That was for me. "Papa" in Russian must mean everything from Pope to Bishop, and on to Father. It was the signal for me to dig out a bar of chocolate, a pack of cigarettes, or a left-over biscuit. He found a pal, a little terrier that we had in the yard. He tried to tell me about his own little dog which he had to leave home on the farm, back in Russia near Kazan. His mother was still at home—he hoped.

It took mountains of patience and self-control to smile when Alexander would swing the machine gun from his shoulder, point it at a cloud or at one of our shacks, and proceed to unload the bullets with a terrifying racket, or when he and his pals would come into our sitting room, put a Russian polka on the victrola, and cavort about the room in their spiked boots. Still, I liked him.

Then there was Captain Berganov. He was in charge of a mechanized unit, consisting of a fleet of American-built Studebaker trucks, all six-wheelers. His mission was to haul the loot to the loading platforms at Mukden. He seemed to enjoy his visits with us. He was polite, respectful, a good disciplinarian. He kept his drivers and guards out of our house.

One day, after several hours of work at the power plant, he stopped at the house for a short visit. Out again, he started up his trucks and made ready for the return. Then he came back into the room. He closed the door, made certain there was no one around, reached into his breast pocket and pulled out a wallet. He took from it a handkerchief, and from the folds of the handkerchief, a little crucifix. His mother had given it to him, he said, when he was leaving home in the Ukraine, when he was first called to the service. She was a good Christian—he had told us about her before—keeping up her religion in secret. It was her prayer, of course, that her son would remain good. He carried the crucifix with him wherever he went with the Russian forces, all through the Finnish campaign, the German campaign and into Hungary, and then during the long trek across Mongolia and into Manchuria. That was the first time anyone else had seen it; he would never dare show it to his fellow army officers. I learned in those days that not all the officers and men of the Soviet army were registered members of the Communist Party.

There were many nightmares during those months following the war. We missed one of the worst; it was the night Russian soldiers broke into our center mission at Fushun. We had not yet returned from the internment camp. They carried off clocks and clothes. One of the soldiers went off with my frock coat, which had been given to me five years before by Bishop James Edward Walsh who explained that it was the proper dress for a bishop and I should wear it.

There was tragedy that night when, to escape the soldiers, a little Chinese Sister jumped from an upper window, and then, with her back broken, crawled through the weeds and mud until the danger passed. She has been a cripple ever since that night.

I remember another terrible night. Just before Christmas that year, I started out for Dairen, taking with me some of our Manchu Sisters, who were to look after our school and dispensaries formerly staffed by our Maryknoll Sisters. The Russians were keeping the country closed, allowing no one to come in. We waited hours for the train in the station at Mukden. Things looked very bad. Drunken Russian soldiers were moving about in groups, some with guns drawn. They had robbery and worse things written in their faces. After about an hour of terrible anxiety, two young men approached us. Both were Russians, and one spoke good English. They asked if they could be of help to us. I explained our plight, and they made themselves our bodyguard. At least five times, during those six hours of waiting for the train, they argued with our would-be molesters and turned them away. When the train came, they helped us with our mountain of baggage and found us seats. At Dairen they told the station guards: "This is the American Consul and his staff," and they saw us safely to the mission. Later, they told me they were Soviets, and that they came from Harbin; but that night they surely looked like Guardian Angels.

I mentioned Alexander, the good little Russian from Kazan, who became the bad little boy with the Soviet army in Fushun. Many of the officers and men, especially the M.P.'s, knew that he lived with us. They knew that we called him Alexander, though that was neither his first name nor his family name. Late one Sunday evening, about six months after the war ended, during a quiet after-supper recreation with our Manchu seminarians, the doors opened suddenly, and a squad of Russian M.P.'s came into our living room. They were headed by a polite young officer who spoke German and, of course, Russian. "Where is Alexander?" he asked. Captain Sogolov and Alexander had departed days before, and we thought that they must be hundreds of miles away on the road back to Russia. Apparently, not. They said that Alexander was in the neighborhood and was wanted. To our naive question, "What has Alexander done?" his reply was simply: "Something serious."

They were invited to look around the house, but the young officer took our word for it. We had not seen Alexander in weeks. They went out quickly. A moment later, one of our Chinese teachers came in, burning up with curiosity. What had happened, he wanted to know; he had been outside when the trucks drew up;

our house had been surrounded with sentries while the patrol was in our living room.

It does not take army vehicles many minutes to cover three miles on roads that are in fair condition. The squad was soon at our mission on the north side of the river and made a similar raid, with the same results.

"Where is Alexander?" I wish I knew. I don't know what he did, nor whatever became of him. I had tried to be kind to him, but when he departed, the job was not yet complete. Now, when I read about Communist armies marching here and moving there, I find myself thinking about Alexander—thinking about the ten million Alexanders, who have been called from their homes, dragged away from their mothers and fathers and sisters, from their rabbits and puppy dogs, to carry a gun and spill their blood for dialectic materialism and other things about which they know nothing and care less, and which, if they are educated, they abhor. Alexander was not interested in the ascendancy of the proletariat and all the cruel crimes committed with that as an excuse. He wanted to be back on the farm with his mother and his puppy.

TO SPREAD THY LOVE

O LOVE that joyest in the sons of men,
Thou knowest this my shameless love,
This throb of heart, this laughing love,
This longing, urging, aching love
I feel for heathen souls that should have been
Ennobled by their love for Thee.

Yes, Jesus, faintly Thou hast let me share
The hunger that has filled Thine eyes,
Thy thirsting eagerness that sighs
To spread Thy love that purifies
The tarnished heathen heart and quickens there
A flame to burn eternally.

—FRANCIS X. FORD

FATHER DAMIEN

by Robert Louis Stevenson

The author of *Kidnapped* and *Treasure Island* rises to
the defense of the Apostle to the Lepers after Father
Damien's memory had been attacked in a sectarian
newspaper by a well-to-do Hawaiian.

AN OPEN LETTER TO THE REVEREND DR. HYDE OF
HONOLULU, BY ROBERT LOUIS STEVENSON

Sydney, February 25, 1890

Sir, it may probably occur to you that we have met, and visited,
and conversed; on my side with interest. You may remember that
you have done me several courtesies for which I was prepared
to be grateful. But there are duties which come before gratitude,
and offences which justly divide friends, far more acquaintances.
Your letter to the Reverend H. B. Gage is a document which,
in my sight, if you had filled me with bread when I was starving,
if you had sat up to nurse my father when he lay a-dying, would
yet absolve me from the bonds of gratitude. You know enough,
doubtless, of the process of canonization to be aware that, a
hundred years after the death of Damien, there will appear a
man charged with the painful office of the *devil's advocate*. After
that noble brother of mine, and of all frail clay, shall have lain
a century at rest, one shall accuse, one defend him. The circumstance is unusual that the devil's advocate should be a
volunteer, should be a member of a sect immediately rival, and
should make haste to take upon himself his ugly office ere the

bones are cold; unusual, and of a taste which I shall leave my readers free to qualify; unusual, and to me inspiring. If I have at all learned the trade of using words to convey truth and to arouse emotion, you have at last furnished me with a subject. For it is in the interest of all mankind and the cause of public decency in every quarter of the world, not only that Damien should be righted, but that you and your letter should be displayed at length, in their true colors, to the public eye.

To do this properly, I must begin by quoting you at large: I shall then proceed to criticize your utterance from several points of view, divine and human, in the course of which I shall attempt to draw again and with more specification the character of the dead saint whom it has pleased you to vilify: so much being done, I shall say farewell to you forever.

Honolulu, Aug. 2, 1889

Rev. H. B. Gage.

Dear Brother:—In answer to your inquiries about Father Damien, I can only reply that we who knew the man are surprised at the extravagant newspaper laudations, as if he was a most saintly philanthropist. The simple truth is, he was a coarse, dirty man, headstrong and bigoted. He was not sent to Molokai, but went there without orders; did not stay at the leper settlement (before he became one himself), but circulated freely over the whole island (less than half the island is devoted to the lepers), and he came often to Honolulu. He had no hand in the reforms and improvements inaugurated, which were the work of our Board of Health, as occasion required and means were provided. He was not a pure man in his relations with women, and the leprosy of which he died should be attributed to his vices and carelessness. Others have done much for the lepers, our own ministers, the government physicians, and so forth, but never with the catholic idea of meriting eternal life.

Yours, etc.

C. M. Hyde.

To deal fitly with a letter so extraordinary, I must draw at the outset on my private knowledge of the signatory and his sect. It may offend others; scarcely you, who have been so busy to collect, so bold to publish, gossip on your rivals. And this is perhaps the moment when I may best explain to you the character of what you are to read: I conceive you as a man quite beyond and below the reticences of civility: with what measure you mete, with that shall it be measured you again; with you at last, I rejoice to feel the button off the foil and to plunge home. And if in aught that I shall say, I should offend others, your colleagues, whom I respect and remember with affection, I can but offer them my regret; I am not free, I am inspired by the consideration of interest far more large; and such pain as can be inflicted by anything from me must be indeed trifling when compared with the pain with which they read your letter. It is not the hangman, but the criminal, that brings dishonor on the house.

You belong, sir, to a sect—I believe my sect, and that in which my ancestors labored—which has enjoyed, and partly failed to utilize, an exceptional advantage in the islands of Hawaii. The first missionaries came; they found the land already self-purged of its old and bloody faith; they were embraced, almost on their arrival, with enthusiasm; what troubles they supported came far more from whites than from Hawaiians; and to these last they stood (in a rough figure) in the shoes of God. This is not the place to enter into the degree or causes of their failure, such as it is. One element alone is pertinent, and must here be plainly dealt with. In the course of their evangelical calling, they—or too many of them—grew rich. It may be news to you that the houses of missionaries are a cause of mocking on the streets of Honolulu. It will at least be news to you that, when I returned your civil visit, the driver of my cab commented on the size, the taste, and the comfort of your home. It would have been news certainly to myself had anyone told me that afternoon that I should live to drag such matter into print. But you see, sir, how you degrade better men to your own level; and it is needful that those who are to judge betwixt you and me, betwixt Damien and the devil's advocate, should understand your letter to have been penned in a house which could raise, and that very justly, the envy and the comments of the passers-by. I think (to employ a phrase of yours, which I admire) it "should be attributed" to you that you have never visited the scene of Damien's life and death. If you had, and had recalled it, and looked about your pleasant rooms, even your pen perhaps would have been stayed.

Your sect (and, remember, as far as any sect avows me, it is mine) has not done ill in a worldly sense in the Hawaiian Kingdom. When calamity befell their innocent parishioners, when leprosy descended and took root in the Eight Islands, a *quid pro quo* was to be looked for. To that prosperous mission, and to you, as one of its adornments, God had sent at last an opportunity. I know I am touching here upon a nerve acutely sensitive. I know that others of your colleagues look back on the inertia of your church, and the intrusive and decisive heroism of Damien, with something almost to be called remorse. I am sure it is so with yourself; I am persuaded your letter was inspired by a certain envy, not essentially ignoble, and the one human trait to be espied in that performance. You were thinking of the lost chance, the past day; of that which should have been conceived and was not; of the service due and not rendered. Time was, said the voice in your ear, in your pleasant room, as you sat raging and writing; and if the words written were base beyond parallel, the rage, I am happy to repeat—it is the only compliment I shall pay you—the rage was almost virtuous. But, sir, when we have failed, and another has succeeded; when we have stood by, and another has stepped in; when we sit and grow bulky in our charming mansions, and a plain, uncouth peasant steps into the battle, under the eyes of God, and succors the afflicted, and consoles the dying, and is himself afflicted in his turn, and dies upon the field of honor—the battle can not be retrieved as your unhappy irritation has suggested. It is a lost battle, and lost forever. One thing remained to you in your defeat—some rags of common honor; and these you have made haste to cast away.

Common honor; not the honor of having done anything right, but the honor of not having done aught conspicuously foul; the honor of the inert: that was what remained to you. We are not all expected to be Damiens; a man may conceive his duty more narrowly, he may love his comforts better; and none will cast a stone at him for that. But will a gentleman of your reverend profession allow me an example from the fields of gallantry?

When two gentlemen compete for the favor of a lady, and the one succeeds and the other is rejected, and (as will sometimes happen) matter damaging to the successful rival's credit reaches the ear of the defeated, it is held by plain men of no pretensions that his mouth is, in the circumstance, almost necessarily closed. Your church and Damien's were in Hawaii upon a rivalry to do well: to help, to edify, to set divine examples. You having (in one huge instance) failed, and Damien succeeded, I marvel it should not have occurred to you that you were doomed to silence; that when you had been outstripped in that high rivalry, and sat inglorious in the midst of your well-being, in your pleas-ant room—and Damien, crowned with glories and horrors, toiled and rotted in that pigsty of his under the cliffs of Kalawao—you, the elect who would not, were the last man on earth to collect and propagate gossip on the volunteer who would and did.

I think I see you—for I try to see you in the flesh as I write these sentences—I think I see you leap at the word pigsty, a hyper-bolical expression at the best. "He had no hand in the reforms," he was "a coarse, dirty man"; these were your own words; and you may think it possible that I am come to support you with fresh evidence. In a sense it is even so. Damien has been too much depicted with a conventional halo and conventional fea-tures; so drawn by men who perhaps had not the eye to remark or the pen to express the individual; or who perhaps were only blinded and silenced by generous admiration, such as I partly envy for myself—such as you, if our soul were enlightened, would envy on your bended knees. It is the least defect of such a method of portraiture that it makes the path easy for the devil's advocate, and leaves for the misuse of the slanderer a considerable field of truth. For the truth that is suppressed by friends is the readiest weapon of the enemy. The world, in your despite, may perhaps owe you something, if your letter be the means of substituting once for all a credible likeness for a wax abstraction. For, if that world at all remember you, on the day when Damien of Molokai shall be named Saint, it will be in virtue of one work: your letter to the Reverend H. B. Gage.

You may ask on what authority I speak. It was my inclement

destiny to become acquainted, not with Damien, but with Dr. Hyde. When I visited the lazaretto, Damien was already in his resting grave. But such information as I have, I gathered on the spot in conversation with those who knew him well and long: some indeed who revered his memory; but others who had sparred and wrangled with him, who beheld him with small respect, and through whose unprepared and scarcely partial communications the plain, human features of the man shone on me convincingly. These gave me what knowledge I possess; and I learned it in that scene where it could be most completely and sensitively understood—Kalawao, which you have never visited, about which you have never so much as endeavored to inform yourself; for, brief as your letter is, you have found the means to stumble into that confession. "*Less than one-half* of the island," you say, "is devoted to the lepers." Molokai—"*Molokai ahina*," the "gray," lofty, and most desolate island—along all its northern side plunges a front of precipice into a sea of unusual profundity. This range of cliff is, from east to west, the true end and frontier of the island. Only in one spot there projects into the ocean a certain triangular and rugged down, grassy, stony, windy, and rising in the midst into a hill with a dead crater: the whole bearing to the cliff that overhangs it, somewhat the same relation as a bracket to a wall. With this hint, you will now be able to pick out the leper station on a map; you will be able to judge how much of Molokai is thus cut off between the surf and precipice, whether less than a half, or less than a quarter, or a fifth, or a tenth—or, say, a twentieth; and the next time you burst into print you will be in a position to share with us the issue of your calculations.

I imagine you to be one of those persons who talk with cheerfulness of that place which oxen and wainropes could not drag you to behold. You, who do not even know its situation on the map, probably denounce sensational descriptions, stretching your limbs the while in your pleasant parlor on Beretania Street. When I was pulled ashore there one early morning, there sat with me in the boat two Sisters, bidding farewell (in humble imitation of Damien) to the lights and joys of human life. One

of these wept silently; I could not withhold myself from joining
her. Had you been there, it is my belief that nature would have
triumphed even in you; and as the boat drew but a little nearer,
and you beheld the stairs crowded with abominable deforma-
tions of our common manhood, and saw yourself landing in the
midst of such a population as only now and then surrounds us
in the horror of a nightmare—what a haggard eye would you
have rolled over your reluctant shoulder toward the house on
Beretania Street! Had you gone on; had you found every fourth
face a blot upon the landscape; had you visited the hospital and
seen the butt-ends of human beings lying there almost unrecog-
nizable, but still breathing, still thinking, still remembering; you
would have understood that life in the lazaretto is an ordeal from
which the nerves of a man's spirit shrink, even as his eye quails
under the brightness of the sun; you would have felt it was
(even to-day) a pitiful place to visit and a hell to dwell in. It is
not the fear of possible infection. That seems a little thing when
compared with the pain, the pity, and the disgust of the visitor's
surroundings, and the atmosphere of affliction, disease, and physical disgrace in which he breathes. I do not think I am a man
more than usually timid; but I never recall the days and nights
I spent upon that island promontory (eight days and seven
nights), without heartfelt thankfulness that I am somewhere else.
I find in my diary that I speak of my stay as "a grinding experience"; I have once jotted in the margin, "Harrowing is the
word"; and when the Mokolii bore me at last toward the outer
world, I kept repeating to myself, with a new conception of their
pregnancy, those simple words of the song—

> " 'Tis the most distressful country
> That ever yet was seen."

And observe: that which I saw and suffered from was a settlement, purged, bettered, beautified; the new village built, the
hospital and the Bishop's Home excellently arranged; the Sisters,
the doctor, and the missionaries all indefatigable in their noble
tasks. It was a different place when Damien came there, and made
his great renunciation, and slept that first night under a tree

amidst his rotting brethren: alone with pestilence; and looking forward (with what courage, with what pitiful sinkings of dread, God only knows) to a lifetime of dressing sores and stumps.

You will say, perhaps, I am too sensitive, that sights as painful abound in cancer hospitals and are confronted daily by doctors and nurses. I have long learned to admire and envy the doctors and the nurses. But there is no cancer hospital so large and populous as Kalawao and Kalaupapa; and in such a matter every fresh case, like every inch of length in the pipe of an organ, deepens the note of the impression; for what daunts the on-looker is that monstrous sum of human suffering by which he stands surrounded. Lastly, no doctor or nurse is called upon to enter once for all the doors of that gehenna; they do not say farewell, they need not abandon hope, on its sad threshold; they but go for a time to their high calling; and can look forward as they go to relief, to recreation, and to rest. But Damien shut to with his own hand the doors of his own sepulchre.

Damien was coarse.

It is very possible. You make us sorry for the lepers, who had only a coarse old peasant for their friend and Father. But you, who were so refined, why were you not there to cheer them with the lights of culture? Or may I remind you that we have some reason to doubt if John the Baptist were genteel; and, in the case of Peter, on whose career you doubtless dwell approvingly in the pulpit, no doubt at all that he was a "coarse, headstrong" fisherman! Yet, even in our Protestant Bibles, Peter is called Saint.

Damien was dirty.

He was. Think of the poor lepers annoyed with this dirty comrade! But the clean Dr. Hyde was at his food in a fine house.

Damien was headstrong.

I believe you are right again; and I thank God for his strong head and heart.

Damien was bigoted.

I am not fond of bigots myself, because they are not fond of me. But what is meant by bigotry, that we should regard it as a blemish in a priest? Damien believed his own religion with the simplicity of a peasant or a child; as I would I could suppose that you do. For this, I wonder at him some way off; and had that been his only character, should have avoided him in life. But the point of interest in Damien, which has caused him to be so much talked about and made him at last the subject of your pen and mine, was that, in him, his bigotry, his intense and narrow faith, wrought potently for good, and strengthened him to be one of the world's heroes and exemplars.

Damien was not sent to Molokai, but went there without orders.

Is this a misreading? or do you really mean the words for blame? I have heard Christ, in the pulpits of our Church, held up for imitation on the ground that His sacrifice was voluntary. Does Dr. Hyde think otherwise?

Damien did not stay at the settlement, etc.

It is true he was allowed many indulgences. Am I to understand that you blame the Father for profiting by these, or the officers for granting them? In either case, it is a mighty Spartan standard to issue from the house on Beretania Street; and I am convinced you will find yourself with few supporters.

Damien had no hand in reforms, etc.

I think even you will admit that I have already been frank in my description of the man I am defending; but before I take you up upon this head, I will be franker still, and tell you that perhaps nowhere in the world can a man taste a more pleasurable sense of contrast than when he passes from Damien's "Chinatown" at Kalawao to the beautiful Bishop's Home at Kalaupapa. At this point, in my desire to make all fair for you, I will break my rule and adduce Catholic testimony. Here is a passage from my diary about my visit to the Chinatown, from which you will see how it is (even now) regarded by its own officials: "We went round all the dormitories, refectories, etc.—dark and dingy enough, with a superficial cleanliness, which he" (Mr. Dutton, the lay brother) "did not seek to defend. 'It is almost decent,' said he; 'the Sisters will make that all right when we get them here.'" And yet I gathered it was already better since Damien was dead, and far better than when he was there alone and had his own (not always excellent) way. I have now come far enough to meet you on a common ground of fact; and I tell you that, to a mind not prejudiced by jealousy, all the reforms of the lazaretto, and even those which he most vigorously opposed, are properly the work of Damien. They are the evidence of his success; they are what his heroism provoked from the reluctant and the careless. Many were before him in the field; Mr. Meyer, for instance, of whose faithful work we hear too little; there have been many since; and some had more worldly wisdom, though none had more devotion, than our saint. Before his day, even you will confess, they had effected little. It was his part, by one striking act of martyrdom, to direct all men's eyes on that distressful country. At a blow, and with the price of his life, he made the place illustrious and public. And, that, if you will consider largely, was the one reform needful; pregnant of all that should succeed. It brought money; it brought (best individual addition of them all) the Sisters; it brought supervision, for public opinion and public interest landed with the man at Kalawao. If ever any man brought reforms, and died to bring them, it was he. There is not a clean cup or towel in the Bishop's Home but dirty Damien washed it.

Damien was not a pure man in his relations with women, etc.

How do you know that? Is this the nature of the conversation in that house on Beretania Street which the cabman envied, driving past?—racy details of the misconduct of the poor peasant priest, toiling under the cliffs of Molokai?

Many have visited the station before me; they seem not to have heard many shocking tales, for my informants were men speaking with the plainness of the laity; and I heard plenty of complaints of Damien. Why was this never mentioned? and how came it to you in the retirement of your clerical parlor?

But I must not even seem to deceive you. This scandal, when I read it in your letter, was not new to me. I had heard it once before; and I must tell you how. There came to Samoa a man from Honolulu; he, in a public-house on the beach, volunteered the statement that Damien had "contracted the disease from having connection with the female lepers"; and I find a joy in telling you how the report was welcomed in a public-house. A man sprang to his feet; I am not at liberty to give his name, but from what I heard I doubt if you would care to have him to dinner in Beretania Street. "You miserable little —," (here is a word I dare not print, it would so shock your ears). "You miserable little —," he cried, "if the story were a thousand times true, can't you see you are a million times lower — for daring to repeat it?" I wish it could be told of you that when the report reached you in your house, perhaps after family worship, you had found in your soul enough holy anger to receive it with the same expressions; ay, even with that one which I dare not print; it would not need to have been blotted away, like Uncle Toby's oath, by the tears of the recording angel; it would have been counted to you for your brightest righteousness. But you have deliberately chosen the part of the man from Honolulu, and you have played it with improvements of your own. The man from Honolulu—miserable, leering creature—communicated the tale to a rude knot of beach-combing drinkers in a public-house, where (I will so far agree with your temperance opinions) man is not always at his noblest; and the man from Honolulu had himself been drinking—drinking, we may charitably fancy, to excess. It was to your "Dear Brother, the Reverend H. B. Gage," that you chose to communicate the sickening story; and the blue ribbon which adorns your portly bosom forbids me to allow you the extenuating plea that you were drunk when it was done. Your "dear brother"—a brother indeed—made haste to deliver up your letter (as a means of grace, perhaps) to the religious papers; where, after many months, I found and read and wondered at it; and whence I have now reproduced it for the wonder of others. And you and your dear brother have, by this cycle of operations built up a contrast very edifying to examine in detail. The man whom you would not care to have to dinner, on the one side; on the other, the Reverend Dr. Hyde and the Reverend H. B. Gage; the Apia bar-room, the Honolulu manse.

But I fear you scarce appreciate how you appear to your fellowmen: and to bring it home to you, I will suppose your story to be true. I will suppose—and God forgive me for supposing it—that Damien faltered and stumbled in his narrow path of duty; I will suppose that, in the horror of his isolation, perhaps in the fever of incipient disease, he, who was doing so much more than he had sworn, failed in the letter of his priestly oath—he, who was so much a better man than either you or me, who did what we have never dreamed of daring—he too tasted of our common frailty. "O Iago, the pity of it!" The least tender should be moved to tears; the most incredulous to prayer. And all that you could do was to pen your letter to the Reverend H. B. Gage!

Is it growing at all clear to you what a picture you have drawn of your own heart? I will try yet once again to make it clearer. You had a father: suppose this tale were about him, and some informant brought it to you, proof in hand: I am not making too high an estimate of your emotional nature when I suppose you would regret the circumstance? that you would feel the tale of frailty the more keenly since it shamed the author of your days? and that the last thing you would do would be to publish it in the religious press? Well, the man who tried to do what Damien did is my Father, and the Father of the man in the Apia bar, and the Father of all who love goodness; and he was your Father, too, if God had given you grace to see it.

TO BLESSED THEOPHANE, MARTYR

Thou, happy martyr, in the hour of death
  Didst taste the deep delight of suffering;
Thou didst declare, e'en with thy dying breath,
  That it is sweet to suffer for the King.
When the stern headsman made thee offer fair
  Thy torture to abridge, how swift thy word:
"Oh, blest am I my Master's cup to share!
  Long let my suffering last with Christ my Lord!"

—SAINT THERESE OF LISIEUX

PATRICK AND THE BIG SNAKE

by Joseph A. Hahn

> Mothers are ferocious people when their offspring are
> in danger. Father Hahn wrote this example from the
> Bolivian jungle when he worked there at the headwaters
> of the Amazon.

Mama Peron walked along the jungle path with eleven-year-old
Patricio just ahead of her. The sun shone in the Sunday morning
calm, but in the deep glades they saw little of it. Traffic on the
paths was light, and it was necessary for the Indian woman to
work her way to Mass by cutting the growth that at times had
become too thick. She manipulated her heavy machete with ease,
now flicking a branch, now sweeping away the tall grass when
young Patrick found the going hard. A lady in the Bolivian low-
land swings a machete as handily as a Park Avenue matron em-
ploys a handkerchief.

Not far from Cavinas, mother and son came upon a sultry
stream, across which a tree trunk had been thrown as bridge. The
trunk was too short, and hence at one end it was submerged in
the slowly moving water. Ahead of his mother, the barefoot
Patricio jumped nimbly to the log and started across.

But he was scarcely out over the stream when drama struck!

A huge anaconda, expertly hidden near the bank, swung its
head swiftly out, grabbed Patricio's left leg in its mouth, and
pulled the boy into the stream. The snake's plan—the pattern
followed by every constrictor—was to encircle its victim, crush

him for a minute or two, and then swallow him whole. Large reptiles of this kind have been known to consume a full-grown man.

But Mr. Anaconda had not counted on Mamma Peron. With an earsplitting shriek, the Indian woman jumped into the stream and, blind to her own danger, slashed furiously, at the snake's head with her machete. It is almost impossible to penetrate the skin of a large anaconda with such a weapon, though a strong man might be able to prick the tough skin with the machete's sharp point. Even that would not kill the serpent, but only discourage it.

The violence of the woman's rage, however, served to deflect the anaconda momentarily from its purpose. It hesitated, opened its jaws—and thus allowed Mamma Peron to grasp Patricio by the shoulders and pull him from the snake's coils. Then still clutching her son, the mother dashed like lightning through the forest to the mission chapel. There I entered the picture. I had already commenced one of the Sunday Masses and was about to read the Gospel. The tremendous stir behind me gave the impression that some Indians were fighting, and I turned with a reprimand on my lips. But the altar boy ran to me with the story.

"Patricio Peron has been bitten by a poisonous snake!" he exclaimed.

I do not blame him for getting things mixed, for Mamma Peron was still beside herself with excitement and babbled incoherently, like a runaway Victrola.

Thinking it was a case of poisoning, I believed that there was not a moment to lose, so I threw off my vestments and took the boy to the rectory. There I discovered twenty or thirty tooth marks on the left leg, from the kneecap to the ankle. I applied an antiseptic, calmed the distracted mother and child, and went back to celebrate the Sunday Mass.

Patricio's father was in the chapel. "But what of the snake, Padre?" he asked after Mass.

"Let's kill it," I said.

With the father and two other Indians, I set off. We pushed through the shoulder-high grass and weeds, which Peron cut away when they were too heavy. How, I wondered again, can little Indian youngsters ever see where to go on such trails! On our hurried trip, the Indians, who are short of stature, cut only what blocked their passage and hence I found myself stooped most of the way through this forest tunnel.

"Do you see the snake?" I asked, as we arrived at the stream.

"Directly ahead of us, Padre, near the other bank," replied Peron.

It took Indian eyes to locate the hideous creature, for I confess that only by an effort could I discover the head, slightly breaking the surface of the water. The body was almost indistinguishable amid the tangle of rotten logs, where the monster waited to strike at another victim.

I fired five charges from my gun, to make sure that I killed the beast. Even then it continued to wind its immense coils desperately about the decayed tree trunks. When at last it lay still, I proposed that we haul it to the bank.

"Not I!" exclaimed Peron. "If I touch it, my boy will die."

This is a local superstition. The remaining three of us dragged out the dead anaconda, and I measured it with a folding rule. It was twenty-one feet long. When we cut off the skin, that was thirty inches in width.

Patricio was pretty sick from the bruises and the horror of his experience, but he recovered. Our Indians are grateful to God for sparing the community from such a terrible tragedy. They do not even call Mamma Peron a heroine. There are no Congressional Medals for mothers in the Bolivian jungle.

LOVE IS CONTAGIOUS

"In a sense, religion is more caught than taught. Fire is enkindled by fire, zeal by zeal, and love for our fellow men by beholding this love in others."
                                                            —A MISSIONER

THE INDIAN WARRIORS

by Peter J. De Smet

One of the most extraordinary figures in American history is the Jesuit, Father De Smet, who was so much responsible for opening the West and pacifying the Indian. His writings are among the most valuable in the National Archives. He traveled over 190,000 miles on his errands of mercy, and negotiated the historic peace treaty with Sitting Bull.

I have now to speak of the Crows. If they are considered as superior in intelligence to all their neighbors, they also surpass them in their wah-kon, or superstitious ideas and ceremonies, which reign in all their movements and actions. In illustration, I will cite the following trait, of which I was innocently and ignorantly the cause.

In 1840, I first met the Crows, in the valley of the Big Horn, a tributary of the Yellowstone. Among all the tribes of the northwest portion of North America, this nation is considered as the most warlike and valiant. It counts about four hundred and eighty lodges, ten individuals to a lodge, and roams over the valley of the Yellowstone, principally in the region of the Wind River Mountains, or Black Hills, and the Rocky mountains. This race is one of the noblest in the desert; they are tall, robust, and well-formed, have a piercing eye, aquiline nose, and teeth of ivory

* From *The History of the Western Missions*. Published, P. J. Kenedy.

whiteness. In my quality of Black-gown, they received me with all possible demonstrations of respect, and with a sincere joy. I had with me a stock of lucifer-matches, which I used from time to time to light my pipe, and the calumet used in the Great Council. The effect of these matches surprised them greatly; they had never seen any. They conversed about them in all the lodges, and called them the mysterious fire which the Black-gown carried. I was at once considered the greatest medicine-man that had ever visited their tribe. They consequently treated me with distinguished respect, and listened to all I said with the greatest attention. Before my departure, the chiefs and principal warriors of the council requested me to leave them a portion of my matches. Unconscious of the superstitious ideas which they attached to them, I readily distributed them, reserving only what was necessary for my journey.

In 1844 I visited them again. The reception they gave me was most solemn. I was lodged in the largest and finest lodge of the camp. All the chiefs and warriors were habited in their embroidered moccasins, leggings, and buckskin shirts ornamented with beads and porcupine quills, while eagle's feathers crowned their heads, and they conducted me in grand ceremony from lodge to lodge. That I might participate in a grand banquet, I was provided with my band of eaters, who would do honor to the viands and eat for me. One of the great chiefs testified a special friendship for me.

"It is to thee, Black-gown," said he to me, "that I owe all my glory in the victories I have gained over my enemies."

His language astonished me greatly, and I begged him to explain. Without delay he took from his neck his wah-kon, or medicine-bag, wrapped in a bit of kid. He unrolled it, and displayed to my wondering view the remnant of the matches I had given him in 1840!

"I use them," said he, "every time I go to battle. If the mysterious fire appears at the first rubbing, I dart upon my enemies, sure of obtaining victory."

In 1843, the great chief of the Crow nation was known by the title of *Tezi-Goe*, a word which sounds bad enough, meaning

Rotten Belly. He was as much renowned for his bravery in war as for his wisdom in council, and the patriotic love that he testified to the whole nation. Seeing with pain the great losses that the continual incursions of so many enemies caused his tribe, he resolved to conclude a solemn treaty of peace, if not with all, at least with a great part of the Black-Feet. He made all suitable arrangements, and convoked his council, to deliberate on the most prompt and the most efficacious means of success in his great design. All the warriors hastened to his aid. After having discussed the different points, it was unanimously decided that a party of twenty-five braves should repair to the Black-Feet camp, to offer them the calumet of peace.

The guide chosen to conduct the band was one of the nation of Black-Feet, taken prisoner by the Crows some years before, and hitherto retained in captivity. In order to attach him more securely to the good cause, the Crows granted him his liberty, with the title of brave, and the permission to wear the eagle's plume. He was, besides, loaded with presents, consisting of horses, arms, and ornaments of every kind. Having received his instructions, he set out joyfully and with signs of gratitude, fully resolved to neglect nothing to obtain and consolidate an honorable and lasting peace between the two nations. A place had been designated in which the two tribes might meet as friends and brothers, to celebrate the grand event. The deputation, therefore, set out for the Black-Feet camp of four hundred lodges, commanded by the great Chief Spotted Deer, which they found encamped in the valley of the Maria River, a pretty large branch of the Missouri River, in the neighborhood of the Great Falls.

About a month before the departure of this expedition, two Crows had been killed, near their own camp, and their scalps carried away, by a war-party of Black-Feet. The two brothers of these unfortunate victims fasted, and took their oaths according to custom. These oaths consisted in vowing that they would each kill a Black-Foot, the first good chance. They communicated their intentions to no one. The bravery and determination of these two men were well known. They were elected to join the band of deputies, and promised ostensibly to forget their private wrongs for the public welfare; but in secret they renewed their first intentions, foreseeing that this excursion would probably furnish an occasion of avenging the double murder of their brothers.

The band progressed slowly, using many precautions, and redoubling them as they approached the camp of the Black-Feet. When within a few days' distance from it, they separated in companies of two or three, to scour the country and assure themselves whether any Black-Feet parties were out of the village.

In the course of the day the two brothers stayed together, and discovered two Black-Feet Indians returning from the chase, with several horses laden with buffalo-meat. Having with them a calumet-handle, they advanced boldly toward their enemies, and offered them the pipe, as on similar occasions. The Black-Feet were entirely reassured, and conceived no suspicions nor suffered the least anxiety. One of them presented his gun to one of the two Crows, and the other gave his horse to the second. They took the same way together towards the camp, but their path led through a deep and lonely ravine. There the snare was discovered.

The two Black-Feet suddenly received mortal blows, and were thus cowardly assassinated by the two Crows, who scalped their victims. They then killed the horses with arrows, and concealed their carcasses beneath the underwood and briars. The two scalps were carefully secured in their bullet-bags. Having removed all traces of blood from their habiliments, they rejoined their companions, without making known the cruel act of private vengeance they had consummated, secretly and in violation of all received Indian usages. The day which followed this atrocious crime the deputation made a solemn entrance into the camp of the Black-Feet, and were received by the chiefs and braves with the greatest cordiality, and with every attention of Indian hospitality.

The Black-Feet declared themselves favorable to the treaty of peace. They received joyfully the proposition which the Crows made by their guide and interpreter, the recent prisoner. All the politeness and attention of which Indians are capable were lavished upon the deputies. They were invited to a great number of feasts, to amusements and public sports, which lasted late in the night. They were afterwards distributed to the lodges of the principal chiefs, in order to repose after their fatiguing journey.

The inclination to steal is very common among the women of several tribes of the Northwest. The Black-Feet women share largely in this bad reputation. One of these feminine pillagers, favored by the darkness of night, silently entered the lodges where the Crows were peaceably sleeping. She relieved their pouches of all that could prove valuable to her. While searching, she laid her hand upon a damp, hairy object, and instantly perceived it to be a scalp. She seized it, quitted the lodge in the greatest possible silence, and, by the glimmering of the watchfire which was burning in the middle of the camp, examined the bloody trophy. It is very difficult to move an Indian, for he is habituated to strange sights. Such an event would have spread alarm among white men, but it only tended to render the Indians more circumspect and more prudent in taking measures. The woman, after reflecting a moment, turned her steps towards the lodge of the great chief, awoke him, and communicated to his ear in the softest whisper the important discovery she had made. He lighted a pine torch, in order to examine the scalp. At the first glance he recognized it as that of a young hunter who had not yet come back from the chase.

The chief instantly formed his plan. He made signs to the woman to follow him, recommended her to retire to her own lodge, because nothing could be done before daylight, and forbade her to divulge her secret, or to excite the slightest suspicion. He feared that in the confusion which would probably arise, and sheltered by the darkness, some of the Crows might escape.

Spotted Deer then, alone and noiselessly made the rounds of his camp. He aroused his bravest warriors, to the number of twenty or thirty, by a single touch, and also those whom he desired to consult in this circumstance. They followed him, asking no questions, and were conducted to a solitary place in the vicinity of the camp. There, forming a circle and lighting a torch, the chief displayed the scalp, and related to them the adventure of the woman.

The youngest of his counsellors desired instant revenge on the

Crows, but the prudent chief represented to them that the night was not a favorable time; besides, that having smoked together the calumet of peace, to kill them in their own lodges, and in the very camp of the Black-Feet, would be at variance with all their customs and practices, and would draw upon them the contempt of all other Indian nations. He, however, commanded them to hold themselves armed and ready at daybreak.

The Crows rose early. They were somewhat surprised to see the lodges they occupied surrounded by a band of four or five hundred warriors, armed and mounted on their fleetest coursers, and with countenances far from friendly, as on the previous eve. But Indians are not easily disconcerted; they awaited the result in silence. As soon as the daylight appeared in the camp, the Spotted Deer convened a grand council and summoned the Crow deputies to appear. They at once obeyed, and took their places with the air of haughty indifference, peculiar to the Indian, in the center of a circle of enemies who were burning with vengeance.

When all were in order, the Spotted Deer arose, and thus addressed the Crows: "Strangers, only yesterday you arrived in our camp. You declared yourselves the deputies of your principal chiefs, sent to conclude with us, hitherto your foes, a solid and durable treaty of peace. We listened to your message. Your words and propositions seemed reasonable and advantageous. All our lodges have been open to you; you have shared in our feasts and hospitality; you joined in our games. Yesterday we had the intention of showing you to-day still greater liberality. But, before discoursing further, I have one single question to ask you, Crows! I must have an answer; and that answer will decide whether peace be possible, or whether a war of destruction must continue." Then drawing the scalp from the bullet-pouch, and displaying it before them, he cried, "Tell me, Crows, whose hair is this? Who among you claims this trophy?"

Those of the Crows who were ignorant of the affair, looked on with amazement, and could only imagine that the Black-Feet sought a pretext for quarrelling. No one replied.

The Chief resumed: "Will no one answer? Must I call a woman to question these Crow braves?" Then beckoning to the stealer of the scalp, he said to her, "Show us to which warrior this trophy belongs."

Without hesitation, she pointed to one of the brothers. Every eye was fixed upon him.

The chief, Spotted Deer, approaching the murderer, said to him, "Knowest thou this scalp? Didst thou take it? Fearest thou now to avow it?"

With one bound the young Crow placed himself opposite the chief, and shouted, "Spotted Deer, I fear not! It is I who took the scalp! If I endeavored to conceal it, I did so with the desire of doing more evil! Thou askest whose hair is this. Look at the hairy fringe of thy shirt and thy leggings. In my turn, I ask, whose hair is that? Belongs it not to my two brothers, slain by thee or thine, hardly two moons ago? or belongs it not to the relations of some Crow here present? 'Tis vengeance brings me here! My brother holds in his shot-bag the companion of this scalp. We determined, before leaving the camp, to cast into thy face these bloody tufts, at the same moment, as our challenge of defiance."

This language determined the Black-Feet. "Young man, thou hast spoken well," replied the Spotted Deer; "thou art valiant and fearest not death, which will strike thee and thy companions in a few moments. Yet we have smoked the calumet together. It is not suitable that the ground on which that ceremony took place should drink thy blood. See, Crows, the hill before you! It is in the way that leads to your lodges. So far we allow you to go. When you get there, we will pursue you. Go on, and leave us."

The Crows instantly left the place, and advanced towards the hill designated by the Black-Foot chief, determined to sell their lives dearly in this unequal combat. Their enemies mounted their horses, and awaited with ardor the order for the pursuit.

As soon as the Crows reached the hill, the terrific war-whoop —the *Sassaskivi*—resounded through the camp. The Black-Feet, burning to avenge the outrage received, rushed forward with the greatest impetuosity. The Crows, after running some moments, found a deep ravine excavated in the plain by the running waters:

judging the position favorable, they took refuge in it, and maintained themselves for some time. As soon as, in their first ardor, the Black-Feet approached the ravine to dislodge them, a general discharge of muskets and arrows from the Crows killed eighty Black-Feet, and wounded a great number. This discharge routed them, and forced them to draw off. The Black-Feet dismounted, and on foot there were several skirmishes between the two bands; but all were disadvantageous to the Black-Feet, for the Crows were protected in the hole, and only showed their heads through necessity, while their enemies fought in the open plain. A great number of Black-Feet lost their lives in these different attempts, while the Crows lost not a man.

Spotted Deer, seeing the danger and the useless destruction of so many warriors, made an appeal to his braves. He proposed to them to place himself at their head, and to fall simultaneously on their enemies. His proposition was accepted; the war-whoop resounded anew through the bloody plain; they attacked the Crows *en masse,* and after having discharged on them their guns and arrows, armed only with their daggers and tomahawks, they darted with confused violence into the ravine, and in a few moments horribly massacred the whole band. In this last attack, it is worth noting that not a single Black-Foot lost his life.

The combat ended, the scalps were carried off by the warriors who had most distinguished themselves in the affair. The women cut the corpses of their slain in such small pieces, that it would be difficult to detect among them the smallest trace of the human form. The scalps, with all the torn scraps of flesh, were then attached as trophies to the extremities of poles and lances, and triumphantly borne through the camp, mid chants of victory, yells of rage, with howling and vociferations against their enemies. There was also a general mourning, caused by the loss of so many warriors fallen in this horrible engagement. Since that day, war continues without relaxation to the present time.

I request you, in a special manner, to pray very particularly for these poor Indians. During fourteen years they have implored the favor of having some of our Fathers sent to them. The scripture, "They asked bread, and there was none to break it to them," may be justly quoted in regard to them. In my short visits to them I have been touched with their affability, their beneficent hospitality, and the respectful attention they gave to my instructions. I augur very favorably of their good dispositions, and am convinced that two or three fervent and zealous missionaries could gather consoling fruits for religion from these barbarians, who sigh to know and practice the Gospel of Peace. Since my last interview with them, in 1851, I have received several letters from them.

LAST LETTER OF A MARTYR

by Theophane Venard

> When the Annamese executioner severed the head from the body of Blessed Theophane Venard, his act was to reverberate around the world. In the United States it has proven the source of many vocations to the missions.

January 2, 1861

My dearest Father, Sister, and Brothers,—I write to you at the beginning of this year, which will be my last on earth. I hope you got the little note which I wrote announcing my capture on the Feast of St. Andrew. God permitted me to be betrayed by a traitor, but I owe him no grudge. From that village I sent you a few lines of farewell before I had the criminal's chain fastened on my feet and neck. I have kissed that chain, a true link which binds me to Jesus and Mary, and which I would not exchange for its weight in gold. The mandarin had the kindness

* From *A Modern Martyr* by James A. Walsh. The Maryknoll Bookshelf.

to have a light one made for me, and treated me, during my stay in his prefecture, with every possible consideration. His brother came at least ten times and tried to persuade me to trample the Cross under foot. He did not want to see me die so young! When I left the prefecture to go on to the capital, an immense crowd came to witness my departure; in spite of the guards and the mandarins, one man, a young Christian, was not afraid to throw himself on his knees three times before my cage, imploring my blessing, and declaring me to be a messenger sent from Heaven. He was of course made a prisoner.

After a couple of days I arrived at Kecho, the ancient capital of the kings of Tong-king. Can you fancy me sitting quietly in the centre of my wooden cage, borne by eight soldiers, in the midst of an innumerable crowd of people, who almost barred the passage of the troops. I heard some of them saying, "What a pretty boy that European is!" "He doesn't look a bit afraid!" "Certainly he can't have done anything wrong!" "He came to our country to do us good and yet they will put him to death!" etc., etc. We entered the citadel by the eastern gate and I was brought at once before the tribunal of the judge of criminal cases. My catechist Khang, bearing his terrible yoke, walked behind my cage. I prayed God's Holy Spirit to strengthen us both and to speak by our mouths according to our Savior's promise; and I invoked the Queen of Martyrs and begged her to help her faithful child.

To begin with, the judge gave me a cup of tea, which I drank without ceremony in my cage. Then he commenced the usual interrogatory: "Whence do you come?" "I am from the Great West, from the country of France."

"What have you come to do in Annam?" "I have come to preach the true religion to those who know it not."

"What is your age?" "Thirty-one." The judge here said aside, with an accent of pity, "Poor fellow! he is still very young!" Then he continued, "Who sent you here?" "Neither the king nor the mandarins of France; but I myself, of my own accord, came to preach the Gospel to the heathen, and my superiors in religion assigned Annam to me as my district."

At this part of the interrogatory the prefect arrived, and he had hardly taken his seat when he cried out to me, in a loud and angry voice:

"Ah! you chief of the Christian religion, you have a clever countenance, you know very well that the Annamite laws forbid entrance into the kingdom to Europeans; what was the use, then, of coming here to be killed? It is you who have excited the Europeans to make war upon us, is it not? Speak the truth, or I will put you to the torture."

"Great mandarin, you ask me two questions. To the first I reply that I am sent as an ambassador from Heaven to preach the true religion to those who scorn it not, no matter in what kingdom, or in what place. We respect the authority of kings on the earth, but we respect more the authority of the King of Heaven. To your second question I answer that I never in any way invited or excited the Europeans to make war on the Annamite kingdom."

"In that case will you tell them to go? And you will then obtain your pardon."

"Great Mandarin! I have no power and no authority in such matters, but if His Majesty sends me I will beg the European warriors to abstain from making war on the Annamites; and if I do not succeed, I will return here to suffer death."

"You do not fear death, then?"

"Great mandarin! I do not fear death. I have come here to preach the true religion. I am guilty of no crime which deserves death. But if the Annamites kill me, I shall shed my blood with great joy for them."

"Have you any spite or ill-will against the man who betrayed and took you prisoner?"

"None at all. The Christian religion forbids us to entertain anger, and teaches us to love those who hate us."

"Chief of the Christian religion! You must declare the names of all the places and people that have sheltered you up to this hour."

"Great mandarin! They call you the father and mother of this people. If I were to make such a declaration it would involve a large number of persons in untold misery. Judge for yourself whether it would become me to do this or not."

"Trample the Cross under foot, then, and you shall not be put to death."

"How! I have preached the religion of the Cross all my life until this day, and do you expect me to abjure it now? I do not esteem so highly the pleasures of this life as to be willing to buy the preservation of it by apostasy."

"If death has such a charm in your eyes, why did you hide yourself when there was fear of your being taken?"

"Great mandarin! Our religion forbids us to presume on our strength, and to deliver ourselves to the persecutors. But Heaven having permitted my arrest, I have confidence in God that He will give me sufficient courage to suffer all torture and be constant unto death."

This is a summary of the questions asked me, and of my answers. The mandarins then proceeded to question my catechist and inflicted ten strokes of the knout upon him. He bore them without flinching, God giving him strength all the while gloriously to confess the faith.

Since that day I have been placed in my cage at the door of the prefect's house, guarded by a company of Cochin-Chinese soldiers. A great many persons of rank have come to visit me and converse with me. They will have it that I am a doctor, an astronomer, a diviner, a prophet, from whom nothing is hid. Several visitors have begged me to tell their fortunes. Then they question me about Europe, about France, in fact, about the whole world. This gives me an opportunity to enlighten them a little on points about which they are supremely ignorant, and on which they have sometimes the most comical ideas. I try above everything to slip in a little serious word now and then so as to teach them the way of salvation. But the Annamites are a frivolous race, and don't like serious subjects; still less will they treat on philosophy or religion. On the other hand, their heart is good, and they do their best to show me both interest and sympathy. My soldier guards have an affection for me, and though they have been blamed two or three times for letting me go out, they still open my cage from time to time, and allow me to take a little walk . . . Sometimes their conversation is not very proper, but I never let pass words of that sort; and I do not hesitate to speak to them strongly. I tell them that they lower themselves in the eyes of everyone by impure thoughts and libertine discourses; and that if they can talk in that way without blushing, they deserve nothing but pity, not to say contempt. My lessons make an impression. They are far more careful in their language now, and some have gone to the length of begging my pardon for having made use of indelicate expressions. Still I cannot say that everything is sweet and pleasant; although many are kind to me, some insult and mock me, and use rough language to me. May God forgive them!

I am now only waiting patiently for the day when God will allow me to offer Him the sacrifice of my blood. I do not regret leaving this world; my soul thirsts for the waters of eternal life. My exile is over. I touch the soil of my real country; earth vanishes, heaven opens, I go to God. *Adieu*, dearest father, sister, brothers, do not mourn for me, do not weep for me, live the years that are yet left to you on earth in unity and love. Practice your religion; keep pure from all sin. We shall meet again in Heaven, and shall enjoy true happiness in the kingdom of God. *Adieu*. I should like to write to each one separately but I cannot, and you know my heart. It is three long, weary years since I have heard from you, and I know not who is taken or who is left. *Adieu*. The prisoner of Jesus Christ salutes you. In a very short time the sacrifice will be consummated. May God have you always in His holy keeping. Amen.

MY ADVENTURE
WITH BILLY THE KID

by Sister Blandina Segale

One of Mother Seton's daughters in religion and a desperate outlaw make an unusual combination. From a little known page in history comes a revealing insight into the men who made America's legends, by a Sister of Charity who was herself a pioneer.

The Trinidad Enterprise—the only paper published here—in its last issue gave an exciting description of how a member of "Billy's Gang" painted red the town of Cimarron by mounting his stallion and holding two six-shooters aloft while shouting his commands, which everyone obeyed, not knowing when the trigger on either weapon would be lowered. This event has been the town talk, excluding every other subject, for the past week.

Yesterday one of the Vigilant Committee came to where I was on our grounds—acting as umpire for a ball game—and said: "Sister, please come to the front yard. I want you to see one of Billy's gang, the one who caused such fright in Cimarron week before last." My informant passed the news to the Nine and their admirers, so that it became my duty to go with the pupils, not knowing what might take place.

When we reached the front yard, the object of our curiosity

* From *At the End of the Santa Fe Trail*. Copyright, Bruce Publishing Co.

was still many rods from us. The air here is very rarefied, and we all are eagle-eyed in this atmosphere. We stood in our front yard, everyone trying to look indifferent, while Billy's accomplice headed toward us.

He was mounted on a spirited stallion of unusually large proportions, and was dressed as the *Toreadores* (Bull-Fighters) dress in old Mexico. Cowboy's sombrero, fantastically trimmed, red velvet knee breeches, green velvet short coat, long sharp spurs, gold and green saddle cover. A figure of six feet three, on a beautiful animal, made restless by a tight bit—you need not wonder, the rider drew attention. His intention was to impress you with the idea "I belong to the gang." The impression made on me was one of intense loathing, and I will candidly acknowledge, of fear also.

The figure passed from our sight. I tried to forget it, but it was not to be. Our Vigilant Club, at all times, is on the alert to be of service. William Adamson, a member of the Club, came excitedly, to say—"We have work on hand!"

"What kind of work?" I asked.

"You remember the man who frightened the people in Cimarron, and who passed our schoolhouse some weeks ago?"

"Yes, William."

"Well, he and Happy Jack, his partner, got into a quarrel, and each got the drop on the other. They kept eyeing and following each other for three days, eating at the same table, weapon in right hand, conveying food to their mouth with left hand.

"The tragedy took place when they were eating dinner. Each thought the other off guard, both fired simultaneously. Happy Jack was shot through the breast. He was put in a dugout 3x6 ft. Schneider received a bullet in his thigh, and has been brought into Trinidad, thrown into an unused adobe hut, and left there to die. He has a very poor chance of living."

"Well, William, we shall do all we can for him. Where did this all take place?"

"At Dick Wootton's tollgate—the dividing line between Colorado and New Mexico."

At the noon hour we carried nourishing food, water, castile

soap and linens to the sick and neglected man. After placing on a table what we had brought, my two companions, William Adamson and Laura Menger, withdrew. I walked towards the bed and, looking at the sick man, I exclaimed, "I see that nothing but a bullet through your brain will finish you!"

I saw a quivering smile pass over his face, and his tiger eyes gleamed. My words seemed heartless. I had gone to make up for the inhuman treatment given by others, and instead, I had added to the inhumanity by my words.

After a few days of retrospection, I concluded it was not I who had spoken, but Fear, so psychologists say.

At our first visit I offered to dress the wound, but to my great relief the desperado said, "I am glad to get the nourishment and the wherewith to dress my wound, but I shall attend to it myself." Then he asked: "What shall I call you?"

"Sister," I answered.

"Well, Sister, I am very glad you came to see me. Will you come again?"

"Yes, two and three times a day. Good-bye."

We continued these visits for about two months, then one day the sick man asked: "Sister, why is it you never speak to me about your religion or anything else?"

I looked and smiled.

He continued: "I want to tell you something. I allude to the first day you came. Had you spoken to me of repentance, honesty, morals, or anything pertaining to religion, I would have ordered you out. 'I see that nothing but a bullet through your brain will finish you.' Sister, you have no idea what strength and courage those words put into me. I said to myself, 'No shamming here, but the right stuff.'"

Dear Sister Justina, imagine what a load was lifted, to know for a certainty I had not added pain to the downtrodden culprit, for so he is at present. The patient seemed to wish to talk. He asked:

"Sister, do you think God would forgive me?"

I repeated the words of Holy Scripture as they then came to my mind. "If your sins were as scarlet, or as numerous as the sands on the seashore, turn to Me, saith the Lord, and I will forgive."

"Sister, I would like to tell you some things I have done—then, I will ask you, if you think God can forgive me."

Seating myself, I waited, as he continued:

"I have done all that a bad man can do. I have been a decoy on the Santa Fe Trail."

He saw I did not grasp his meaning, so he explained:

"I dressed in my best when I expected to see horsemen or private conveyance take to the Trail. Addressing them politely, I would ask, 'Do you know the road to where you are going?' If they hesitated, I knew they were greenies. I would offer to escort them, as the Trail was familiar to me, and I was on my way to visit a friend. We would travel together, talking pleasantly, but all the while my aim was to find out if the company had enough in its possession to warrant me carrying out my purpose.

"If I discovered they did not have money or valuables I would direct the travelers how to reach the next fort. If they possessed money or jewelry, I managed to lose the trail at sunset and make for a camping place. When they slept, I murdered them and took all valuables. The fact of being off the Trail made it next to impossible for the deed to be discovered.

"Another thing I took pleasure in doing was to shoot cows and steers for their hides. I remember one time I shot several cows that belonged to a man from Kansas. I left the carcasses for the coyotes. The old man had a great deal of spunk in him, so he and his herders trailed and caught me with the hides.

"They had a rope with them which they threw over the limb of a tree and placed me under the rope. Before going any farther the old man said to me, 'Say your prayers, young man; you know the law of the plains, a thief is hanged.' I said, 'I'm not a thief, I shot at random. When I saw my shots had taken effect, I took the hides of the animals I had shot. What would you have done?'

" 'I would not have shot at random into a bunch of cows,' he added. 'Did none of you ever make a mistake? I acknowledge I did wrong.' All but the old man said, 'Let the fellow go,' and waited for the old man to speak. 'Well, if you all think he ought to be let go, I don't say anything against it,' he said. So they let me go. As soon as I got where my pals were, I told them how near I came to being strung up. They all laughed and said I had the young ones to thank that I was able to tell the tale. I added, 'I'll wager ten cents I'll scalp the old man and throw the scalp on this counter.' They laughed and took up my wager.

"The next day I went to find in what direction the cattle I had fired into had gone. I soon discovered the herd trail and followed it, and at noon I saw the cattle. The old man was sitting on a stump with his back to me. I slipped up quietly behind him, passed my sharp knife around his head while holding his hair, and carried his scalp on a double run to where I had left my bronco; then, whirled to where my pals were. They each had told some of the deeds he had done, and Happy Jack had just finished telling an act which I will not tell you, but I added: 'Here is my last achievement. Scalped a man on a wager of ten cents.' While saying this I threw the scalp on the counter. 'Give me my dime.'

"Sister, now do you think God can forgive me?"

I answered: "Turn to Me in sorrow of heart and I will forgive, saith the Lord."

"Sister, I do not doubt that—you believe that God will forgive me: I'm going to tell you what I think God would do. Through you, God is leading me to ask pardon for my many devilish acts.

"He is enticing me, as I enticed those who had valuables; then, when He gets me, He will hurl me into hell, more swiftly than I sent my victims to Eternity. Now what do you think about that, Sister?"

"I will answer you by asking you a question. Who was the sinner who asked Christ to remember him when He came into His kingdom?"

"I don't know, Sister."

"It was the malefactor dying at the side of Christ on the cross who called for mercy at the last moment. He was told by the very Christ-God—'This day, thou shalt be with Me in Paradise.' "

"That sounds fine, Sister; but what will my pals think of me?

Me, to show a yellow streak! I would rather go to the burning flames. Anyhow, when I get there, I will have to stay chained."

"Experience is a great teacher."

"You bet it is, Sister."

"I'm going to give you an experience." I got the fire shovel and placing two burning coals on it, brought it to the bedside of the patient. "Now place one finger over these coals, or let me tie your hand, so that one finger will burn for ten seconds, then tell me if, in either case, the pain will be diminished."

"Say, Sister, let me think this thing over."

At our next visit the patient did not allude to our last conversation. I do not speak on religious subjects to him unless questioned. This routine work of taking him nourishment, linens, etc., continues. We had been doing it for about four months when this particular incident took place.

On a Saturday morning we arrived at our patient's adobe house when, for the first time, we heard voices in his room. Rapping at the door, the patient in a loud irritated voice called out: "Come in, Sister, and look at these hypocrites and whited sepulchres. Do you know what brought them here? Shame! You shamed them, you, a Catholic Sister, who has been visiting me for over four months and bringing wherewith to keep me alive. You never once asked me whether I was a Jew, Indian, or devil. You shamed them into coming. They say I belong to their church!"

Not noticing the aggressive language, I remarked: "I'm so glad your friends have found you. Should you need us in the future, we will be at your service."

Then one of the ladies of the company said: "It was only yesterday that a member of our Methodist congregation was told that the sick man was a Methodist. She went at once to our minister and he appointed this committee, and we are here, ready and willing, to attend to the sick man."

I told her that it made me happy to know the patient will have his own visiting him.

With a pleasant good-bye, we took our leave. On returning to the Convent, while making our program for sick calls, I remarked: "Billy the Kid's partner has found friends. Rather they have found him, and they intend to give him all the aid he needs. So we will withdraw, but be on the alert, in case we should have to continue our visits." This was said to a member of the Vigilant Club, who always accompanied my companion and myself to this particular patient.

Two weeks had elapsed when our protector of the Vigilant Committee came to the schoolhouse to say: "Sister, Billy's pal needs us again. I visited him several times during the past two days. He told me that no one has been to see him for a week."

So this noon we visited the desperado, the same as we had done at first. His being neglected by those who had promised to attend to him made me think that the ladies we met in his room are perhaps mothers of families, and cannot spare the time from their home. Again, some of the ladies maybe were as much afraid of him, as I had been, so it is easy to see why they could not keep their promise, but it would have been more just to let me know they were going to discontinue aiding him. Perhaps their husbands did not approve of their visiting a bandit. The general sentiment is, "Let the desperado die."

Today when we got to the adobe, everything was deathly quiet and the door was ajar. I noiselessly walked in. This is the scene that met me. The patient stretched full length, his eyes glazed and focused on the ceiling; his six-shooter in his right hand with the muzzle pointing to his temple. Quick as a flash I took in the situation and as quickly reached the bedside. Placing my hand on the revolver and lowering the trigger while putting the weapon out of his reach, I remarked: "The bed is not a good place from which to practice target shooting."

He said, "Just in the nick of time, Sister," as though we had not been absent a day. I named the different edibles we had brought him. The subject of the act he was about to commit was never mentioned. By intuition he understood he was not to speak against those who had promised to attend him and did not do so.

Another month passed by and the patient was visibly losing strength. I managed to get his mother's address. She lives in California.

After a week we resumed our visits. At the noon call our patient was quite hilarious. I surmised something unusual had taken place. He lost no time in telling me that Billy and the "gang" are to be here, Saturday at 2 P.M., and I am going to tell you why they are coming.

"Do you know the four physicians who live here in Trinidad?"

"I know three of them," I answered.

"Well, the 'gang' is going to scalp the four of them" (and his tiger eyes gleamed with satisfaction) "because not one of them would extract the bullet from my thigh."

Can you imagine, Sister Justina, the feeling that came over me? One of the gentlemen is our Convent physician!

I looked at the sick man for a few seconds, then said: "Do you believe that with this knowledge I'm going to keep still?"

"What are you going to do about it?"

"Meet your gang at 2 P.M. next Saturday."

He laughed as heartily as a sick man could laugh and said, "Why, Sister, Billy and the gang will be pleased to meet you. I've told them about you and the others, too, who call themselves my church people," but seeing the conversation did not please, he said no more.

In the interval between this visit and the Saturday 2 P.M., which was to be such a memorable day for me, I wrote to his mother not in an alarming strain, but enough to give her to understand he might not recover. Fourteen days later, she arrived. That was quick time, for she depended on mules and horses for conveyance. I cannot give you any idea of the anxiety of the days previous to the coming ordeal of meeting the gang.

Saturday, 2 P.M., came, and I went to meet Billy and his gang. The introduction was given. I can only remember, "Billy, our Captain, and Chism."

I was not prepared to see the men that met me, which must account for my not being able to recall their names.

The leader, Billy, has steel-blue eyes, peach complexion, is young, one would take him to be seventeen—innocent-looking, save for the corners of his eyes, which tell a set purpose, good or bad. Mr. Chism, of course this is not his real name—has a most bashful appearance. I judge he has sisters. The others, all fine looking men. My glance took this description in while Billy was saying: "We are all glad to see you, Sister, and I want to say, it would give me pleasure to be able to do you any favor."

I answered, "Yes, there is a favor you can grant me." He reached his hand toward me with the words: "The favor is granted."

I took the hand, saying: "I understand you have come to scalp our Trinidad physicians, which act I ask you to cancel." Billy looked down at the sick man who remarked: "She is game."

What he meant by that I am yet at a loss to understand. Billy then said: "I granted the favor before I knew what it was, and it stands. Not only that, Sister, but at any time my pals and I can serve you, you will find us ready."

I thanked him and left the room. How much of this conversation was heard by my companion who waited in the corridor, I do not know. Here are the names of the physicians who were doomed to be scalped:

Dr. Michael Beshoar, our Convent and Academy physician. The two Menger brothers; the elder has a large family, the younger is a bachelor. The fourth is Dr. Palmer, whom I know only by reputation. They will never know from me what might have happened.

Life is a mystery. What of the human heart? A compound of goodness and wickedness. Who has ever solved the secret of its working? I thought: One moment diabolical, the next angelical.

The patient's mother is going to have her son removed to a private family. I am unable to judge how much the mother knows of the life of her boy. His tiger expression must have developed since he left her side, and she is too happy to be with him to notice anything except that life is losing all attractions for him.

Feast of All Saints, 1876

Our poor desperado is fast approaching the shores of eternity. He has become more thoughtful, even his tiger eyes are softening. The mother is all attention and goodness to her son, but neither will hear to our discontinuing our visits. This is the ninth month of our work with this patient who now never mentions "the Gang" though Trinidad often hears of the atrocities committed by it—only say "Billy the Kid" and every individual is at attention.

Dear Sister Justina, were I to write many of the incidents of daily occurrence, this journal kept for you instead of giving you a little diversion, and perhaps a wee bit of knowledge, might bring you only sadness and weariness.

Billy and his gang are terrorizing the country between this place and La Glorieta, the historic battleground of Texans and Mexicans.

Our school is rehearsing for a concert to be given during the Christmas holidays. We are not depending upon outside talent for our vocal numbers, but we will be assisted by two Italian musicians—violin and harp.

Our desperado patient has the comfort of his mother's presence, yet neither her love nor sacrifice can stay his fast dissolution. *December 2.* This morning I felt quite uneasy about him, so made an early visit to be on time for the morning school session. When we entered the patient's room we saw plainly he could not survive many hours. Kneeling, we said prayers, which included an act of contrition, he repeated them, then said "good-bye." We felt this was the end of our services to the tiger desperado. We left him to the mercy of God.

The sick man's mother came to the Convent after the funeral and told me some minister had come to see her son shortly after our last visit. He said to the minister: "Do not disturb me. I want to keep in mind the prayers said by the Sisters." *Miserere mei Deus, secundum magnam misericordiam tuam.* He is in God's just, yet merciful, hands.

NIGHT BY A JUNGLE LAGOON

by Tom Gill

A sensitive word portrait of a night spent in the Mexi‹ can rain forest by a distinguished author, forester, natu‑ ralist, cartographer and explorer.

Pedro's wrinkled face smiled. "After all, it is only at night when the jungle speaks. In two short months here in our Mexican forests, you think, perhaps, you have learned something of the way of the wild things. But it is not really so. For only at night, senor, the bitter fight for life begins. Then the jungle things awaken and come forth."

My old Mexican guide was right. Two months knocking about through the mahogany forests of southern Mexico had certainly not rewarded me with much knowledge of the abundant wild life that I knew must exist there. I waited for old Pedro to speak again.

"Always the eyes of the children of the jungle are upon us— they follow us and signal about us, and know our coming and going. Yes, even the Caribe Indians know we are here. And I think, if they wished it, we should not see tomorrow's dawn."

Now, I had already heard of the Caribe Indian and his play‑ ful way with blow-gun and poisoned arrow. Farther to the south, where they are unfriendly, white men had lost their lives, but here they were thought a peaceful people.

"Sometimes when we are caught out at night," Pedro's soft,

* Originally published and copyrighted by *Nature Magazine*, republished by *The Reader's Digest*.

lisping Spanish went on, "sometimes we hear the jungle awaken. The bats, and the great moths and puma, the big cat, watch us. But soon we light a campfire, and everything moves back."

My curiosity was so aroused by this talk that the following sunset I took leave of Pedro and his comfortable campfire, to spend the night on the banks of a lagoon.

Already night had fallen. Behind me loomed the jungle, black and impenetrable. The vampire bats were out. Back and forth before me, three of them kept me eerie company for an hour, flying so close that I could dimly trace their evil, hairy faces, and distinctly feel the rush of wind beneath their wings. Curious fellows. More than once they hung motionless, so close I could have struck them with my hat, peering at me.

Far out in the lagoon I heard the muffled ripple of moving water. I could see nothing, and flashed on my flashlight, playing it back and forth over the smooth water of the lagoon. At last I held it steady where two dull red eyes glowed like garnets in the darkness. The alligator, that old killer of the jungle, was abroad.

Held by the spell of the flashlight, he came almost to the bank of the lagoon, and there beneath my feet he waited, with upturned wicked, bloodshot eyes. Soon from the left, out of the darkness, came another cautious ripple, and farther on still another. And before half an hour had passed 12 pairs of ruby eyes were ranged down there before me, all looking hungrily, expectantly up into the flashlight. Above them, attracted by the illumination, great giant moths were fluttering on soft, brilliantly-colored wings just over the water's edge.

I thought of the Indian legend that tells how the souls of good children, in dying, are sometimes favored by the gods, and pass into these moth bodies, abiding there until they are born again.

Tired at last of that solemn scrutiny of steady eyes, I chose a large stone and dropped it carefully on the nose of the biggest alligator. Followed an indignant snort, a mad lashing of the water beneath, and a sudden extinction of all those pairs of eyes. Once more I was surrounded by silence and jungle blackness.

Just at midnight rose the sound of a jaguar. Now it is one thing to hear the midnight rumble of a jaguar when you are lying in the comparative security of a campfire's glow, but it was somewhat different perched upon the edge of an alligator-infested lagoon. From the crackling and trampling, it sounded unmistakably as if he were working my way. With cocked automatic in my right hand, I flashed a stream of light down into the tangled mass of bamboo and palms.

The rest is a confused memory—a snarl of surprise, a mottled, sinewy form not ten feet away, and the flash of my automatic as twice I fired wildly. I must have missed by yards. The shots shattered the peace of the surrounding jungle. Parrakeets chattered and swore, while from afar off a band of monkeys shrieked and howled. It was hours before quiet returned to the jungle.

Just as dawn was painting its first silver over jungle and lagoon, and I had almost given up hope of seeing more—just then my long vigil was rewarded by something I would have journeyed many miles to see.

Beyond the rising mists I first noticed a clump of palms shaking in a way no movement of wind could have accounted for. Then I saw two dark arms push the palms aside, and a moment later the almost naked figure of an Indian had moved silently down to the water's edge. In his left hand he grasped a bow and several arrows. His long black hair fell below his shoulders. I knew then that I was looking upon one of that little known, mysterious Caribe tribe, those furtive, almost legendary people so few travelers ever see. For no other Indian of southern Mexico allows his hair to grow long and to hang loosely about his shoulders. No other Indian wears only a band of stringy burlap-like bark about his waist.

Noiselessly the Caribe crept to a point of land not far from where three mallard ducks were swimming lazily about. He had laid aside his bow and arrow and held some large object about the size and shape of a pumpkin, but darker in color. Slowly he slipped into the water. As it reached his shoulders he put over his head that hollow spherical object, then let himself sink until only that strange headdress was visible above the surface. It bobbed and moved and stopped and moved again, as naturally as any light object might be blown about by some soft morning breeze, but always with a kind of menacing certainty it approached nearer and nearer its quarry. Once a duck turned as if to paddle away, but apparently changing its mind, resumed feeding. The hidden Caribe was only a few feet away, and I found myself straining forward to catch the end.

The end came quickly. The unseen hunter was floating quietly now, directly among the feeding ducks. A hush, almost of expectancy, had fallen. Suddenly a frightened squawk broke the morning silence.

With a terrified flapping of wings one duck arose and sped back into the jungle. The other two were nowhere to be seen! Beneath that quietly floating object, two dark hands were grasping the ducks that only a moment before had been feeding in such complete security. In another moment my Caribe had thrown off his camouflage and gained the farther bank, where he stood glistening and streaming with water, holding in either hand the prizes of his hunt. Silently he turned back into the jungle and was gone.

Hungry and weary, an hour later, I was telling Pedro my story. He listened without comment, but as I finished he said quietly, "Give thanks to the Mother of God, senor, that the Caribe did not see you. They do not greatly like to be spied upon, those jungle people."

THE DOG WHO DIDN'T LIKE PROVERBS

A Maryknoller welcomed a Chinese gentleman to his residence, wrote Father Edwin J. McCabe from Kweilin. But the mission watchdog growled his disapproval of the visitor. The missioner assured his guest, "A barking dog never bites." The Chinese smiled ruefully: "Spiritual Father, you know the proverb; I know the proverb; but does the dog know the proverb?"

FORLORN PEOPLE

by Roger Buliard

> The Oblates of Mary Immaculate have won for them-
> selves an outstanding reputation because of their work
> in Arctic wastelands. No other group of men have their
> knowledge of Eskimo customs and habits.

Among the Eskimos, lying, as we understand it, is certainly not
a sin, and clever lying is almost a virtue. What counts is what
you can get away with. Daily, during his entire life, the Eskimo
matches his wits with nature and is continuously exposed to
hazard. Hunting is no sport for him, but a grim business upon
which he depends for survival, and it is his life or the animal's.
In his social life, it is he or his rival. Necessity makes him a
supreme egocentric, and of course he lies, shamelessly, until he
is caught. Then he laughs. The trick has failed.

Returning to camp after a long absence, I once discovered that
my precious dog line, the only one of its kind within a couple
of hundred miles, had disappeared. I kept my eyes open for
several weeks, and, sure enough, I spotted it at Minto, in an
Eskimo settlement. After a while, between cups of tea, with
everyone in the settlement around, I asked quite innocently,
"Has anyone seen my dog line? Or perhaps someone took it, eh?"
Offended airs, emphatic denials! No, Falla! Certainly not, Falla!
They didn't know a thing about it. I smiled at the guilty one.

* From *Inuk*. Copyright, Farrar, Straus and Cudahy.

"Well, my boy, your dogs are tied up with it, or didn't you know? When did you steal it? Come on!"

"Why, Falla!" the fellow said, all smiles. "I thought you had given it to me."

I was angry and said, "You lie! You all lie!"

The Eskimos just laughed and laughed, and after a while one of them went out to get the dog line and brought it back to me.

Thieving and lying are just two ways of making a living, just easier than other ways such as hunting and fishing, that's all. As in ancient Sparta, it isn't the stealing but the being caught that constitutes evil. To acquire, even unjustly, is still to acquire. Of course, they are all so poor that temptation is hard to resist, even for the best disposed among them. Petty theft is the most common source of trouble in their camps.

Once, while I was visiting a camp on Victoria Island, I became so discouraged with their thieving habits that I wrote in my diary:

"I should leave this place for a while, I guess. They steal my fish, and many other things, during the night, right under my nose. They are a bunch of confirmed thieves. They accuse each other and always loudly protest their innocence, but they are always careful to blame one too stupid to be held responsible, or one so unlucky as is always caught.

"Moreover, their morals are absolutely dumbfounding—a striking spectacle of nature shamelessly displayed in the raw. This is one of the few remaining tribes of the old style, and their practices would put the most licentious ancient to shame."

Most missionaries, at one point or another in their careers, have awakened on a certain morning so disillusioned that they are ready to leave the North forever. But something holds them, something persuades them to go on, and they find in their hearts pity and forgiveness for the Eskimo tribesmen.

But one never becomes used to their hypocrisy, or reconciled to it. It is their hallmark, and even the dreaded Mounted Police have been taken in by Eskimo cunning on more than one occasion.

At Tree River, some time ago, a constable of the Mounted Police took into custody a notorious Eskimo murderer—one

Alikamek, a tough specimen if there ever was one. The police-man was bringing Alikamek to Hershell Island, 1000 miles away, for trial, and at first, having heard of the Eskimo's murderous character, he was careful with his prisoner. But Alikamek played the servile savage. He laid it on thick, cringing, bowing, offering to perform all kinds of menial service for the officer. The police-man gradually relaxed his vigilance, and after a while he and Alikamek were like master and servant rather than officer of the law and prisoner. One fine morning the Mountie said, "Hey, there, Alikamek, pass me my boots will you?"

Alikamek went to the corner where the policeman's boots were lying, but when he turned around his hands held, not boots, but the constable's rifle. Alikamek grinned at the Mountie, enjoying his triumph, and shot him as he sat on the bed. Then he stood by the window, watching, his rifle ready. After a while the Hudson's Bay Company trader next door, observing that no smoke was coming from the chimney of the Police barracks, decided to investigate. As he came out of the H.B.C. store, Alikamek got him in his sights and put a bullet through his fore-head. The opportunity was just too good to miss—a stupid Big Eyebrow, like that.

Then, feeling sure that he had earned the rifle, Alikamek slung it over his shoulder and made his way back north to his camp, delighted with his new firearm and eager to show it off to his friends. Until they caught him again and took him in to hang him, Alikamek enjoyed quite a reputation as a hunter of the Big Eyebrows.

Of course, Alikamek saw nothing wrong with what he had done, nor did his people. Their standards are different, their at-titudes not like ours. So have our own standards been different in the past, and we should not forget that even if all people do have a basic platform of values common to all mankind, these may vary, in application and detail, in accordance with the culture and time. For instance, the duel of bygone days was accepted by Western Europeans as quite natural and lawful. So was slavery. So was a rigid class system. So was capital punish-ment for trivial offences. All these have gone. Under our present system, built upon Christian ideals, human life is considered sacred, and we regard the man who kills another human with repugnance and horror. But among other, non-Christian peoples, where self-preservation is the sole guide to human conduct, one sees displayed a shocking disregard for human life, of one's own life and that of his neighbors. I am told that this is true among the Chinese and other Orientals, and it is certainly true among the Eskimos. So if, according to our standards, the Eskimo does kill too often, we must not condemn him without thought. And we should not forget that, in the past especially, many Eskimo murders were not really murders at all, but dispensations of civil justice, according to their own rude legal code. In their country, until recently, there were no Police and no courts, and in many cases the people were obliged to take individual action in defence of their homes, property or families. Often, too, the Eskimo, trained in the hunting field and suspicious, wary, by nature, would think he saw in another's sidelong glance, or trivial sneer, a threat to his own safety. He would take no chances. But the murder he did would, in his mind, be a matter of self-defence.

OF FATHER DONOVAN

Oh, pity not this fallen one,
  This eager one with ravaged frame—
For, falling low, he scaled the heights
  To bear his torch in deathless flame!

But oh! that he might pity us,
  Who, glimpsing stars, still walk in night—
That he might strike our earthbound souls
  With restless fire of burnished light!

—MARGUERITE GILBERT

A GUARDIAN ANGEL SMILES

by Francis X. Ford

> Bishop Ford was the first Maryknoll student, and the
> first American priest to die at the hands of the Chinese
> Communists. He was a great proponent of the native
> clergy, as this article shows.

When we began work in Hakkaland, in 1925, we firmly resolved
not to build anything anywhere till we were well settled, both in
knowledge of the place and language, but more especially in
funds. We made a solemn promise to ourselves not to take any
forward step until our financial credit warranted it. We borrowed
this axiom from Ben Franklin without blushing, for experience
in the past had shown that early wrinkles and gray hairs are the
result of living up to your income without reserve. It seemed a
splendid chance to begin a new mission correctly from the very
start.

The guardian angel of the mission surely must have smiled at
our shortsightedness. We poor mortals were trying to imitate
the "children of this world" in being prudent, but, that no flesh
might glory in itself, Providence simply stepped in and ran things
from God's viewpoint, and we were helpless. First, the wee, small
voice spoke to the boys of our schools, and vocations to the
Catholic priesthood superabounded. Then the Holy Father, as if

* From *Stone in the King's Highway* by Raymond A. Lane. Copyright, Maryknoll Fathers.

he had seen the whole affair, wrote his letter to the missions, saying that we were not to refuse vocations.

There were ten boys waiting for us when we arrived in this hinterland of the port city of Swatow. Without budging an inch in our resolution, we gave the mission's guardian angel a knowing glance, and started the seminary in our own house. Of course, our conscience whispered that it would not do at all, but we were deaf. We took the boys in, and, as happened in the schools of Charlemagne, the youngsters became part of our household.

The rectory, with two bedrooms upstairs and three rooms on the ground floor, was not overlarge, but by putting the boys' beds on the enclosed porch and using one of our bedrooms for the teachers we managed to be cosy. The pastor made his bedroom in the hallway, by blocking off a corner with his bookcase. The next school term found us with thirteen boys. The hall room was released for the seminarians' use, by fixing up the attic for the pastor. We could still claim financial victory in the battle for economy.

Our defenses were rapidly crumbling, however. Before we could catch our breath, we had twenty-one seminarians. We crowded them into our two-bedroom dwelling, but at the expense of order and discipline. Only Chinese boys would have put up with the discomforts of those narrow quarters. We made place for the latest recruits by sawing off the beds of the smaller boys, which gave us room for two more bunks. All spare clothing was stored in boxes in the yard. Outside of the hours for meals, the dining room served alternately as classroom and as study hall. Two Protestant missionaries from the Baptist university paid a call, and they had to be received on the porch. There was no room vacant except the pastor's bedroom, and three chairs could not fit in there.

At length, we conceded what we had known all along; a seminary is not a camp; and there were certain essentials which had to be provided. As we acknowledged defeat, we could hear the mission's guardian angel chuckling. "God has given you all those seminarians," he seemed to say. "Why should you be so stupid as to doubt that He would help you to build a seminary?"

The angelic chuckles did not irk us because we were remarkably happy ourselves. The joy of training Chinese youth for the Catholic priesthood far outweighed the sacrifice of worldly prudence. Under our fostering care, there would take place in China the miracle of the birth of "other Christs," all linked with Bethlehem's First-born. Each of those Chinese priests nurtured in our seminary would be God's "star in the East," calling men of good will from the shadow of death to the everlasting splendor of Redemption.

Recently the seminary has been called upon to make its sacrifice in the death of one of its students, John Yap Tet-hon. This young man was the first applicant for admission when the seminary was begun, in 1925. He was a boy only thirteen years of age, finishing his course at the parochial school in Kaying, but he had already entertained for several years the desire to offer himself for the priesthood.

He came from a family that has been Catholic for several generations, which is not unusual in this section of the mission. This particular family has, moreover, nourished a Catholic spirit that has sent the eldest son to the Catholic University at Peiping, while it generously encouraged the two younger boys in their vocation at the seminary.

John, although not a naturally bright student, often led his class because of his steady application. But, better still, as associated with the institution from its beginning he was the leader of the other boys in a quiet, unconscious piety. He came from what would be considered one of the "better families" of our mission, and in China class consciousness is a strong element; yet in practice, he went beyond his classmates in little acts of humility and mortification.

The manual-labor period at the seminary—especially in its earlier days—was strenuous enough, and irksome to the average Chinese boy, who sharply distinguishes as a student between menial and other tasks. Yet John again set the example. He would work during the hour, digging in the garden or removing heaps of rubbish, in his bare feet. When asked why, he replied that the cloth shoes were too easily torn by such work, and he wished to save us that expense.

During his seven years with us, I never knew him to commit a deliberate violation of the rules; his interpretation of their spirit was generous and showed reflection. He could accuse himself occasionally of interior feelings of anger, though not of their outward expression, and in basketball or handball he had a mastery over his feelings even in moments of excitement. He entered into the spirit of any student activity, whether study or games, without losing himself in it, and he preserved a mature purpose in his actions rare in so innocent a life.

The scourge of the student class in China is lung trouble; and John developed symptoms. His lingering illness terminated in a characteristic act. He was conscious to the end, begging his father to be resigned to God's will. When his father finally assented, John, as though waiting for his permission, quietly closed his eyes and breathed his last.

He was the John Berchmans of the seminary, set in pagan surroundings where his virtues are emphasized by contrast. God chose our worthiest. It is a reassuring thought that we are represented in the Eternal Sanctuary by one who was so grateful here below for what we gave him.

THE IRON DUKE AND THE MARCHING ORDERS

A Protestant Minister in England once asked the Duke of Wellington if he believed in foreign missions. "Sir," asked the Iron Duke, "what are your marching orders?" Thus the old soldier put his finger on the preacher's difficulty: we are not asked; we are *commanded* by God Himself: "Go ye into the whole world and preach the gospel to every creature."   —MARK XVI:15

THE MAIDEN AND THE BELL

by *Thomas J. Malone*

For countless centuries the great teaching in China has been respect of parents. Now the Communists are attempting to destroy filial piety. The following legend is an example of the old teaching.

Near Peking is a temple called the Great Bell Temple. The huge bell that gives this shrine its name measures fifteen feet high and thirty-four feet around. Inside and outside, the bell is covered with Chinese writing, the sayings of China's greatest sages. There is a quaint but pathetic legend connected with the bell.

Once upon a time (so the story goes), a great emperor ordered the making of a bell whose voice should be heard thirty-three miles distant. He directed that gold and silver should be melted with the other metals for the bell, to make it sound beautiful as well as loud. The most famous bell maker in the land was given the task of making the bell. This man had a small daughter, who grew frightened when she heard of the work her father had accepted.

She said to him: "Father, please think well before you promise the emperor. If you fail to please His Highness, he will be angry, and I fear for your welfare."

The father paid no heed to his daughter, but set about making his bell. When it was time for the first casting, the emperor was on hand. The metals were poured into a mold and allowed to cool; then the mold was removed.

The bell maker, with confidence and pride, struck the bell to sound its voice for his sovereign. Alas, the tone was neither loud nor beautiful! A second time the bell maker tried, and the result was equally poor.

The emperor became wrathful and said: "After the first failure, I felt sorry for you, but now I am angry. Unless you achieve satisfactory results on the next casting, you die!"

The bell maker's little girl heard those words and was terrified. In an effort to help her father, she hastened to a wise and venerable soothsayer.

That sage told her, "Gold cannot mix with silver, or brass with iron, unless the blood of a pure and good girl be mixed with them."

The little girl returned to her father's house and said nothing about what the wise man had told her. For the third time, the metals were made ready. Again the emperor was on hand to watch. Just as the bell maker was about to draw off the metal for the mold, his little daughter dashed past him and threw herself into the melting pot. Her father rushed to pull her out, but too late! All he could save was one of her shoes.

Brokenhearted, the bell maker proceeded with the casting, for the emperor's command was urgent. At last the mold was taken off, and the new bell tried. The first stroke gave a sonorous and successful sound. Never had the emperor heard more beautiful music; moreover the pealing could be heard much farther than he had hoped. However, between each sound of the bell there seemed to be an echo: it was like the voice of a little girl crying, "Haai! Haai!"—which in Chinese means, "Shoe! Shoe!"

WANG AND HIS COFFIN

by John J. Considine

> Wang had his coffin and was up-to-date in his burial
> club dues. But a bitter turn of fortune intervened which
> robbed him, yet blessed him wonderfully.

Wang sat in his sunny courtyard and smoked contentedly. Before
him was his coffin, with which he was immensely pleased. It was
made of camphor wood six inches thick, with a high, curved lid.
It was lacquered with ten coats of lustrous black, while gold
spirals adorned the cover and long gold dragons ran down each
side.

"Father," the eldest of Wang's five sons had said that morning,
the morning of his sixtieth birthday, when they made him this
precious gift, "we have always loved you and respected you. We
have been mindful of the saying of the ancients, 'The most important thing in life is to be buried well at death.' We bring you
this coffin."

Now he was ready for death whenever it might come. For years
he had paid dues to a funeral club; thus there was money for the
ceremony. Preparations were complete; all was well.

Yet all was not well. Dark rumors about invaders proved too
true. Before the week was out they had swept like a plague
through the valley. Wang found himself, he knew not how, on a
refugee boat, moving up the Yangtze River, without his sons,
without money, without anything from home—even his precious
coffin.

The vessel unloaded at Wanhsien. Wang realized that he was very hungry, and the fact frightened him. He had been hungry at times in his life, but there had always been his home to go to, with its carefully stocked granary in times of difficulty, his friends with whom he could arrange regarding his needs. Now there were no home, no food, no money, no sons, no friends.

"I have nothing to eat," he said distractedly to a passer-by.

"Sorry, Uncle, but you're not much worse off than the rest of us. Guess you'll have to grub for it."

Late that afternoon, an old woman in a hovel was ladling out rice to her children when he wandered in. The sweet fumes of the steaming kettle made his head swim.

"Have you any work for me?" he asked weakly.

"Uncle, you don't want work, you want food," said the matter-of-fact grandmother. "We'll spare you a bowl of this rice, but you're robbing the children."

When night came, Wang crawled into an abandoned lean-to outside the city. Those there before him regarded him as an intruder, but they allowed him to remain on his promise that he would leave in the morning.

The new sun gave him courage. He had slept well, and his head was clearer.

"I will get work," he said to himself. "It shouldn't be hard to earn the few dollars for the fare to my sons down the river."

But work for a man of sixty was not easy to find. Toward noon he came upon a big-boned fellow standing with a burden pole.

"Work, Uncle? Are you strong? Perhaps you could take Wu's place. Wu used to carry with me, but he died yesterday."

The two men hurried to a warehouse near the docks. They mingled with other pairs, who were attaching great cases to their poles.

"Ready, Uncle—up!" cried his new-found companion. Straightening himself with the pole on his shoulder, Wang helped lift a heavy case from the ground.

"What a murderous load!" he gasped to himself. All went blank for a moment, but he doggedly kept his knees from crumpling. The owner of the pole was impatient at first, but Wang was determined not to show weakness. He had to get his stride, he explained; and by nightfall they were friends. The pole owner took his helper to an empty warehouse where with some twenty others, they threw themselves on the ground and slept deeply.

Every bone in Wang's body ached the next day, but he persisted. On the third morning he yielded, for a sizable lump protruded from his side.

"That's bad, Uncle, very bad. You have a rupture. Hard luck!"

Wang had money from the previous day, to buy rice. A doctor fastened a pad over his rupture; it was uncomfortable but permitted him to go back to his work. The doctor charged an exorbitant fee, and Wang was weeks paying it.

Then work ceased; there was no trade on the river. Wang, exhausted, gave little concern. He listened to the other coolies bewailing their lot, but did not join in their lamentations. He merely lay on his back in the sun, with his eyes closed.

Rest was very welcome—but a man must eat to live. Since the war still raged down the river, Wang followed the drift in the opposite direction and soon reached teeming Chungking. There he took such odd jobs as he could find.

He preferred to work with a gang; there was a sense of help from the others. The carriers possessed a carefully evolved technique. When a load was ready, the signal was given. Then the men moved with the rhythm and precision of dancers. All used a short, staccato step; and the front and rear carriers alternated with weird cries, as strange as the cries of animals in a jungle.

"*Hai-ya!*" "*Ho-ya!*" came the ceaselessly uttered versicle and response from one little procession. "*Hoh-Hoh!*" "*Yo-hoh!*" were the calls form another group.

But in addition to the cries were the odor of reeking perspiration, the staring eyes straining from their sockets; veins on every face and body taut as if ready to burst, the contorted muscles quivering, as if in mortal fear that they could not hold.

At last would come surcease. The carriers would throw themselves on the ground and be gripped by a sleep of exhaustion.

Wang felt himself growing increasingly more tired. "I cannot! I cannot!" he would repeatedly murmur to himself. The pennies he earned were not many, and the purchase of a passage to Ichang was postponed.

The aging man sought to find something less taxing for his meager strength. He spoke to the chair carriers.

"You are much too old," they replied as one man. Yet he would try the work. For some months he succeeded in getting odd jobs as assistant to men who owned a chair. Chance threw him into the country along the route to Chengtu. He shuttled backward and forward, some days overworked, some days idle. The chair took its toll. The bar resting on his shoulders pressed cruelly into the flesh and formed welts of angry red and purple. Then one day a splintered bar cut beneath the skin and caused a fester. Pus gathered in the wound and exuded under the pressure, as he trotted miserably along the road.

One autumn morning, after a night in a cold, damp shelter, Wang awoke trembling with ague. Toward evening he called to a passing coolie.

"You must help me get to a bowl of hot soup," he said.

"Very well, Uncle. But it is not soup you need; it is the puff of an opium pipe."

Wang's face darkened in horror. "Never!" he cried. "Never! My brother took opium and ended badly."

"Well, Uncle, you are not ending very famously yourself."

"Perhaps not," agreed poor Wang, cut to the heart. "And perhaps you are a downright scoundrel, with your rude remarks! Know that I am the father of five sons, that I have a home and a beautiful coffin. Soon—"

"Listen, Uncle, I have an idea for you. You must get to Chengtu before winter comes, and you must go to the home for old men. The home is conducted by the Sisters of the Lord of Heaven religion. They will have a bed for you, and rice for you."

There was a chilly whir of falling leaves, when Wang trudged slowly through Chengtu, to the gate of the House of St. Helen. A Sister answered his knock.

"I am very tired," he said.

"Come in and rest awhile, Uncle," replied the Sister quietly, her appraising eyes regarding him. "Yes, you are very tired."

Wang slept. The next morning his bones did not ache from the dampness, because he was dry and warm. But he was sick as well as tired, and he was obliged to remain in bed.

"That Man on the cross there, Sister," Wang remarked slowly one day. "I have been thinking about Him. What did He do?"

He liked the story. He felt very kindly toward this God who wanted men to love each other, and who sent people like the Sisters and priests to take care of men like himself who had bad fortune. One morning a priest came and baptized Wang. It was well that he did, for spring did not bring strength to the ex-hausted man. Rather, his life seemed slowly to ebb away. Deeply peaceful, like a man in sleep busied with a pleasant dream, he lay in repose.

In the hospital yard sounded the ring of a hammer on nail heads. Kung, the chief carpenter, was making coffins. "You must know," any of the Sisters would explain, "that the desire of every Chinese, even the lowliest, as the end comes, is to have a coffin in which to be buried."

A servant entered the yard. "Have you a coffin ready, Kung?" he asked. "Wang is dead."

ALL HONOR TO
CHING SIN SANG

When we pay tribute to Father Robert J. Cairns, who met violent death in South China at the hands of the Japanese, let us sing the praises of his "Man Friday." Ching Sin Sang was long of doubtful reputation; many of Father Sandy's friends had warned him against this Chinese. But Father Cairns trusted the man, and Ching repaid the trust. He could have left Sancian when he sent his family to safety; he could have fled into the hills. But he stood shoulder to shoulder with his priestly master in the hour of danger, voluntarily accepted capture with him, and presumably died with him. Like Father Cairns, Ching Sin Sang was never heard of after he was taken on the invaders' boat, out into the South China Sea, the night of December 16, 1941.

PASCUAL STRIKES IT RICH

by George L. Krock

When a flaming commercial airliner crashed in wooded
Missouri hills while on a routine flight, Maryknoll lost
one of its most talented writers, as this sample from
Guatemala will show.

Pedro Almengor left Spain in the 17th century, to seek his fortune. Silver had been discovered in Guatemala, and thither went
Pedro, with every cent he could scrape together. In the towering
mountain range that rises in northwestern Guatemala, Pedro
found a site where silver ore showed at the surface. By the time
he had bought a Royal patent to the site, had built a smelter,
waterways, a few crude shelters, and had purchased some slaves,
his capital was almost gone.

We are told that Pedro, before the digging was begun, went
down to the Dominican church in Chiantla. Kneeling there before the statue of the Virgin, he vowed that, if his mine produced,
he would have a mantle of pure silver fashioned for the Virgin's
statue; he would also give her two silver crowns—one for her and
one for the Christ Child in her arms. The Virgin smiled on
Pedro. And she smiled on little Pascual, the Indian slave at the
Spaniard's side. Poor Pascual, with his flashing smile and his
brown, bare feet. He was always running back and forth, serving his master. Every chance he got, Pascual slipped down to
Chiantla, to pray and to burn his candle in front of the Virgin's
statue.

Some years later, Pedro added up his wealth. It was great, and he was pleased. He had but one idea: to make his fortune and then return to Spain. He said, "When I have twice this much, I will sell out and go back to Spain."

On the next day, he rode down to Chiantla to fulfill his vow. It almost broke his heart to give the Padres five heavy bags of silver for the Virgin's mantle and one more to pay the silversmith to fashion the mantle. However, he made another vow. He promised the Virgin that, if she would help him double his fortune in five years, he would place before her shrine a candle as big as a cypress tree.

Pascual, kneeling beside his master, heard the vow and was much impressed. He wished he had enough money to do the same, because the tiny candles he could afford seemed to burn out before he could say even ten "Our Fathers." Little Pascual was not jealous, only a bit sad. Suddenly, his master slapped him with a riding whip and told him to bring the horse around to the front of the church. Pascual snuffed out the stump of his candle and slipped it into his belt. Soon Pedro was galloping off, with Pascual puffing along behind.

Five years passed. During all that time, Don Pedro never went near the church, although he often rode down to Chiantla when he wanted liquor. Nightly he threw himself on the bed without a word of night prayers. Pascual, his slave, never thought of sleeping without praying first. Whenever he could get permission, he went down to Chiantla to burn his candle and say his prayers as fast as he could. He thought the prayers had to be said while the candle burned. He always went away, wishing he could have a candle as big as a cypress tree.

At the end of the five years, Pedro's fortune had doubled. But he lay drinking in his hammock, day after day, as if he had not noticed. Pascual finally reminded him of the great vow. The lad's eagerness to see the huge candle overcame his fear of the master.

Pedro was furious. He thought that Indians should be kept in their place and taught to respect authority. He shouted at Pascual: "So, it has come to this, that a slave tells his master how

to run his affairs. You go out now and cut me a nice long switch
—and we shall see who is the master here."

Pascual cut a switch two feet long, and Pedro beat him with it
fiercely. When his arms grew tired, he flung the bloody whip at
the slave and snarled: "There, take it to the cook, and tell her to
make a candle of the same size. Then take the candle down and
give it to your Virgin. You see, I am a man of my word: the
switch you brought me is a small cypress tree."

Pascual was horrified and shamed when the master told him to
carry the two-foot candle down to the shrine, and to stay there
and see that it was all burned before he came back. The Indian
knelt down in front of the statue and began to weep. He apologized to the Virgin: "Here is your candle, Mother, but my master
is cheating you. I think he is the richest man in the world after
the King; yet he sent me here with this shameful little candle."

Finally he went back to the mine to report. As soon as he got
inside, a fellow slave told him that there was a Senora waiting
outside, who wanted to see him immediately. Pascual hurried to
obey. As he left the mine, the earth began to quake. He heard a
great noise and saw a cloud of dust belch out, as the whole mine
caved in.

Pascual stood in the bright sunshine. He felt very frightened
and terribly alone, as he looked on the ruins of the mine, closed
forever, with the master inside. He ran to look for the Senora, but
of course he did not find her. Then Pascual slowly made his way
to the only place of consolation he knew, to the shrine of Our
Lady in Chiantla. He knelt there, asking her to pray for all who
had perished that day.

THE INDIAN AND THE BABY

by Francis X. Lyons

A chance encounter of a Maryknoller and an Andean
Indian drives forcibly home the terrible need for more
priests in Latin American countries.

There was a dusty vocational placard hanging on the sacristy wall.
It read: "In the United States, one priest for every six hundred
Catholics; in Peru, one priest for every thirteen thousand souls."

It caught my eye that morning, as it did every morning while I
was unvesting. I was studying the drawing of a chalice raised in
benediction over the upturned faces of a great crowd, when I
heard a noise behind me. An Indian had come in.

Since he was chewing coca, I really smelled his presence before
I saw him. I laid the vestments on the scarred dressing table in
the dingy sacristy and turned toward the visitor. When I bowed,
he dropped on one knee, and before I was aware of his intention,
he kissed my hand.

"*Tatai*," which means "Father" in his language, was all he
said, so I asked how I could serve him.

The Indian stood there shyly for a moment, grasping his
woolen cap in his gnarled and twisted hands. His body, clothed
in homespun trousers and jacket, was bent slightly from years of
heavy work. His calloused feet shifted nervously in their thonged
sandals.

"A baby, *Tatai*," he said.

"To be baptized?"

"Yes, *Tatai*."

"Is it very sick?" I asked.

"Very sick, *Tatai*. It rests at the church entrance."

I took off the other Mass vestments, put on the surplice and stole for baptism, and followed the man down the long, dark nave of the church to the baptismal font. When he had picked up the little bundle of blankets from the corner near the door, I opened the ritual.

"What do you ask from the Church of God?" I inquired in Latin, and then continued with the ceremony. Reaching out to make the sign of the cross on the baby's forehead, I removed the blankets from the tiny face.

The baby was dead. It had been for days.

I put the blanket back over the face, and said as gently as I could: "The baby is dead. I can do nothing."

The Indian's face fell. His body began to shake silently, and I knew he was crying in a quiet, suppressed way. Slowly he sank to the wooden flooring and laid the baby at his side. Then he grasped me around the knees.

"*Tatai*," he begged, "baptize the baby!" I looked down at his tear-wet face, and explained as best I could: I would baptize a live baby—yes; a dead baby—no. I also pointed out, so that his sorrow might not be repeated for another child, the fact that, if it is certain a baby is going to die, and no priest is near, any Catholic can perform the baptism.

Apparently the Indian was not listening, for when I finished he said, "But *Tatai*, a dead baby baptized must surely be better than a dead baby not baptized!"

He would not be consoled. When he saw that there was nothing I could do, he picked up the lifeless bundle and shuffled out into the sunlight, tears still in his eyes. Through the doorway, I watched him go, wondering how many days he had walked with his sad little burden, seeking a priest.

I thought, too, how inadequate was that vocational poster that I had seen in the sacristy. If only it could show how great is the need of these Indians—how terrible the disappointment and heartbreak of such a one as the man who had come with his dead child—it would be far more convincing than it is with cold, impersonal statistics.

ONE HUNDRED DUCKS A NIGHT

by Thomas J. Brack

> Old Uncle made a bet that he could eat a hundred
> ducks in the space of one night. Father Brack tells how
> the feat was accomplished.

Maan Kung was getting old. The fact was evident in his unsteady crossing of the stream that separated his village from the mission, and in his labored climbing of the stone steps that led from the rice field up to our compound. The fact was manifest in the trembling of his slender hands as he lit his long pipe, which had been filled from my tobacco tin.

The old man's visits usually were made this way: I supplied the tobacco, and he the stories—especially the story about the ducks.

"Now, Maan Kung," I said, "do you mean to sit there and tell me that your uncle actually ate one hundred ducks in one night?"

"So help me!" he answered. "That was long before Father Mac came here to build this church; long before these two villages adopted the Faith. You see, my uncle worked for Old Man Lai, the rich farmer who owned these rice fields long ago. Uncle lived in Lai's house, worked with him, and ate with him. And all the time Old Man Lai taunted Uncle about his appetite. For my uncle could eat! He ate with enthusiasm and completeness. Yet all the while he complained that he was being starved.

"One night, when they had visitors and the wine was very good, Old Man Lai said he thought my uncle could eat four or five ducks, all by himself. 'Five ducks?' asked Uncle. 'Why, I could put away a hundred in one night!'

"They drank one cup of wine, and it became a wager. If on the following night Uncle could eat a hundred ducks, then Old Man Lai would give him the rice field near the bamboo grove. If he should fail, then Uncle would have to pay Old Lai for the ducks he ate, and nevermore complain of his frustrated appetite.

"The next day was a difficult one for Uncle. He wasn't particularly worried but he became extremely hungry. He went without breakfast and ate only two bowls of rice gruel to sustain him during the day. But Uncle's hunger was mild compared to that of the ducks. There is nothing hungrier than a hungry duck, and Uncle didn't give them a grain of rice all day.

"Instead, he kept rattling the rice measure, so that the ducks would be reminded of how hungry they were. At six o'clock, when Old Lai locked Uncle and the hundred ducks in the kitchen, starvation was written in one hundred and one pairs of eyes!

"Uncle had until six the next morning to win the rice field. Stimulated by hunger, he built a roaring fire, and the caldron sang as it boiled. As fast as he could dress the ducks, Uncle popped them into the boiling water. The other ducks couldn't figure what was happening, but they knew they were hungry, and they smelled good food cooking. Soon they were gulping down whole morsels of boiled duck as fast as Uncle could feed them!

"Uncle spent a busy hour, dressing ducks, cooking ducks, and feeding the ones that were left. Fifty ducks disappeared before their companions were sated. Then Uncle sat down and limited himself to five more. It was just a snack, but he had much work to do before morning. After that, he dampered the fire, and he and the forty-five remaining ducks went to sleep.

"At nine o'clock, Uncle woke up and started in again. The ducks were hungry and wanted more. Uncle fed them nineteen, and ate one himself just to keep the number even. Another nap until midnight—and then ten more ducks disappeared. At three in the morning, Uncle had a duck, and his dwindling companions accounted for four more. That left only ten, which were easily disposed of in the final assault.

"At six o'clock, Old Man Lai unlocked the kitchen door. He found Uncle sound asleep, with the peace that follows enjoyable labor on his face. And in the corner piled neatly—for Uncle was neat—was a mound of feathers and duck bones.

"There is Grandson, plowing in the field that Uncle won that night," concluded my guest, pointing with his shaky finger. Then he was gone, down the stone steps and across the stream, picking his uncertain way in the waning April sunlight.

AMERICA NEEDS A SAINT

by Fulton J. Sheen

> Probably no clergyman is as widely heard and loved as
> Bishop Sheen. Most Americans know him as a TV per-
> sonality. In his role as editor of *Worldmission* magazine
> he wrote the following editorial.

America needs a Saint, an American saint. After three hundred years of Catholic life, we can point to no saint who was born in this great land, who was educated in our schools and showed in crisis how an American Catholic can relive the life of Christ Crucified. We have the greatest Catholic school system in the world, the widest forms of charity work, the most compact army of teachers and religious, but the niches of our churches are empty.

Our dollars are cleansing lepers, digging wells for Moslems, setting up chapels in Nigeria and orphanages in Japan, but we must be more than hewers of schools and drainers of dollars. We must give to the world more than our gifts. We ought also to present it with a saint—a saint to prove we are not as materialistic as some believe; a saint who would be a priest, and preferably a Bishop, to prove that sanctity in a nation must begin with the Bishops, then the clergy and finally the faithful; a saint who needs must be born here but need not die here, to prove that the "boiling pot" of America boils over in its love of humanity and pays back the debt of immigration that made us great; a saint who might have been so American as to have gone to school in Brooklyn—for what city has such a ring of Americanism about it; a saint who would have served the Church in other lands, for though we want a saint from America we do not want a saint who was only for America. We ought to present the world with a saint so American that his grandfather might have fought in the Civil War and his uncle might have lost his life when the Merrimac sank the Cumberland, whose father might have been the first newspaperman to publish a paper with a circulation of a million, whose grandfather, on his mother's side, might have driven one of the first trains into Des Moines, and whose parents might have been married by an American Bishop. We need a saint so American that as a boy he would, like all American boys, make fun of anyone with a foreign accent, and then prove that he meant it in such good faith, that he would make the message the ideal of his life; in a word, a saint so American that he might have the same name as one of our automobiles.

Saying that we want a saint like this is not to say we have one, or will ever have one, but we believe we have a candidate to submit to the Church for her decision in our great American missionary to China, Bishop Francis Ford.

Francis Ford walked the streets of Brooklyn and New York; his confessor was the present Archbishop of Brooklyn. When he was twelve years of age, he heard an Italian missionary lecture on his work among the lepers. He gave a nickel in the collection which was much for a boy in those days and still is highly valued in some congregations. What stuck in his heart were the last words of the missionary, "My one ambeesch is to die a martyr." He kept repeating them over and over again; false ambition seemed squelched in the accent, but true ambition was satisfied in a Communist jail, as the accent now became Chinese: "My one ambition is to die a martyr."

One need never throw a log into a stream to see which way the current is flowing; a straw will tell us just as well. The little things of life more often indicate a character than some great burst of heroism or affection. It may very well be that a turtle and a wounded bird were the preface and the postscript to his episcopal motto which in its turn was the prophecy of his life. In his late teens just beginning to study for the missions, he wrote a little note to his superior: "I don't like to annoy you, but would you ask someone to let my turtle free. I left him near the pump and had not time to attend him." . . . Years pass and as a Bishop in China, he one day was carrying a box through the yard to put over an outdoor crucifix. He saw beneath his feet, a wounded bird. Under the image of the Wounded Lord, the Bishop stopped to heal the creature with the scarred flight, but it died in his hands.

In between the turtle and the bird incident, he was consecrated a Bishop and what motto would this great missionary be expected to choose than the one word which summed up his reaction to the turtle and the bird: "Compassion." Written across his episcopal shield was the word "condolere" which he took from St. Paul's description of the great High Priest and Bishop of our souls: "Who can have compassion on them that are ignorant and that err, because He Himself also is compassed with infirmity."

The superior could release the turtle out of compassion, but the Lord in heaven would not release Bishop Ford from a Communist cell. The wounded bird, the Bishop could not restore to life, even under the eyes of the Crucifix, but the Savior, Who would not release him from captivity because He willed that "he should be compassed with infirmity," will give healing to his wings and one day raise him to new life in the Resurrection of the just.

Late in 1950 as the Communist police began to close in on the mission and as the news filtered in of the arrest and persecution of priests, Bishop Ford's reaction was like that of his Master on the occasion of the visit of the Greeks. As the seed produces new life only by falling to the ground, so now he sees the Communist persecution as the Cross-condition of China's Easter: "We may lose a few lives, but that is what is needed to convert China." As some of the Sister catechists were arrested, he said: "Remember the Church is not only a triumphant Church, but also a suffering Church; with Christ you may expect not only joy, but sorrow, but He is with you."

One often wonders why of all the details in the life of Christ, that only one man is mentioned in the Creed, and that is the name of the representative of Caesar: "He suffered under Pontius Pilate." Judas is not named, nor Caiphas, nor Herod, nor the Pharisees, but only a political figure. This is not only to record an historical fact, but also to be a prophesy of how the Mystical Christ in various rehearsals through history, and then in the final conflict of the forces of good and evil, will go to His Death, "suffering under Pontius Pilate," suffering under the power of the omnipotent state.

"Thou art not a friend of Caesar" has echoed back from the balustrade of Pilate's court and now rings through Eastern Europe and China as the devout followers of Christ are accused of undermining Caesar.

To be like the Savior, and to be a model of resistance in this totalitarian era, it was fitting that Bishop Ford should be charged with "harboring Kuomintang agents and Kwangsi landlords, and of slanders against the People's Government." When Caesar becomes God, then a new crisis arises, the crisis of believing in God who is not Caesar. As the Communists often said to the missionaries: "Do you not know the Devil is the head of our government?"

As the Lord started the Procession to Calvary, the Cyrenian and the pious women consoled Him while the crowds buffeted and mocked Him. Bishop Ford had his consolation in the shopkeepers and their families who bowed low to him as he was led bound from his mission at Kaying. But there were also those who spat at him, threw stones and offal as some boasted: "I gave him a good wallop." To show that the curtain never goes down on the drama of Calvary, but merely has new actors, instead of the sarcastic banner carried before Christ bearing His name and His alleged crime, there was the sarcastic banner carried before Bishop Ford reading, "The people's Government welcomes the spy, Bishop Ford." While all this was going on, Bishop Ford was seen blessing and making the sign of the cross, as best he could with his handcuffed hands.

Many a missioner in China when asked: "Why do you not ask God to help you now?" answered: "I would not ask Him. I prefer to suffer for Christ." Another, when asked: "What can your God do for you now?" answered: "He can teach me to forgive you." Our Divine Lord is never without witnesses in every age of His Passion and Death. But how sweetly Providence watches over those who heralded the Cross in their lives. Out of all the prisoners in jail, no one was given bread and wine except Bishop Ford.

Too weak to stand, he leaned against the prison wall,
His hair was long and white, his beard matted,
His face emaciated and pale from torture.
On his lap was a tin tray for an altar stone,
His own burnt eyes were the candles.
His unconscious servers, fellow prisoners,
His Cathedral, a prison,
His cathedra, a cold cement floor,
His vestments, a black padded Chinese gown,
His mitre, a stocking cap,
His music, the groans of the suffering,
His missal, the memory of Calvary,
His sanctuary bell, the death knell about to strike.
But what Mass in a Gothic Cathedral
With forest aisles of stones,
Sunset panes and rose windows,
With chant, bright robes, and candles
Could equal the Golgothian splendor of that prison Mass,
As Bishop Ford moved his fingers over the tin tray
Saying, "Qui pridie quam pateretur."

If the Mass be the memorial of the death of Christ, then this was it par excellence. The great High Priest whose death was being renewed in the lower room of a Chinese death-cell, was inseparably Priest and Victim. Hence Our Lord on the Cross was upright as a Priest and prostrate as a Victim. We who possessed of His powers, call ourselves priests, but we never call ourselves victims, yet, in us, as well as in the Master, the two are meant to be inseparable. Who shall deny that Bishop Ford at this moment, was both priest and victim; priest because he was strong enough to make oblation; victim because he was too weak to do it standing. Tremendous is the significance of the words of the Consecration when pronounced in circumstances such as these, for how deep must have been the identification of Bishop Ford with the words of the Consecration, "This is My Body; this is My Blood." . . . No parasite was he on the Mystical Body of Christ! Here was a new body and new blood for Christ to live and die . . . and be born again.

The murderer returns to the scene of his crime. I wonder if anyone in history has ever speculated about the idea that Judas might have hanged himself on the naked Cross of Calvary after Our Lord had been laid in the sepulchre? It would seem the fitting place for him to avenge in himself his crime. What is particularly interesting in the life of Bishop Ford is that the Chief of Police who supervised the investigation, a certain Tsong K'i Yao, was a vacillating individual who became a Red because it paid off. He knew Bishop Ford well, was acquainted with the good repute he enjoyed in the mission field, how he aided the poor, started pagans in business, taught the young, solaced the sick and buried the dead. But as a Communist, he persecuted the Bishop. All of this must have been done with the consciousness that it was wrong, just as Judas knew he was wrong in betraying. Bishop Ford finally died as a dry-martyr in February, 1952. One month later, the Chief of Police committed suicide . . . Where? Of all places, he went back to Bishop Ford's room, and there hanged himself, as his bowels burst asunder.

America needs a saint, a saint who scratches initials in our school desks, who is ordained here, who seems just like the rest of us; a saint popular with most everyone who knows him well, unpopular with a few who think they knew him better; a saint who mingles sanctity with humor, a mixture that is indispensable to holiness from our American point of view; a saint who brings American methods to the missions, and yet who is American enough to love all nationalities and who seeks to build up native clergy for the Church and prays that his successors may be Chinese.

America needs a saint who has done more than most priests and bishops will ever be called upon to do, namely to die for the faith, but who thus will always make us humbly realize how far short in all successes we fall from the ideal to "take up the cross daily": a saint who dies outside our shores as Our Lord died outside Jerusalem to prove

"It was not life alone he gave,
But country up for man."

We are not saying that Bishop Ford is a saint, for in this we must wait upon the judgment of Our Mother, the Church. But in any case, he comes closer to being a saint than we know ourselves to be in the honesty of our hearts.

We plead with all American Catholics, with all mission societies to beg the Church to study his life, and to tell us if we may venerate him, and if we may hope one day to see his statue on our altars, the figure of an American, an American priest, an American Bishop, an American who died at the hands of the Reds for the love of the Red Blood of Calvary.

We Americans are good administrators, but lest our love for counting, for statistics and for buildings make us forget that we are shepherds, and that the temple we must build above all others is the Temple of the Holy Ghost, we need the example of a man who so combined Americanism and the Faith as to make us love them not as irreconcilables, but father and mother.

The United States is now giving to the Holy See 70 per cent of all that is distributed to mission lands, but we are giving only about 5,000 out of over 100,000 missionaries to the pagan world. Lest our offering be thought to be only material, may God give us a Saint that we can give to the world, that the world may see that American progress and methods are not obstacles, that the good natured, free, easy and comfortable lives we live in the routine of our priestly existence do not make us any less prepared for martyrdom than those to whom charity means a long face on top of a hair shirt.

It would be wonderful if this American Bishop who prayed that he might be "ground underfoot and spat upon and worn out" as a doorstep in the King's Highway "to China," might also deign to become the stone on which our faithful, our clergy, might climb to such a spiritual eminence, that other nations, who now take our money, may take our holiness and learn that America has another "business," the business of the salvation of souls.

LINES FOR A DRAWING OF OUR LADY OF THE NIGHT

This, could I paint my inward sight,
This were Our Lady of the Night:

She bears on her front's lucency
The starlight of her purity:

For as the white rays of that star
The union of all colours are,

She sums all virtues that may be
In her sweet light of purity.

The mantle which she holds on high
Is the great mantle of the sky.

Think, sometimes, 'tis our own Lady
Spreads her blue mantle over thee,

And folds the earth, a wearied thing,
Beneath its gentle shadowing.

—FRANCIS THOMPSON

DESCRIPTION OF A MISSIONER

by James Edward Walsh

> When he was head of the Kongmoon diocese, Bishop
> Walsh wrote this classical portrait of the missioner. A
> veteran missioner himself, he was Maryknoll's second
> Superior General.

It is better to be a saint than a good missioner; but is it harder?

A saint is a man of logic, or, in other words, one who lives what he believes. Incidentally it is not strange that he is seldom or never seen outside of that home of logic which is the Catholic Church. The good missioner, in his role of being all things to all men, would qualify rather as a man of psychology. The saint luxuriates in the strong beauty of a divinely exigent religion to the extent of converting himself; whereas the good missioner, while he does not necessarily go to such a length, at least approximates it in a measure by trying to mirror that same divine appeal in all manner of multifold ways in order to convert others. To accomplish this he need not be a saint, but he must come close to passing for one. And in order to achieve this hoax he must be so many things that a saint is, and he must do so many things that a saint does, that it becomes for him a serious question if the easiest way to the goal is not simply to be a saint in the first place and be done with it. In short, is it easier to imitate a saint, or to be one? The good missioner has this much of a choice.

Merely to be an average missioner is, of course, a superlatively easy thing. All that is required is to cross the ocean on a ship, buy a dictionary, and get to work (not necessarily too hard). Some add a typewriter and a camera; others grow a beard; still others learn to smoke a pipe: each one abounding in his own sense, which is to say, his own nationalism, as to the various little incidental appendages of his international vocation. At any rate, it is with some such simple preliminaries as this that a missioner qualifies for his role, and thereupon he can proceed to be as average as he pleases, while remaining a missioner—that is to say, of a kind.

He may fail to master the language of his people and spend a score of years trying to convert them in a jargon they cannot understand, but he is still a missioner. He may see nothing good in his adopted land, and set to work to recommend his ministry to the people around him by a continual disparagement of their country and themselves, but he does not cease to belong to the clan. He may lose patience fifty times a day with the strange, and, therefore, in his eyes reprehensible, customs and mentalities that surround and assail him, until he who came to attract remains only to repel; but not to lose his title of missioner. All this he can do and more; and, in fact, all this and more is very hard not to do; for not to do this is one way of being a good, instead of an average, missioner: and that, if it is not sanctity, is at least art. The missioner, and the good missioner, are as far apart as two men in the same profession can well be; the difference is that between Socrates and Squeers.

The task of a missioner is to go to the place where he is not wanted to sell a pearl whose value, although of great price, is not recognized, to people who are determined not to accept it, even as a gift. To do this he must so conform to the place as to make himself first tolerated, then respected, finally esteemed; and yet his conformity must not be total, for all the time he must conserve that precious foreign *elan* that will unceasingly nerve his campaign of active propaganda until his people begin to see some value in his offering. He must become Chinese while remaining American, thus conforming and resisting at the same time. It is easy to become wholly oriental, and it is easier still to remain wholly occidental; but the adaptation needed by the good missioner is a judicious combination of the two, and that is a feat.

He must absorb a new and fascinating civilization, while eschewing its philosophy; he must adopt new viewpoints, while retaining old ones; he must learn and wield a new language, while clothing in it, not its own shopworn tags, but his own vigorous foreign thoughts. He must absorb not only the language itself, but what lies behind the language; the mentality that made it and is at once expressed and revealed, and even at times disguised, by it. He must know and adopt many customs that are quite strange to him; other some he must know without adopting. He must doff all sorts of habits and prepossessions, and must don many others, so that he finds himself obliged to maintain through life a flexibility of both mind and body that makes of him a perpetual gymnast.

There is no gentle settling into the pleasant groove of old age for him, for his surroundings fail to recognize and allow for that natural process. Nobody knows that he must have his morning coffee before being corralled by importunate visitors, and nobody cares. Nobody is aware that his afternoon siesta is supposed to partake of the nature of a religious rite, as he is made to realize when he opens his eyes in the middle of it, to find genial faces peering at him through the mosquito net. In a thousand and one ways, he is denied the privilege of growing old. He must live as well as die with his boots on. It is true that his teeth fall out, and his hair grows gray; he may look old, and even feel old: but in all the essentials that make the man, he is condemned to eternal youth, for the Orient will forever demand of him the resiliency of a rubber ball, and only when he is finally punctured will he cease to bounce. Ponce de Leon should have sailed eastward.

He sallies out to convert the world, but the world does not convert. He meets disappointments. They multiply to make discouragement. Meanwhile he is a stranger in a strange land. All his overtures require just a little extra effort; meet just a little extra ridicule, fancied or real; remain just a little against the grain. He does not know it, but soon, in his heart, he is looking for some graceful way to feather his nest. Here is one made to order: the necessity to be pious. He begins to pray long prayers and to do voluminous spiritual reading. He becomes an expert in mystical theology; he is an authority on prayer; he reads many lives of the saints, maybe even writes a few. All good in its place and in its measure; but not missionary work.

Not a substitute for climbing mountains and riding horses and floundering in rice fields and visiting villages and entertaining mandarins and jollying shopkeepers and encouraging students and curing sick people and tending lepers and teaching children and harboring abandoned babies, not to mention the thousand and one other active works that make up the real vocation of the man who was sent to be all things to all men. Not a substitute, and not even an excuse. "To me, the least of all the saints, is given this grace, to preach among the gentiles, the unsearchable riches of Christ" (Eph. III, 8). And unless he is preaching that gospel in some active fashion designed to reach the hearts of men, he may be many things, but he is not a missioner.

Is it possible, then, for a man to be a good missioner without at the same time being a saint? The answer is that it would take an exceedingly clever man; so clever indeed that he probably does not exist. And if such a man could be found, it would cost him far more time and effort and study and care to manoeuvre successfully through this maze, than it would require to perform the same work through the automatic means of becoming a saint. He would be taking ten times as much trouble to attain the same result. Sanctity is therefore the easiest way, because it is the straightest road; and being the easiest way, it is for most of us the only way, since the average man is not looking for hard and unusual ways to perform this or any other stunt. In fact, when the average man once wakes up to the startling fact that he, the least of all the saints, with all his blushing imperfections thick upon him, has been chosen through some mystery of Divine Providence to walk in the giant footsteps of Paul and Xavier, he thereupon begins to look about him in desperation for the easiest way, or indeed for any old way, that will enable him to cope with the colossal task.

He lacks abysmally the brains and the character needed for his job of work, and unless he is simply to make a fantastic fiasco

of the whole business, he is forced to seek and find the one adequate means open to him. It is his only hope. When God
fashioned him into the weak and stupid creature he is, and then
sent him out as a child to do a man's work, He thereby sentenced
him to sanctity. And so, instead of trying to imitate the saint, it
would be better for him to concentrate on the less complex
process of being one. For him it is at once the easiest and the
only way. And, incidentally, it is doubtless the reason why missioners abound, while the good missioner is almost as rare as the
saint whose vocation his own so closely resembles.

MY MATCHSTICK ROSARY

by Robert W. Greene

> Put on public trial, condemned to death, almost insane
> from Communist brutality, Father Greene lived to re-
> turn to America and tell his story to the world. This is
> an excerpt from his book.

I refused to acknowledge again or even reply to the charge that
I had given money to the guerrilla quartermaster with instructions to kill certain Communist soldiers who were stationed on
the mission property. The quartermaster said that for each soldier
of the People's Government killed by the guerrillas I "offered the
sum of sixty dollars in United States currency." I looked at
the man and said: "You know that your charge is a lie."

The judge angrily rose from his chair and started around the table toward me, and I was preparing for a blow from his fist. With my hands this time bound tightly with rope behind my back, it would have been impossible to ward off his assault. But instead of striking me, he uttered some curses, and stuck under my eyes a page of his law book which, he said, told how a criminal should conduct himself in the presence of his judge. Then he told the soldiers to release my arms so I could sign a statement admitting that I was guilty for the second time of contempt of court. I signed the contempt charge, realizing that I had now been sentenced to life imprisonment, plus ten years!

I did not see Ah-Hiu Palm Sunday night until he stepped out of one of the small rooms. He was calmer now than in the afternoon. He came before the judge and, without preliminary remarks, he made this accusation: "You recall," he said to me angrily, "the day you threw a soldier of the People's Government out of the kitchen?" Then turning to the judge he added: "I remember how this American spy not only insulted that innocent soldier, but he ordered one of his hirelings to kill him with a knife."

I was too weary any longer to attempt to deny or explain. I simply said: "The whole story is fantastic."

Ah-Hiu wished to continue, but the quartermaster interrupted to say that he recalled the very day on which the transaction took place. He insisted that he was present and had heard everything that was said at that time.

I muttered something to the effect that since everyone seemed so certain of it, what could I say?

The judge snarled at me: "It is strange that *you* cannot remember. These men recall the details so vividly. Obviously you are lying."

My mind was incapable of reflection, but the thought kept vaguely presenting itself to me that possibly my cook and these other men were to be punished for the various crimes of which they accused me if I should be freed. I stood wearily through the haggling for what seemed an interminably long time. At that weird and weary hour all I was interested in was reaching the end of this interminable Palm Sunday. When finally they returned me to my cell I let myself drop with a lifeless thud on the boards and passed immediately into unconsciousness.

But it was still dark when I awoke. I felt a painful twitching in my right leg. As I rubbed the circulation back, I began slowly to recollect parts of what had transpired the night before. The story of the Communist soldier whom, according to Ah-Hiu's testimony, I had caused to be stabbed with the knife, came back to my mind. I remembered there in the darkness of my foul cell the actual event as it had taken place about two years before. The soldier had accidentally cut his hand in our kitchen and Ah-Hiu had run for me to come and attend the man. Why had I said last night, as the judge asserts I did, that I had ordered someone to knife the Communist soldier?

I called the guard and started to explain to him that I did not understand what I was doing last night when I admitted committing a crime that I had never done. He said: "Don't bother me with that nonsense. All you are supposed to do is think over all your crimes and confess them."

On Monday evening of Holy Week, as had happened on two or three of the previous nights, the soldiers put my arms in tourniquets. They pulled the rope tightly and my shoulders were held back in a painfully awkward position. I could just see the backs of my hands hanging high and limp at the level of my chest. After a while a large white ring appeared on the back of each hand, and a red spot in the middle of each white ring. At first there was considerable needlelike pain shooting through both limbs, and then they became numb. Later that night as I looked at the backs of my hands, devoid of feeling and hanging by my chest, I would think: "This can't be happening to me." It was as if I were standing over at one side of the room, looking at this figure with the tourniquets, upright before the bright lamp and the judge in black. It was like watching a movie. I could see myself as if in the picture—and then suddenly I'd realize that it wasn't a picture, that it was real. Then I'd mumble to the judge: "Look at my hands, they have no feeling in them."

Utterly without the least touch of human compassion, he cursed me and told me to pay attention to the witnesses and to the court. It seemed unbelievable when he ordered the soldiers to apply the tourniquet more tightly because of my misconduct before the court.

I recall that more angry words were directed at me, but I don't think I could any longer follow their meaning. Then it seemed that everything gradually went black, and I went down in a heap on the floor. A soldier must have picked me up, for when I came to I was sitting in a chair. This, far from eliciting a bit of pity from the heartless judge, merely angered him the more. Cursing me, he said: "You American spies think you are such good actors. But even as spies you are not so good."

I was about to tell him for the one hundredth time that I was not a spy, when he surprised me by asking if I had ever heard of the German Gestapo. I told him that I knew a little about it. He explained that while they were ruthless and efficient, they could not compare with the Russian Secret Police; they are the best, he said, pointing with his hand high over his head. Then he said disdainfully, "You Americans, you are way down here." And he gestured toward the ground.

I felt no urge to comment. What would be the use? They would merely laugh at me, or get more angry with me. I merely nodded and let it go at that. The only thing I must not do, I knew, was to deny my priesthood, nor must I involve the Legion of Mary in any of my confessions, no matter how often they accused me or tormented me. I reminded myself that other priests were no doubt having far worse torments than I. Perhaps this ordeal of mine, all these misunderstandings and lies could be endured for them as well as for my Christians. I prayed the *Memorare* for strength.

That night, as on several previous nights, the guards very seriously warned me not to attempt to jump from the upper balcony of the Sisters' Convent as we walked out of the large room. Many times recently the soldiers had made remarks intimating that they thought I might be thinking of suicide. Each time I told them: "Have no fear. I would not take my own life." Perhaps I shall never know whether they were afraid I might commit suicide or whether they were trying to put the idea in my upset and weary mind. It seems now unthinkable that such thoughts ever entered my head, yet I know there were in those dreadful days many long gaps during which I could recall nothing I said or did.

During the half-waking, half-delirious hours of the painfully long days I would try to remove from my mind the sinister look of the inhuman judge, and the evil intentions of all those who had come together against me. For some small comfort I would try to pray. I would try to say the Rosary on my fingers. The prayers came hard and distractedly. It was impossible to keep count of the number of prayers I said. Then for the first time I noticed five or six burnt safety matches lying in one of the foul corners of my cell. I picked up the matchsticks and broke each one in half, making ten pieces about an inch long. I placed them in a row on the board bed, and I squatted in front of the matches and started slowly to say the Hail Marys of the Rosary. After each prayer I would move a matchstick about two inches to the left, then go on to the next prayer. When I had completed one decade, I would move them back to the right again one by one as I said my Aves.

For each decade of the Rosary I would pray for a special intention: that my mind might remain clear; that my body might remain strong; that my dysentery might clear up; that the infection in my ear might get better; that my Christians might remain faithful; that Ah-Hiu might regain his mind and his faith. I felt stronger after these moments of prayer. And at such moments of respite my mind would go back to the disturbing fact of the Blessed Sacrament lying in my quarters.

As I prayed I had not noticed the surly guards at the window and the door gazing at me in wonderment. No doubt about it, the sight of my squatting there on the boards staring at broken bits of burnt matches and moving them occasionally from side to side must have convinced these men that I had reached an advanced stage of dementia praecox. However, according to their plans I was apparently somewhat ahead of schedule—they had still some more use for me, and they sounded rather anxious as they shouted out: "What are you doing there with those sticks?"

"Thinking," I replied slowly, "just thinking."

And otherwise I would ignore them.

I didn't know, until the end, that the guards had informed the judge about this queer thing they had seen me doing in my cell. When the officials heard about my inexplicable matchstick moving they were certain that I was very close to losing my mind. So anxious were they about that possibility that for the next three nights the judge and the officials were rather lenient to me. I have no doubt that those men, at least the shrewd judge, realized just how far the mind could be taken before it crossed the line from sanity to insanity. My judge and his team of officials knew the system well. As I observe it now, it is the same detailed procedure followed in each trial for each victim of the Reds, whether the victim is in China or in Europe.

MISSIONER'S FAMILY

by John J. Considine

> The kidnaping of Father Jerry Donovan from his mission in Manchuria was a headline story in the United States some years ago. Father Considine gives us one facet of its tragic ending.

Pittsburgh's Tipton Street, where the Donovans lived, is very steep. Hence perhaps it was the climb that made Father Conroy and the gentleman with him breathe so heavily as they entered the Donovan home that October morning in 1937. Mrs. Donovan sensed nothing in their manner to make her uneasy. When

* From *When the Sorghum Was High*, Longmans Green and Co. Copyright, Maryknoll.

Father Conroy said they wished to see Katie, the mother merely seated them in the room and went off about her work.

Katie was more intuitive and, as soon as she glanced at the pair, she asked quickly, "What has happened in China?"

"This man is a reporter," said Father Conroy. "He says Father Gerard has been captured by bandits and is being held for ransom."

"Well, let's not talk about it here," said Katie, thinking immediately of her mother; and the three went into the living room. Father Meenan of St. Stephen's joined them, and in low tense voices the kidnaping was discussed.

When the group left, Katie in the *melee* of her racing thoughts found one concern which stood above the others—her father and mother. How tell them? Distractedly for half an hour she walked from room to room through the house, attempting to decide what to do.

Then a shrill call drifted in from Tipton Street—a newsboy's call: "Pittsburgh priest captured by bandits!"

"No use," she sighed, "I must tell them."

But indeed her fears from the boy on the street were groundless; neighbors saw to that. Neighbors possess something very beautiful, that quality which, when one family among them is in trouble, draws all instinctively to its aid.

"Go right along, son," said a motherly old lady who came down her front steps and approached the youngster with the big voice. "Don't go back to that house on the terrace. And don't shout so loudly, son."

Katie's father was preparing to go out, and she saw that delay would be dangerous. She approached her mother first. "Mother, don't be alarmed, but Father Gerard has been captured by bandits. Everybody's sure he'll be released very soon."

Mrs. Donovan appeared stunned, but made no demonstration. She seemed to wish to speak but could not form the words. However, she showed no excitement—only the calm and the quiet which characterized her always.

It was different with the father. He was deaf and Katie had to raise her voice.

"What did you say?" he asked at first, rather listlessly, for he did not understand. Katie repeated. "Captured by bandits!" he cried and started as though struck. "My heavens, that's terrible!" Excitable, and accustomed to solving all his problems, he demanded a score of details which Katie could not give.

At noon a reassuring telegram arrived from Bishop Walsh of Maryknoll: "Cable received Father Gerard captured by bandits from Fushun chapel but good hopes early release Stop Little fear of any other than successful outcome for such an able and seasoned missioner Stop Be assured of our sympathy prayers efforts."

Many friends and neighbors called during the afternoon, and the newspapers kept the family busy. Hence, Katie found little time to think until late that night after everyone had left. When she was alone in her room a sickening realization came over her.

"I shall never rest," she whispered to herself, "until Gerard is found." (While friends and acquaintances everywhere used the affectionately familiar "Father Jerry," to Katie and her mother a strong preference remained always for the more formal "Gerard.")

Next morning there was no news—at least, no good news; and so it was on many successive days. The first report had arrived in warm and sunny weather, but later chill and rain came. Katie found herself distinctly worried.

Then, late in the evening of October 19, one of the Pittsburgh papers called to say that a short-wave radio amateur in Los Angeles had picked up a report that Father Jerry had been released. "Stand by for a further report at one a.m.," said the newspaper office.

Joy approaching ecstasy reigned in the Donovan home. But Katie, secretly, was distrustful. She had a horror of being disappointed.

No confirmation came, but the family did not seem to notice. They reveled in the good news. Katie, however, felt herself racked with the torture of it all.

Then two days later came a letter from Father Joe at Maryknoll. Jerry was free! Had they heard the report? Katie saw that her brother was but feeding hope to the old parents on the flimsy story from Los Angeles. She said nothing.

The next day the newspapers definitely denied the false rumor of the release. However, the first edition received at the Donovan home made no mention of it, and Katie took the sudden resolve to hide from both father and mother this denial. Why hurt them unnecessarily? she argued to herself.

Henceforth it was a daily struggle against any and every circumstance which might reveal the truth to the parents. Each evening Katie hurriedly examined the paper before letting it fall into their hands. On the few occasions when there were items, she managed to remove the page unnoticed. She never left the house for an hour without some ally to take her place, lest a stray caller upset the illusion. It was heartbreaking to hear the dear old lady, her mother, explain to visitors how happy and thankful she was that her Gerard had been freed.

But then came the time when a letter should have arrived from her boy. Twice a day the mother watched for the mailman. "Go down and see if he has something for us from Gerard," she would say.

Dutifully Katie would descend the stairs and return with some such remark as, "No, not yet, Mother."

"Perhaps he was injured or very sick when they freed him," ruminated Mrs. Donovan. Katie watched her sharply for some sign of fading faith and slowly discovered that what she was trying to do for the mother, the mother in turn was seeking to do for her. Each was attempting to protect the other. Neither revealed her thoughts till the end.

As the weeks passed, the vigil became ever more unbearable to Katie. She awoke each morning and a sickening dread passed over her; yet hiding it within her, she sought to be blithe and cheerful through the day. To prepare meals was an ordeal, and to eat them a greater one. Every footstep and knock on the door caused her alarm. She could not read, and formed the habit of walking long hours aimlessly through the house.

And there was the weather, the deepening winter. It hurt to step out into the cold, and it hurt to come back into the heat.

"Gerard is out in this cold," she would say. "Gerard has none of this heat," would come the thought.

There was no help but in prayer, and in this she found comfort. Katie had no earthly enthusiasms and regarded as shallow any artificial, baseless buoyancy of spirit. But she had deep confidence in God.

Curiously, not until the Saturday before the news of Father Jerry's death did hope completely wane. That morning she was in town and met a woman friend on the street. "Any news of Father Jerry, Katie?" asked the friend.

"No, not yet. But I'm sure we'll have something very soon now." This had become her routine response through the months.

"Well, I wish I could feel optimistic with you, Katie. But I wouldn't be too sure if I were you. I had a brother among the missing in the World War. I was certain for months that he was alive and finally found that he had been dead all the while."

Dazedly, Katie sought the support of the near-by store front and leaned heavily against it. What a cruel thrust! Others had spoken discouragingly, but this seemed to shatter her last support. When she returned home, she carefully avoided her mother lest she break down before her and admit that she was plagued with the temptation to despair.

At ten on the morning of February 11, the woman from the tenement below came up, attempting to be nonchalant. "You are wanted downstairs," she said.

Katie immediately surmised. She edged from the room where her mother stood, taking the woman with her. "What is it?"

"There are two reporters down there. They say Father Jerry's body has been found."

All reason for restraint was gone. Katie fairly flew back to her mother. "There it is, there it is at last!" she cried. "Gerard is dead!"

The mother made no reply, uttered no sound, but fell against the wall. Katie wept hysterically, releasing the pent-up feelings of the dreadful months. Slowly the mother came to her. "It is God's will, Katie," she whispered softly. "I gave him to God, Katie. I am sure He has made good use of him."

THE CITY

by Alan Paton

Through the eyes of a country Negro, Alan Paton allows the reader to see the squalor, misery and tragedy that is non-white Johannesburg, South Africa's race-wracked mining metropolis.

All roads lead to Johannesburg. If you are white or if you are black they lead to Johannesburg. If the crops fail, there is work in Johannesburg. If there are taxes to be paid, there is work in Johannesburg. If the farm is too small to be divided further, some must go to Johannesburg. If there is a child to be born that must be delivered in secret, it can be delivered in Johannesburg.

The black people go to Alexandra or Sophiatown or Orlando, and try to hire rooms or to buy a share of a house.

—Have you a room that you could let?

—No, I have no room.

—Have you a room that you could let?

—It is let already.

—Have you a room that you could let?

Yes, I have a room that I could let, but I do not want to let it. I have only two rooms, and there are six of us already, and the boys and girls are growing up. But school books cost money, and my husband is ailing, and when he is well it is only thirty-

* From *Cry, The Beloved Country.* Copyright, Charles Scribner's Sons.

five shillings a week. And six shillings of that is for the rent, and three shillings for traveling, and a shilling that we may all be buried decently, and a shilling for the books, and three shillings is for the clothes and that is little enough, and a shilling for my husband's beer, and a shilling for his tobacco, and these I do not grudge for he is a decent man and does not gamble or spend his money on other women, and a shilling for the Church, and a shilling for sickness. And that leaves seventeen shillings for food for six, and we are always hungry. Yes, I have a room but I do not want to let it. How much would you pay?

—I could pay three shillings a week for the room.

—And I would not take it.

—Three shillings and sixpence?

Three shillings and sixpence. You can't fill your stomach on privacy. You need privacy when your children are growing up, but you can't fill your stomach on it. Yes, I shall take three shillings and sixpence.

The house is not broken, but it is overflowing. Ten people in two rooms, and only one door for the entrance, and people to walk over you when you go to sleep. But there is a little more food for the children, and maybe once a month a trip to the pictures.

I do not like this woman, nor the way she looks at my husband. I do not like this boy, nor the way he looks at my daughter. I do not like this man, I do not like the way he looks at me, I do not like the way he looks at my daughter.

—I am sorry, but you must go now.

—We have no place to go to.

—I am sorry, but the house is too full. It cannot hold so many.

—We have put our name down for a house. Can you not wait till we get a house?

—There are people in Orlando who have been waiting five years for a house.

—I have a friend who waited only one month for a house.

—I have heard of such. They say you can pay a bribe.

—We have no money for a bribe.

—I am sorry, but the house is full.

Yes, this house is full, and that house is full. For everyone is coming to Johannesburg. From the Transkei and the Free State, from Zululand and Sekukuniland. Zulus and Swazis, Shangaans and Bavenda, Bapedi and Basuto, Xosas and Tembus, Pondos and Fingos, they are all coming to Johannesburg.

I do not like this woman. I do not like this boy. I do not like this man. I am sorry, but you must go now.

—Another week, that is all I ask.

—You may have one more week.

—Have you a room to let?

—No, I have no room to let.

—Have you a room to let?

—It is let already.

—Have you a room to let?

Yes, I have a room to let, but I do not want to let it. For I have seen husbands taken away by women, and wives taken away by men. I have seen daughters corrupted by boys, and sons corrupted by girls. But my husband gets only thirty-four shillings a week—

—What shall we do, those who have no houses?

—You can wait five years for a house, and be no nearer getting it than at the beginning.

—They say there are ten thousand of us in Orlando alone, living in other people's houses.

—Do you hear what Dubula says? That we must put up our own houses here in Orlando?

—And where do we put up the houses?

—On the open ground by the railway line, Dubula says.

—And of what do we build the houses?

—Anything you can find. Sacks and planks and grass from the veld and poles from the plantations.

—And when it rains?

—Siyafa. Then we die.

—No, when it rains, they will have to build us houses.

—It is foolishness. What shall we do in the winter?

Six years waiting for a house. And full as the houses are, they grow yet fuller, for the people still come to Johannesburg. There has been a great war raging in Europe and North Africa, and no houses are being built.

—Have you a house for me yet?

—There is no house yet.

—Are you sure my name is on the list?

—Yes, your name is on the list.

—What number am I on the list?

—I cannot say, but you must be about number six thousand on the list.

Number six thousand on the list. That means I shall never get a house, and I cannot stay where I am much longer. We have quarrelled about the stove, we have quarrelled about the children, and I do not like the way the man looks at me. There is the open ground by the railway line, but what of the rain and the winter? They say we must go there, all go together, fourteen days from today. They say we must get together the planks and the sacks and the tins and the poles, and all move together. They say we must all pay a shilling a week to the Committee, and they will move all our rubbish and put up lavatories for us, so that there is no sickness. But what of the rain and the winter?

—Have you a house for me yet?

—There is no house yet.

—But I have been two years on the list.

—You are only a child on the list.

—Is it true that if you pay money—

But the man does not hear me, he is already busy with another. But a second man comes to me from what place I do not see, and what he says bewilders me.

—I am sorry they have no house, Mrs. Seme. By the way my wife would like to discuss with you the work of the Committee. Tonight at seven o'clock, she said. You know our house, No. 17852, near the Dutch Reformed Church. Look, I shall write down the number for you. Good morning, Mrs. Seme.

But when I make to answer him, he is already gone.

—Ho, but this man bewilders me. Who is his wife, I do not

know her. And what is this committee, I know of no committee.

—Ho, but you are a simple woman. He wants to discuss with you the money you are willing to pay for a house.

Well, I shall go there then. I hope he does not ask too much, one cannot pay too much on thirty-seven shillings a week. But a house we must have. I am afraid of the place where we are. There is too much coming and going, when all decent people are asleep. Too many young men coming and going, that seem never to sleep, and never to work. Too much clothing, good clothing, white people's clothing. There will be trouble one day, and my husband and I have never been in trouble. A house we must have.

—Five pounds is too much. I have not the money.

—Five pounds is not too much for a house, Mrs. Seme.

—What, just to put my name higher on the list?

—But it is dangerous. The European manager has said that he will deal severely with any who tamper with the list.

—Well I am sorry. But I cannot pay the money.

But before I can go, his wife comes into the room with another woman.

—There must be a mistake, my husband. I do not know this woman. She is not on the committee.

—Ho, I am sorry, my wife. I am sorry, Mrs. Seme. I thought you were on the committee. Go well, Mrs. Seme.

But I do not say stay well. I do not care if they stay well or ill. And nothing goes well with me. I am tired and lonely. Oh my husband, why did we leave the land of our people? There is not much there, but it is better than here. There is not much food there, but it is shared by all together. If all are poor, it is not so bad to be poor. And it is pleasant by the river, and while you wash your clothes the water runs over the stones, and the wind cools you. Two weeks from today, that is the day of the moving. Come my husband, let us get the planks and the tins and the sacks and the poles. I do not like the place where we are.

There are planks at the Baragwanath Hospital, left there by the builders. Let us go tonight and carry them away. There is corrugated iron at the Reformatory, they use them to cover the bricks. Let us go tonight and carry it away. There are sacks at the Nancefield Station, lying neatly packed in bundles. Let us go tonight and carry them away. There are trees at the Crown Mines. Let us go tonight and cut a few poles quietly.

This night they are busy in Orlando. At one house after another the lights are burning. I shall carry the iron, and you my wife the child, and you my son two poles, and you small one, bring as many sacks as you are able, down to the land by the railway lines. Many people are moving there, you can hear the sound of digging and hammering already. It is good that the night is warm, and there is no rain. Thank you, Mr. Dubula, we are satisfied with this piece of ground. Thank you, Mr. Dubula, here is our shilling for the committee.

Shanty town is up overnight. What a surprise for the people when they wake in the morning. Smoke comes up through the sacks, and one or two have a chimney already. There was a nice chimney-pipe lying there at the Kliptown Police Station, but I was not such a fool as to take it.

Shanty Town is up overnight. And the newspapers are full of us. Great big words and pictures. See, that is my husband, standing by the house. Alas, I was too late for the picture. Squatters, they call us. We are the squatters. This great village of sack and plank and iron, with no rent to pay, only a shilling to the Committee.

Shanty Town is up overnight. The child coughs badly, and her brow is as hot as fire. I was afraid to move her, but it was the night for the moving. The cold wind comes through the sacks. What shall we do in the rain, in the winter? Quietly my child, your mother is by you. Quietly my child, do not cough any more, your mother is by you.

The child coughs badly, her brow is hotter than fire. Quietly my child, your mother is by you. Outside there is laughter and jesting, digging and hammering, and calling in languages that I do not know. Quietly my child, there is a lovely valley where you were born. The water sings over the stones, and the wind cools you. The cattle come down to the river, they stand there under the trees. Quietly my child, oh God make her quiet. God have mercy upon us. Christ have mercy upon us. White man, have mercy upon us.

—Mr. Dubula, where is the doctor?

—We shall get the doctor in the morning. You need not fear, the committee will pay for him.

—But the child is like to die. Look at the blood.

—It is not long till morning.

—It is long when the child is dying, when the heart is afraid. Can we not get him now, Mr. Dubula?

—I shall try, mother. I shall go now and try.

—I am grateful, Mr. Dubula.

Outside there is singing, singing round a fire. It is Nkosi sikelel' iAfrika that they sing, God Save Africa. God save this piece of Africa that is my own, delivered in travail from my body, fed from my breast, loved by my heart, because that is the nature of women. Oh lie quietly, little one. Doctor, can you not come?

—I have sent for the doctor, mother. The Committee has sent a car for the doctor. A black doctor, one of our own.

—I am grateful, Mr. Dubula.

—Shall I ask them to be quiet, mother?

—It does not matter, she does not know.

Perhaps a white doctor would have been better, but any doctor if only he come. Does it matter if they are quiet, these sounds of an alien land? I am afraid, my husband. She burns my hand like fire.

We do not need the doctor any more. No white doctor, no black doctor, can help her any more. Oh child of my womb and fruit of my desire, it was pleasure to hold the small cheeks in the hands, it was pleasure to feel the tiny clutching of the fingers, it was pleasure to feel the little mouth tugging at the breast. Such is the nature of woman. Such is the lot of women, to carry, to bear, to watch and to lose.

The white men come to Shanty Town. They take photographs of us, and moving photographs for the pictures. They come and wonder what they can do, there are so many of us. What will the poor devils do in the rain? What will the poor devils do in the winter? Men come, and machines come, and they start building rough houses for us. That Dubula is a clever man, this is what he said they would do. And no sooner do they begin to build for us, than there come in the night other black people, from Pimville and Alexandra and Sophiatown, and they too put up their houses of sack and grass and iron and poles. And the white men come again, but this time it is anger, not pity. The police come and drive the people away. And some that they drive away are from Orlando itself. They go back to the houses that they left, but of some the rooms are already taken, and some will not have them any more.

You need not be ashamed that you live in Shanty Town. It is in the papers, and that is my husband standing by the house. A man here has a paper from Durban, and my husband is there too, standing by the house. You can give your address as Shanty Town, Shanty Town alone, everyone knows where it is, and give the number that the committee has given you.

What shall we do in the rain? In the winter? Already some of them are saying, look at those houses over on the hill. They are not finished, but the roofs are on. One night we shall move there and be safe from the rain and the winter.

THEOPHANE VENARD — MARTYR

A lily clad in surplice white
Is severed from its slender tree
And laid within the Master's sight
To blossom all eternity.

—WALTER J. LAMBERT

BIG BOYS DON'T CRY

by Richard McMonigal

> Rosalino was lonely, sixteen, and looking for a father.
> What happened when Father McMonigal came along
> was quite natural. This is a memorable true story from
> the heart of the Bolivian jungle.

I missed Rosalino when I went into the little dining room in the orphanage in Riberalta, Bolivia. It was suppertime. With the ingrained habits of an ex-prefect of discipline, I counted noses when I sat down to eat with the orphans the simple meal of rice, yucca, and charqui.

I waited awhile, carrying on the usual chatter with the boys. For once I wasn't speculating where tomorrow's rice would come from! At last, when the meal was half over, I left the table to look for Rosalino. Something must be wrong, because mealtime is one of the most important times of the day, and no orphan would miss it willingly.

When I went around the long open porch of the orphanage, I saw Rosalino leaning against one of the posts, looking out into space.

"What's the matter, Rosalino? Is there something wrong?" I asked.

"Nothing, Padre," he replied in the stock answer.

"Are you sick?" I inquired, looking for signs of ever-present malaria.

"No, Padre."

"Is it your father?" I continued.

Rosalino turned away. His lower lip began to quiver, and his eyes filled with tears. That was the reason! Just a few days before, I had been called to visit the old man after he suffered a heart attack.

"Come over to my room," I invited, "and we'll talk about it there."

I knew Rosalino was afraid that the other boys might see him crying, and everyone knows that sixteen-year-olds never cry— especially in the jungles of Bolivia, where life is so competitive and boys grow old before their time.

In my tiny room, I gave the youth the one chair I had, while I took a seat in the hammock. For a few moments the tears gushed, as he struggled to get control. Brokenly the story tumbled out. He had gone home to visit his father, and had found the old man lying on the floor with only a blanket between his body and the dirt. The father was in great pain, and hadn't eaten all day. There were no relatives or friends to take care of him. Rosalino was all he had. The whole problem was just too much for a sixteen-year-old.

"Come," I said. "Let's go over to the kitchen and get a meal to take to your father."

I picked up some candles and matches, some clean clothes, and a plate loaded with rice and dried meat. Then we went down to the little house. After José had eaten, we bathed him and fixed up a bed under the mosquito netting. At first he was reluctant to put on a clean shirt of mine. He had such tremendous respect that he thought it would be sacrilegious to wear a Padre's shirt.

Old José lingered on. Every day Rosalino would pick up meals in the kitchen and take them to his father. At times I gave the boy money to buy some bread or fruit for the old man. Sometimes, when Rosalino ran a personal errand for me, I gave him candy, sent me from home. I noticed that he put the candy aside, and knew that he was saving the treat for his father.

Then I went away for two weeks, inspecting one of our schools in another part of the jungle. One afternoon after I had returned, Rosalino came and told me that his father wanted to see me.

José was having another attack. After I heard his confession and anointed him, I gave him a couple of aspirins and began rubbing his chest with a soothing salve. Sister Vivian, the mission's doctor, told me that no medicine could help José. But interest and sympathy worked wonders.

"Padre," José began between labored breaths, "I know I have not long to live. Except for the Padres and Madres of Maryknoll, I haven't a soul in the world to turn to. I am ready to die, and would die happily if you could promise me two things. Would you see that I am properly buried? Would you take care of Rosalino? I have talked to him, and have told him that he must do whatever you tell him, go where you go, and be like an obedient son to you."

The sick man's eyes studied my face anxiously. I assured him that Father Fritz and I would arrange for him to have the proper Christian burial, and that Rosalino could continue to live at the orphanage. We would keep an eye on him, and see that he should have a chance to make a decent start in life. I was deeply moved as I went out of that poor little house and made my way back to the mission in pouring rain.

I never saw José again. The next day I fell sick with jungle fever, and was soon in our little hospital, under the watchful care of Maryknoll Sisters.

Late one evening, one of the orphans came to the window of my hospital room to tell me that old José had died. Rosalino had gone that morning to the house and had found his father dead in bed. The old man had died alone during the night.

Father Fritz sent some women of the parish to arrange the body. He found a couple of generous men to build a coffin, but they had to rip up some of the long school desks for wood. Late that evening the funeral procession traveled the three miles to the little cemetery. It was dark when they arrived, and the cemetery was locked. The coffin had to be left at the cemetery gate.

The next day some of the bigger orphans went to the cemetery with Rosalino, and they worked for many hours in the hot sun, digging the grave. Father Thomas Higgins came over, and with the solemn and consoling blessing of the Church, the body of José was put in the earth.

I was confined to my hospital bed, disappointed because disease had made me inactive when a boy needed help. Anxiously I counted off the hours, as I waited for Rosalino to come and see me. Late in the afternoon he came. He entered my room and began sobbing. I let him cry for a while, before I explained to him the wonderful teaching of the Church about death, and life after death.

One question he asked will always remain in my mind. "Padre Ricardo," he said, "you won't forget what you promised my father, will you? I am all alone now. I have no one but the Padres to help me."

"No, *hijito*. No, little son," I replied. "I will not forget what I promised your father."

And I won't forget.

THUNDER RESOUNDING AFAR

by *Albert J. Nevins*

Energy, linguistics, personality and modern methods formed the combination that made up this successful China missionary who was said to have died of a broken heart because of tragedy caused by the Reds.

In a little house on the outskirts of Chungking, an old man lay dying. Doctors sent by Generalissimo Chiang Kai-shek could not discover the ailment. But the simple people of the city knew, and they passed the word from one to another:

"Lei Ming Yuan dies of a broken heart."

Lei Ming Yuan (Thunder Resounding Afar) is the Chinese name for Father Vincent Lebbe, a Belgian-born, Chinese-naturalized priest. It is a name which ranks high in the apostolic history of China.

Father Lebbe was born in Ghent, Belgium, on August 19, 1877. In 1895, he journeyed to Paris and entered the Vincentian seminary to study for the priesthood; six years later, although not yet ordained, he was assigned to China. When he arrived in the Flowery Kingdom, the fires of the Boxer Rebellion were still smoldering.

The energy of the young Belgian was tremendous. A master of the Chinese language, gifted with a strong and impressive personality, the new missioner attracted throngs of pagans to hear his preaching.

So successful was he that he rented the largest hall in Tientsin, Canton Guild Hall, and lectured there every night to some three thousand pagans. After each lecture, he would answer questions until midnight. Large numbers of converts were gained through this lecture-hall system, and soon the movement spread all over the district.

In 1912, Father Lebbe founded the weekly Catholic paper, *Kwen I Lo (Spread Abroad Benefits)*. Another weekly followed later. Then after three years, the editor decided to begin a daily Catholic paper, a feat impossible even in most Christian countries of the West. Space in the eighty Tientsin street cars was purchased for an advertising campaign, and large signs in flaming red characters challenged, "What Is Going to Happen on October 10?" October 10 is a great day in China, corresponding to our Fourth of July. Because the Chinese revolution had taken place only four years previously, there was much speculation as to what might happen. The whole of Tientsin became so concerned that the police commissioner finally went to Father Lebbe and asked him to remove the signs. Next day, in place of the questions, placards appeared, stating, "On October 10, *Ishepao (Social Welfare)* will appear."

The advertising campaign was successful. Within a few months the paper had a daily circulation of 40,000 copies, which was enormous for China.

In 1920, Father Lebbe returned to Europe. He was immediately called to aid a large group of Chinese students who had been invited to France by Premier Herriot, and then had been left stranded when Herriot quit office. Father Lebbe organized the Chinese Students' Association and helped the youths with funds. He even gave his own watch to one of them—a small, smiling scholar, named Chou En-lai.

Father Lebbe traveled back and forth to Rome, where he assisted in the preparation of the famous encyclical of Pius XI on native clergy. In 1926, he was present in Rome for the consecration of six Chinese bishops, and with one of them, Bishop Melchior Sun, he returned to China. There he began a promotion of Chinese Catholic art, particularly in reference to Chinese martyrs; this was a new form of Catholic action.

In 1928, at the age of fifty-one, Father Lebbe became a Chinese citizen. He had already founded several mission societies, three newspapers, two magazines, and a half-dozen other organizations —enough for the lifetime of any man. But this zealous missioner was not content to rest on his oars.

Firmly convinced that China's conversion would come through its own sons and daughters, he persuaded Bishop Sun to allow him to found two native communities, one for men and the other for women. Father Lebbe traveled through the countryside, searching out recruits, begging money for the enterprise, and seeking suitable locations for the projects. Finally, on December 16, 1928, the Monastery of the Beatitudes was blessed, and the first fifteen novices were received.

The new society for men was called Little Brothers of Saint John the Baptist, because, as the founder said, it was their task to prepare the way for Our Lord. The Brothers take four vows: poverty, chastity, obedience, and personal mortification. At the monastery they sing the Divine Office in Chinese, daily; they keep complete silence, save for two half-hour recreation periods; they are forbidden by rule to eat meat, fish, and eggs, or to use wine or tobacco. When traveling, the Little Brothers are not allowed to use trains, but frequently bicycles are provided for their journeys. An interesting point of their rule is the requirement to take ten minutes of setting-up exercises in the morning, and a daily bath.

With the exception of the scapular they wear, the Little Brothers make all their own clothes, even to shoes and socks. Cotton grown on their own fields is spun and made into cloth in native fashion.

When the Little Brother is sufficiently trained, he is sent to a mission station, where he lives in a mud-brick house adjoining a chapel. He labors with his hands for a living. He explains Catholic doctrine and catechizes both children and adults. Once a year he returns to the monastery to have his spiritual energies restored and invigorated.

What has been said concerning the Little Brothers is equally true of the Little Sisters of Saint Therese. Both communities prospered and within a few years numbered several hundred members and some twenty-five houses.

When war broke out in 1932, and again in 1937, the Little Brothers joined the army as stretcher bearers in Red Cross units. Father Lebbe was given the honorary title of General in the Chinese Army, but he refused to allow his Little Brothers to bear arms, and once he expelled one from the community because the Brother carried a gun while gathering wounded men from the front lines.

Father Lebbe served the army well, even though at times the army was under the domination of Chinese Communists. The missioner was helping Chinese, and that was his primary concern. From the front lines, he sent the following report:

"Concerning the monastery at the front, the biggest difficulty is to maintain an intense religious life among our Brothers. Wherever we stop, our monastic life is at once organized, including the novitiate with its thirty novices, and our little monks keep the rule with admirable precision. The Brothers' habit has become extremely popular in the army. . . . Today Catholic soldiers, nurses, and stretcher bearers are in furious demand. For this, glory to God!"

The section of China in which Father Lebbe and his Little Brothers served was in the possession of the Chinese Communist troops. Many of them would go to Father Lebbe and ask to have Mass offered for them. One high Communist officer wrote Father Lebbe a letter in which he thanked him "for the beautiful Mass you offered for us today." The Little Brothers were making many converts.

Then into the Chinese Communist territory came Communist refugees from Spain. When those European Reds discovered Father Lebbe, they were furious and immediately sent a message to Moscow. Within a short time, an answer returned. The Communist leader told Father Lebbe that the priest and his Little Brothers must leave the territory. Without protest, Father Lebbe gathered his little community and set out for the long trek back to his base in Honan Province.

After he reached home, he drew up the final constitutions of his religious societies, made his will, and put all his affairs in order. Then he "sat back" to wait for a message that he seemingly expected. Finally, through the underground, a letter reached the waiting priest. It was from the Communists, and it requested Father Lebbe and his Little Brothers to return to the Communist army.

Unquestioningly, Father Lebbe and his Little Brothers set out again. As soon as they reached the Communist territory, they sent word of their arrival to headquarters. A reply was received; it was an order for their arrest.

The entire group of priest and Brothers was condemned to death. Because Father Lebbe was the superior, it was announced that he should be the last to die. The days that followed were ones of agony and torture for Father Lebbe. One by one, he saw his forty Little Brothers being executed. Some were buried alive, with only their heads exposed, and then trampled to death by horses. Others were shot; others were decapitated.

Finally, only Father Lebbe was left. One day a man entered Father Lebbe's cell. The priest strove to recall where he had seen that man before. Then he remembered: his visitor was Chou En-lai, to whom years before, in France, Father Lebbe had given his watch. Chou En-lai had become supreme over all Communist China. He told Father Lebbe that he was sorry about the executions of the Little Brothers, but that he had received orders and he had to carry them out. He said that the priest's own execution was scheduled for the morrow, but that he hoped to save him.

Chou sent a message to Chiang Kai-shek, telling the Generalissimo that he could have Father Lebbe for $20,000, provided a plane would be sent to take the missioner out. Chiang, who knew the great services that Father Lebbe had rendered China, readily agreed to the ransom. At six o'clock on the morning of the execution, the personal plane of General Chiang Kai-shek landed at Communist headquarters. Father Lebbe was hastily placed aboard, and within a few hours he was safe in Chungking.

Friends who knew the priest were saddened at the change in him. They had seen a vigorous, strong man, but now they saw a broken, sorrowing one. His spirit was deeply wounded by the barbarities inflicted on his Little Brothers when the entire community was wiped out.

Father Lebbe was taken to a little house on the outskirts of Chungking. He had often told friends that he hoped to die on the feast of Saint John the Baptist. This wish was to be fulfilled. It was on June 24, 1940, the feast day of Saint John, that this zealous missioner died.

Father Lebbe's funeral was held from the Chungking Cathedral, and official China turned out to pay him the last homage. In accordance with Chinese custom, Chinese officials brought presents of food, which were left to be buried with the body.

Just before the funeral, Bishop Yu-pin arose and asked one of the priests to go outside and bring in some of the poorer Chinese who were mourning their departed friend. When the poor were brought in, Bishop Yu-pin gave them the food. "It is the way Father Lebbe would wish it," he explained to the gathered officials and diplomats.

And outside, too, the poor Chinese wept. They said, "Lei Ming Yuan died of a broken heart."

PERILS ON THE ROAD TO TIBET

by Abbé Huc

> Behind an almost impassable mountain barrier lay the
> mysterious and forbidden land of Tibet. Over the per-
> ilous trail came a band of Catholic missioners. Here is
> an excerpt from the journal of one of the first white men
> to penetrate this hidden country.

One day, as we were following the windings of a valley, our hearts
oppressed with sad thoughts, all of a sudden we perceived two
horsemen make their appearance on the ridge of an adjacent
hill. At this time we were traveling in the company of a small
party of Tibetan merchants who, like ourselves, had allowed the
main body of the caravan to precede them in order to save their
camels the fatigue of a too-hurried march. "Tsong-Kaba!" cried
the Tibetans. "See, there are horsemen yonder, yet we are in the
desert, and everyone knows that there are not even shepherds in
this locality."

They had scarcely uttered these words, when a number of other
horsemen appeared at different points on the hills and, to our
extreme alarm, dashed down towards us at a gallop. What could
they want with us? The case was clear: we had fallen into the
hands of thieves! Their appearance, as they approached, was anything but reassuring. A carbine slung at the saddlebow, two long
sabers in the girdle, thick black hair falling in disorder over the

shoulders, glaring eyes, and a wolf's skin stuck on the head by the way of cap: such was the portrait of each of the gentlemen who now favored us with their company. There were twenty-seven of them, while we numbered only eighteen, and of these eighteen all were by no means practiced warriors. However, both armies alighted, and a valorous Tibetan of our party advanced to parley with the chief of the brigands, who was distinguished from his men by two red pennants which floated from his saddle back.

After a long and somewhat animated conversation, "Who is that man?" asked the chief of the robbers, pointing to Father Gabet, who, fastened upon his camel, was the only person who had not alighted.

"He is a Grand Lama of the western sky," replied the Tibetan merchant; "the power of his prayers is infinite."

The bandit chief raised his clasped hands to his forehead, in token of respect, and looked at Father Gabet, who, with his frozen face, and his singular envelope of many-colored wrappings, was by no means unlike those alarming idols that we see in pagan temples. After contemplating for a while the famous lama of the western sky, the brigand addressed some further words, in an undertone, to the Tibetan merchant. Then he made a sign to his companions, and they all jumped into their saddles, set off at a gallop, and soon disappeared behind the mountains.

"Do not let us go any farther today," said the Tibetan merchant, "but set up our tents where we are. These men are robbers, but they have lofty and generous souls; when they see that we place ourselves without fear in their hands, they will not attack us. Besides," added he, "I believe they hold in much awe the power of the lamas of the western sky."

We adopted the counsel of the Tibetan merchant and proceeded to encamp. The tents were scarcely set up, however, when the bandits reappeared on the crest of the mountain, and once more galloped down upon us with their habitual impetuosity. The chief alone entered the encampment, his men awaiting him at a short distance outside. He addressed the Tibetan who had previously conversed with him.

"I have come," said he, "for an explanation of a point that I don't at all understand. You know that we are encamped on the other side of the mountain, yet you venture to set up your tents here, close by us. How many men, then, have you in your company?"

"We are only eighteen. You, I believe, are twenty-seven in number; but brave men never run away."

"You'll fight, then?"

"If there were not several invalids amongst us, I would answer, 'Yes'; for I have already shown you robbers that I am not afraid of you."

"Have you fought us before? When was it? What's your name?"

"I fought five years ago at the affair of the Tchanak-Kampo, and here's a little souvenir of it"; and, throwing back the sleeve of his right arm, he showed the scar of a great saber cut. The brigand laughed, and again requested his interlocutor's name.

"I am called Rala-Tchembe," said the merchant; "you ought to know the name."

"Yes, all of us know it. It is the name of a brave man." So saying, he dismounted, and taking a saber from his girdle, presented it to the Tibetan. "Here," said he, "accept this saber; 'tis the best I have. We have fought enough; in the future, when we meet, it shall be as brothers."

The Tibetan received the brigand's present and gave him, in return, a handsome bow and quiver which he had bought at Peking.

The robbers who had remained outside the camp, upon seeing their chief fraternize with the chief of the caravan, dismounted, fastened their horses to each other, two and two, by the bridles, and came to drink a friendly cup of tea with the travelers, who now at last began to breathe freely. All these brigands were extremely affable. They asked us various questions about the Tartar-Khalkhas, whom, they said, they were particularly anxious to see for the reason that, in the preceding year, these warriors had killed three of their companions, and they were eager to avenge them. We had a little chat about politics, too. The brigands affirmed that they were warm friends of the Grand Lama and irreconcilable enemies of the Emperor of China. On this account they seldom failed to pillage the embassy on its way to Peking, because it was altogether fitting that the Emperor should send gifts to the Grand Lama.

After having done honor to the tea and *tsamba* of the caravan, the brigands wished us a good journey and returned to their own encampment. All these fraternal manifestations did not prevent our sleeping with one eye open; our repose, however, was not disturbed, and in the morning we resumed our way in peace. Of the many thousands of pilgrims who have performed the journey to Lhasa, there are very few who can boast of having had so close a view of the robbers, at so small a cost.

We had escaped one great danger; but, we were informed, another awaited us, far more formidable in its character though different in kind. We were beginning to ascend the vast chain of the Tangla Mountains. On the plateau of these, our traveling companions assured us, the invalids would die, and those who were now well would become invalids, with but a small chance of living. The death of Father Gabet was considered quite a matter of certainty.

After six days' laborious ascent of several mountains, which rose, one above another, like tiers in a natural amphi-theater, we at length reached the famous plateau—the most elevated point, perhaps, on the earth's surface. The snow there appeared to have identified itself with the soil. It cracked beneath our feet, but the feet left scarcely any impression upon it. The only vegetation consisted of occasional tufts of a low, sharp-pointed, smooth grass, woody within and hard as iron, but not brittle; so that it might very well be used for mattress needles. The animals were, however, so famished that they were fain to attack even this atrocious forage, which actually cracked between their teeth and could be gathered only by vigorous efforts and at the cost of infinite lip bleeding.

From the brow of this magnificent plateau we could see below us the peaks and needles of numerous ridges, the ramifications of which were lost in the horizon. We had never witnessed anything at all comparable to this grand, this gigantic spectacle.

During the twelve days that we were journeying along the heights of Tangla, we enjoyed fine weather; the air was calm, and it pleased God to bless us each day with a warm, genial sunshine that materially modified the ordinary coldness of the atmosphere. Still, the air, excessively rarified at that enormous altitude, was very piercing, and monstrous vultures, which followed the track of the caravan, were daily provided with a number of dead bodies.

The small caravan of missioners itself paid its tribute to death; but, happily, that tribute was only in the shape of our little black mule, which we abandoned with regret but at the same time with resignation. The dismal prophecy that had been announced with reference to Father Gabet was not fulfilled. The mountains which were to have been fatal to him proved, on the contrary, highly favorable, restoring to him, by degrees, health and strength. This blessing, almost unexpected by us, even at the hands of the God of Mercy, made us forget all our past miseries. We regained all our courage, and firmly entertained the hope that the Almighty would permit us to accomplish our journey.

The descent of Tangla, though long in duration, was rapid in itself. Throughout four whole days we were going down, as it seemed, a gigantic staircase, each step of which consisted of a mountain. At the bottom we found some hot springs, of an extremely magnificent description. Amongst huge rocks are a great number of reservoirs, hollowed out by the hand of nature, in which the water boils and bubbles, as in a vast cauldron over a fierce fire. Sometimes the active fluid escapes through the fissures of the rocks, and leaps in all directions by a thousand capricious jets. Every now and then the ebullition, in particular reservoirs, grows so furious that tall columns of water rise into the air, as though impelled by some tremendous pump. Above these springs, thick vapors, collecting in the air, condense into white clouds.

The water of these hot springs is sulphurous. After bubbling and dashing about in its huge granite reservoirs, it boils over and, quitting the rocks, which had seemed to wish to keep it captive, pours down by various currents into a valley below. There it forms a large stream flowing over a bed of flint, yellow as gold.

These boiling waters do not long preserve their fluidity. The extreme rigor of the atmosphere cools them so rapidly that, within a mile and a half from its source, the stream they have formed is almost frozen through. These hot springs are of frequent occurence in the mountains of Tibet; and the lama physicians, who attribute to them considerable medicinal virtue, constantly prescribe their use, both internally and externally.

From the Tangla Mountains to Lhasa, the ground constantly declines. As the traveler descends, the intensity of the cold diminishes, and the earth becomes clothed with more vigorous and more varied vegetation. One evening we encamped in a large plain, where the pasturage was marvelously abundant. As our cattle had been for some time past on very short rations indeed, we determined to give them the full benefit of the present opportunity, and to remain where we were for two days.

Next morning, when we were quietly preparing our tea, we perceived in the distance a troop of horsemen galloping towards our encampment at full speed. The sight seemed to freeze the very blood in our veins: we stood for a moment perfectly petrified. After the first moment of stupor, we rushed out of our tent. "Robbers! Robbers!" cried we. "Here's a great body of bandits advancing against us."

The Tibetan merchants, who were boiling their tea and mixing their *tsamba*, laughed at our alarm, and told us to sit down quite at our ease. "Take breakfast with us," said they. "There are no robbers to fear here; the horsemen you see yonder are friends. We are now entering upon an inhabited country. Behind the hill there, to the right, are a number of black tents, and the horsemen, whom you take to be robbers, are shepherds."

These words restored our equanimity, and with our equanimity returned our appetite, so that we were very happy to accept the invitation to breakfast. We had scarcely taken up a cup of buttered tea before the horsemen made their appearance at the door of the tent. Far from being brigands, they were worthy fellows who came to sell butter and fresh meat; their saddles were regular butchers' stalls hung with joints of mutton and venison, which rested on the sides of their horses. We purchased eight legs of mutton, which, being frozen, were easily susceptible of transport. They cost us an old pair of Peking boots, a Peking steel, and the saddle of our defunct mule, which luckily could also boast of Peking origin.

Everything coming from Peking is highly prized by the Tibetans, more especially by that portion of the population which has not advanced beyond the pastoral and nomadic life. The merchants who accompany caravans take care, accordingly, to label every package "Goods from Peking." Snuff is especially an object earnestly sought for among the Tibetans: all the shepherds asked us whether we had snuff from Peking. Father Huc, who was the only snuff-taker of our party, had formerly possessed a quantity of the precious commodity, but it had all been used, and for the last eight days he had been reduced to the necessity of filling his snuffbox and his nose with a frightful mixture of dust and ashes. Those who are devotees of snuff will at once comprehend all the horrors to poor Father Huc of this deplorable position.

Condemned for the two last months to live upon barley meal moistened with tea, we found that the mere sight of our legs of mutton seemed to fortify our stomachs and invigorate our emaciated limbs. The remainder of the day was occupied in culinary preparations. By way of condiment and seasoning, we had only a little garlic, and that little was so frozen and dried that it was almost imperceptible in its smell. We peeled, however, all we had, and stuck it into two legs of mutton, which we set to boil in our great cauldron. The argols, which abounded in this blessed plain, supplies ample materials for cooking our inestimable supper.

The sun was just setting, and Samdadchiemba, who had been inspecting one of the legs of mutton with his thumbnail, had triumphantly announced that the mutton was boiled to a bubble, when we heard in all directions the frightening cry, "Fire! Fire!" At one bound we were outside our tent, where we found that the flame, which had caught some dry grass in the interior of the encampment and threatened to assail also our linen tents, was spreading about, in all directions, with fearful rapidity.

All the travelers, armed with their felt carpets, were endeavoring to stifle the flame, or at all events to keep it from reaching the tents, and in this latter effort they were quite successful. The fire, repulsed on every side, forced an issue from the encampment and rushed out into the desert. There, driven by the wind, it spread over the pasturages, which it devoured as it went. We thought that we had nothing further to fear; but the cry, "Save the camels! Save the camels!" at once reminded us how little we knew of a conflagration in the desert.

We then saw that the camels stolidly awaited the flame, instead of fleeing from it as the horses and oxen did. We therefore hastened to the succor of our own beasts, which, at the moment, seemed tolerably remote from the flame. The flame, however, reached them as soon as we did, and at once surrounded us and them. It was to no purpose we pushed and beat the stupid brutes; not an inch would they stir; but there they stood, phlegmatically gaping at us with an air that seemed to ask us what right we had to come and interrupt them at their meals. We really felt as if we could have killed the impractical beasts. The fire consumed so rapidly the grass it encountered, that it soon assailed the camels and caught their long, thick hair; and it was only with the utmost exertion that, by the aid of the felt carpets we had brought with us, we extinguished the flame upon their bodies. We got three of them out of the fire, with the ends of their hair singed, but the fourth was reduced to a deplorable condition. Not a bristle remained on its entire body; the whole coat of hair was burned down to the skin, and the skin itself was terribly charred.

The extent of pasturage consumed by the flame was about a mile and a quarter long by three quarters of a mile broad. The Tibetans were in ecstasies at their good fortune in having the progress of the conflagration so soon stayed, and we fully participated in their joy after we had learned the full extent of the evil with which we had been menaced. We were informed that, if the fire had continued much longer, it would have reached the black tents, in which case the shepherds would have pursued and massacred us. Nothing can equal the fury of these poor children of the desert when they find the pastures, which are their only re-source, reduced to ashes, no matter whether by malice or by mischance. It is much the same thing to them as destroying their herds.

When we resumed our journey, the broiled camel was not yet dead, but it was altogether incapable of service. The three others were obliged to yield to circumstances, and to share among them the portion of baggage which their unlucky traveling companion had hitherto borne. However, the burdens of all of them had very materially diminished in weight since our departure from Koko Nor: our sacks of meal had become little better than sacks of emptiness; so that, after descending the Tangla Mountains, we had been compelled to put ourselves upon an allowance of two cups of *tsamba* each, a day. Before our departure we had made a fair calculation of our reasonable wants, but no such calculation could cover the waste committed upon our provender by our two cameleers—by the one through indifference and stupidity, by the other through malice and knavery. Fortunately we were soon approaching a large Tibetan station, where we should find the means of renewing our stores.

OUR LADY OF CHINA

Thou art as pale as the pear-blossoms, and more lovely than the lotus;
The grace of the willow is thine—and thy voice is its sighing, O Lady!
In the courts of mandarins there is no woman like to thee,
And thy handmaids are the daughters of princes.
Thy name is costly incense rising, or moonlight on a lily pond
When the shadows steal down from the mountains;
And white as frost on the moon; the tall bamboos
Bow to the ground at thy passing, even as our hearts, O Lady!

—MARION PALMER

LETTERS TO A MISSIONER

by Saint Therese of Lisieux

> The Little Flower wanted to be a missioner and go to
> the Carmel established in the land now known as Viet-
> nam. Ill health kept her home but she adopted several
> missioners, offering her prayers and sufferings for them.

Lisieux, 30 July 1896

My Brother,

I hope you will allow me from now on to call you by no other
name, seeing that Jesus had deigned to unite us in the bonds of
the apostolate. It is very sweet to think that from all eternity our
Lord formed this union, which is to save Him souls, and that He
created me to be your sister. . . . Yesterday we got your letters;
it was with joy that our good Mother brought you into the
cloister. She has allowed me to keep *my brother's photograph*,
it is a *very special* privilege, a Carmelite has not even the portraits
of her nearest relations; but Our Mother realises that yours, far
from reminding me of the world and earthly affections, will raise
my heart to regions far above, will make it forget self for the
glory of God and the salvation of souls. So, Brother, while I shall
cross the sea with you, you will remain with me, hidden in our
poor cell. . . .

I am surrounded by things that remind me of you. I have
pinned the map of Su-Chuen on the wall of the room in which I

* From *The Letters of St. Therese*, translated and edited by F. J. Sheed. Copyright, Sheed and Ward.

work, and the picture you gave me lies always on my heart in the book of the Gospels, which never leaves me. I thrust it in haphazard, and this is the passage it came to: "Whoever has left all to follow me, shall receive a hundredfold in this world, and in the world to come eternal life." Jesus' words are already fulfilled in you, for you tell me: "I start out happy."

I realise that this joy must be wholly spiritual. It is impossible to leave father, mother, native land without feeling all the rending of separation. . . . O my brother! I suffer with you, I offer your great sacrifices with you, and I beg Jesus to pour His abundant consolations upon your dear family, until the union in heaven where we shall see them rejoicing in your glory, a glory which will dry their tears forever, and fill them with joy overflowing for a blissful eternity.

This evening, at prayer, I meditated on passages of Isaias which seemed to me so appropriate to you that I felt I simply must copy them out for you:

"Enlarge the place of thy tents. Thou shalt spread out to the right hand and to the left, and thy seed shall inherit the Gentiles and shall inhabit the desolate cities. . . . Lift up thy eyes round about and see: all these are gathered together, they are come to thee, thy sons shall come from afar and thy daughters will rise up at thy side. Then shalt thou see and abound, and thy heart shall wonder and be enlarged when the multitude of the sea shall be converted to thee, the strength of the Gentiles will come to thee."

Is not that the hundredfold promised? And can you not cry out in your turn: "The spirit of the Lord is upon me, because the Lord has anointed me. He has sent me to announce his word; to heal the contrite of heart, to preach a release to the captives, and console those who are in chains."

"I shall rejoice in the Lord, for he has clothed me with the garments of salvation and with the robe of justice he has covered me. As the earth brings forth her bud, so shall the Lord God make justice to spring forth and praise before all the nations. My people will be a people of the just, they will be the shoots that I have planted . . . I shall go unto the islands afar off to those who have never heard of the Lord. I shall announce his glory to the nations and shall give them as a gift to my God."

If I wanted to copy all the passages that touched me most, it would take too long. I conclude, but first I have one more request to make. When you have a moment free I should be very glad if you would write me the principal dates of your life, thus I could unite myself especially with you to thank God for the graces He has given you.

Goodbye, Brother . . . distance can never separate our souls, even death will only make our union closer. If I go to Heaven soon, I shall ask Jesus' permission to visit you in Su-Chuen, and we shall continue our apostolate together. Meanwhile I shall always be united to you by prayer, and I ask our Lord never to let me be joyful when you are suffering. I would even wish that my Brother should always have joys and I trials, but perhaps that is selfish! . . . but no, because my only weapon is love and suffering, and you have the sword of the word and of apostolic labours.

Goodbye once more, Brother, deign to bless her whom Jesus has given you for a Sister.

Thérèse of the Child Jesus and the Holy Face
rel. carm. ind.

Lisieux Carmel,
19 March 1897

Brother,

Our good Mother has just given me your letters, in spite of Lent (a time when we in Carmel do not write). She most kindly permits me to answer you today, for we fear that our November letter has paid a visit to the depths of the Blue River. Your letters, dated September, made a prosperous journey and arrived to rejoice your Mother and your little Sister on the feast of All Saints; the one of January 20 reaches us under the protection of St. Joseph. Since you follow my example, and write on every line, I must not lose so good a habit, but it makes my wretched writing still harder to decipher.

Ah! how long must we wait till we have no need of ink and

paper to tell one another our thoughts? You very nearly went, Brother, to that magic country where they convey what is in their mind without writing or even speech; I thank the good God with all my heart for leaving you on the battlefield, that you may win Him many a victory. . . . Already your sufferings have saved many souls. St. John of the Cross says: "The smallest movement of pure love is more useful to the Church than all works put together." If so, how profitable to the Church must your pains and trials be, since for the sole love of Jesus you suffer them with joy.

Truly, Brother, I cannot pity you, because in you are fulfilled the words of the Imitation: "When you find suffering sweet and love it for the love of Jesus Christ, you have found Paradise upon earth." That is, in fact, the Paradise of the Missionary and the Carmelite; the joy the worldly seek from pleasure is a fleeting shadow, but our joy, sought and savoured in labour and suffering, is a most sweet reality, a foretaste of the bliss of heaven.

Your letter, shot through with holy gaiety, interested me deeply; I followed your example and laughed heartily at your cook: I can see him bashing in his saucepan. . . . Your visiting-card amused me too, I don't even know which way up to turn it, I am like a child trying to read a book upside down.

But, to come back to your cook, would you believe that we too sometimes have amusing incidents in Carmel? Carmel, like Su-Chuen, is to the world a foreign country where the world's most elementary usages are lost; here is a small example. A charitable person recently made us a present of a little lobster, all tied up in a hamper. Naturally no such marvel had been seen in the Convent for a very long time; but our dear Sister Cook did remember that the little thing had to be put into water to be cooked; she did it, with much lamentation at having to treat an innocent creature so cruelly. The innocent creature was apparently asleep and let itself be handled without protest; but the moment it felt the heat, its mildness turned to fury. It knew its innocence, and without so much as a by-your-leave, leapt out onto the kitchen floor, for its soft-hearted executioner had not yet put the lid on the pot.

So poor Sister armed herself with tongs and rushed after the lobster which was leaping about frantically. The struggle lasted quite a time: at last, weary of battle, the Cook, still armed with the tongs, came to our Mother and told her that the lobster was certainly possessed. Her face was even more expressive than her words (poor little creature, a moment ago so mild, so innocent, now possessed! Truly you can't trust the praise of "creatures"!). Our Mother couldn't help laughing to hear the judge demanding justice; she went straight to the kitchen, seized the lobster—which, not having made a vow of obedience, offered some resistance—put it in its prison and went off after closing the door—that is, the lid—tight. In the evening at recreation the whole Community laughed till the tears ran at the little lobster possessed by the devil, and next day everyone was able to enjoy a mouthful. . . .

The donor wanted to give us a treat, and certainly succeeded; for the famous lobster, or rather its story, will serve again and again as a feast not in the refectory but at recreation. Maybe my little story does not strike you as very funny, but I can assure you that had you been present you would not have kept your gravity. . . . Still, Brother, if I bore you please forgive me.

I now begin to speak more seriously. Since your departure, I have read the lives of several missionaries (in the letter you may not have received, I thanked you for the life of Pere Nempon). Among others I read Theophane Venard's, which interested me and touched me more than I can say; under the impression it left on me I composed some verses, which are entirely personal; I am sending them to you, all the same; our good Mother told me she thought these verses would please my brother in Su-Chuen. The last stanza but one requires certain explanations: I say I should be happy to set out for Tonking. . . . No, indeed! it is not a dream; in fact I can assure you that if Jesus doesn't come soon and get me for the Carmel of Heaven, I'll start off one day for the Carmel of Hanoi—there is one in that city now, founded from the Saigon Carmel. You have visited the lastnamed, and you know that in Cochin-China an Order like ours cannot maintain itself without French subjects; but alas! vocations are very rare, and often Superiors are unwilling to let sisters go whom they think capable of being useful to their own community. Thus in her youth our good Mother was prevented, by the will of her Superior, from going to help the Saigon Carmel; I am the last one to complain of that! I thank the good God for giving so true an inspiration to His representative; but I remember that the desires of mothers are often fulfilled in their children and I should not be surprised if I went off to the infidel shore to pray and suffer as our Mother wanted to. . . . It must be admitted, however, that the news we get from Tonking is not very comforting: at the end of last year, thieves got into the poor monastery, and made their way into the Prioress's cell; she did not wake, but in the morning she could not find her crucifix beside her (at night a Carmelite's crucifix lies always near her head, attached to the pillow), a small cupboard had been broken open and the handful of money which was all the Community's material treasure was gone. The Carmels of France, touched by the distress of Hanoi, clubbed together to give her the money for a wall high enough to keep thieves from getting into the monastery.

Perhaps you are wondering what our Mother thinks of my desire to go to Tonking? She believes in my vocation (truly a rather special one is needed, not every Carmelite feels the call to go into exile); but she does not believe my vocation can ever be fulfilled: for that, the scabbard would have to be as strong as the sword and perhaps (thinks our Mother) the scabbard would be thrown into the sea before it got to Tonking. . . . As a matter of fact, it's no great convenience to be composed of a body and a soul! miserable Brother Ass, as St. Francis of Assisi called the body, often hinders his noble sister and prevents her from darting off where she would. . . . Still, I won't abuse him, for all his faults; he is still good for something, he helps his companion to get to heaven, and gets there himself. I am not in the least worried about the future, I am sure the good God will do what He wills: that is the one and only grace I desire—one must not be more royalist than the King. . . .

To accomplish His work, Jesus needs no one, and if He accepted me it would be sheer kindliness; but to tell you the truth,

Brother, I think it more likely that Jesus will treat me as a little idler; I don't want that, for I should be most happy to work and suffer for Him a long time: so I ask Him to act in me for His own satisfaction—that is, to pay no attention to my wishes, whether my wish to love Him in suffering, or my wish to come and enjoy Him in heaven. I do not forget your promise to pray for me; you have received all my requests so kindly that I venture to make this one more. I don't want you to ask God to deliver me from the flames of Purgatory. St. Teresa said to her daughters, when they wanted to pray for themselves: "What care I if I stay in Purgatory till the end of the world, if I save a single soul by my prayers." That phrase finds an echo in my heart, I want to save souls and forget self for them; I want to save them even after my death, so I should be happy if—instead of the little prayer you say, which will be eternally fulfilled—you would say: "My God, permit my sister to go on making you loved." If Jesus hears you, I shall be well able to show you my gratitude.

You ask me, Brother, to choose between the two names, Marie or Thérèse, for one of the girls you are to baptise; since the Chinese don't want two saints to protect them but only one, they must have the more powerful, so the Blessed Virgin wins. Later, when you baptise a great many children, you would give great pleasure to my sister (a Carmelite, like me) by calling two little sisters Céline and Thérèse, the names we bore in the world.

Céline, nearly four years older than I joined me here, after she had closed our good Father's eyes; this dear sister of mine does not know the close relation that exists between you and me; but as we often speak at recreation of Our Mother's missionary (the name you bear at the Lisieux Carmel), she recently told me of her desire that, through you, Céline and Thérèse might go to China to start life over again.

Please, Brother, forgive my requests and my too lengthy chatter, and in your goodness bless your unworthy little sister,

Thérèse of the Child Jesus and the Holy Face
rel. carm. ind.

A SAINT IN THE SLAVE TRADE

by Arnold Lunn

> One of the great failures of Western civilization was in
> permitting slavery to exist in Christian nations for so
> many centuries. Yet Catholic missioners were in the
> front of the fight against this evil. The Jesuit, St. Peter
> Claver, labored among the New World's negroes for
> forty years.

Cartagena, which was founded by Pedro de Heredia in 1533,
owed its great commercial importance to its superb harbour. It is
situated in the Caribbean Sea near the most northerly point of
South America, to the east of the Isthmus of Panama. It is in the
tropics, about 700 miles north of the Equator.

When Peter Claver first set foot in Cartagena, he kissed the
ground which was to be the scene of his future labours. He had
every reason to rejoice, for the climate of Cartagena was dis-
agreeably hot and moist, the country around was flat and marshy,
the soil was barren, the necessities of life had to be imported, and
in the time of Peter Claver fresh vegetables were almost unknown. In the seventeenth century Cartagena was the happy
hunting ground of fever-bearing insects from tropical swamps.
These, the natural disadvantages of Cartagena, might have been
wasted on a robust saint, but Claver must have been consoled to
feel that the fine edge of these discomforts would not be blunted

* From *A Saint in the Slave Trade*. Copyright, Sheed and Ward.

by a naturally healthy constitution. He had, indeed, been warned that delicate health might easily succumb to excessive heat.

Cartagena was the chief centre for the slave trade. Slave-traders picked up slaves at four crowns a head on the coast of Guinea or Congo, and sold them for 200 crowns or more at Cartagena. Lest the reader be tempted to raise the cry of "profiteer," it is only just to remember that the voyage lasted two months, slaves cannot live on air, even foul air, and that the overheads may fairly be credited with 33 per cent or so of slaves who died en route. Further, when we take into consideration the low esteem in which the honourable profession of slave-trading has always been held, we cannot consider that the profits, though large, were excessive.

Father Claver, whose life's work was to be the instruction, the conversion and the care of the negroes who landed in Cartagena, began his ministry under the guidance of Father Alfonso de Sandoval.

Father Claver never experienced that momentary weakness which always overcame the heroic Sandoval when a slave ship was announced. The horror with which Sandoval contemplated a return to these scenes of squalid misery only serves to increase our admiration of the courage with which he conquered these very natural shrinkings of the flesh.

Father Claver, on the other hand, was transported with joy when messengers announced the arrival of a fresh cargo of Africans. Indeed, he bribed the officials of Cartagena with the promise to say Mass for the intentions of whoever was first to bring him this joyful news. But there was no need for such bribes, for among the simple pleasures of life must be counted the happiness of bringing good news to a grateful recipient. The Governor himself coveted this mission, for the happiness of watching the radiant dawn of joy on the saint's face. At the words "Another slave ship" his eyes brightened, and colour flooded back into his pale, emaciated cheeks.

In the intervals between the arrival of slave ships, Father Claver wandered round the town with a sack. He went from house to house, begging for little comforts for the incoming cargo. Claver enjoyed the respect of the responsible officials of the

Crown in Cartagena, devout Catholics who approved warmly the work of instruction which the good Father carried on amongst the negroes. They felt this responsibility for the welfare of these exiles. Such opposition as Claver encountered amongst the Spaniards came from the traders and planters, who were often inconvenienced by Claver's zeal on behalf of his black children.

The black cargo arrived in a condition of piteous terror. They were convinced that they were to be bought by merchants who needed their fat to grease the keels of ships, and their blood to dye the sails, for this was one of the favourite bedtime stories with which they had been regaled by friendly mariners during the two months' passage.

The first appearance of Father Claver was often greeted with screams of terror, but it was only a matter of moments to convince these frantic creatures that Claver was no purchaser of slave fat and slave blood. He scarcely needed the interpreters who accompanied him for this purpose, for the language of love survived in the confusion of Babel, and readily translated itself into gesture. *Cor ad cor loquitur*. Long before the interpreters had finished explaining that the story which had so terrified them was the invention of the devil, Father Claver had already soothed and comforted them by his very presence. And not only by his presence, for Claver was a practical evangelist. The biscuits, brandy, tobacco and lemons which he distributed were practical tokens of friendship. "We must," he said, "speak to them with our hands, before we try to speak to them with our lips."

After a brief talk to the negroes on deck, Claver descended to the sick between decks. In this work he was often alone. Many of his African interpreters were unable to endure the stench and fainted at the first contact with that appalling atmosphere. Claver, however, did not recoil. Indeed, he regarded this part of his work as of special importance. Again and again he was able to impart to some poor dying wretch those elements of Christian truth which justified him in administering baptism.

It is recorded that the person of Father Claver was sometimes illumined with rays of glory as he passed through the hospital wards of Cartagena. It may well be that a radiance no less illuminating lit the dark bowels of the slave ship as Father Claver moved among the dying. There they lay in the slime, the stench and the gloom, their bodies still bleeding from the lash, their souls still suffering from insults and contempt. There they lay, and out of the depths called upon the tribal gods who had deserted them, and called in vain. Then suddenly things changed. The dying Africans saw a face bending over them, a face illumined with love, and a voice infinitely tender, and the deft movement of kind hands easing their tortured bodies, and—supreme miracle—his lips meeting their filthy sores in a kiss. . . . A love so divine was an unconquerable argument for the God in whom Father Claver believed.

When Father Claver returned next day he was welcomed with ecstatic cries of child-like affection.

Two or three days usually passed before arrangements at the port could be completed to allow the disembarkation of a fresh cargo of slaves. When the day of disembarkation arrived, Father Claver was always present, waiting on shore with another stock of provisions and delicacies. Sometimes he would carry the sick ashore in his own arms. Again and again in the records of his mission, we find evidences of his strength, which seemed almost supernatural. His diet would have been ridiculously inadequate for a normal man living a sedentary life. His neglect of sleep would have killed a normal man within a few years, but in spite of his contempt for all ordinary rules of health, in spite of a constitution which was none too strong at the outset of his career, he proved himself capable of out-working and out-walking and out-nursing all his colleagues. He made every effort to secure for the sick special carts, as otherwise they ran the risk of being driven forward under the lash. He did not leave them until he had seen them to their lodgings, and men said that Father Claver escorting slaves back to Cartagena reminded them of a conqueror entering Rome in triumph.

It was after the negroes had been lodged in the magazines where they awaited their sale and ultimate disposal that Claver's real work began. In the case of the dying, Claver was satisfied if he could awaken some dim sense of contrition of sin, and some faint glimmering of understanding of the fundamental Christian belief. The healthy slaves, however, had to qualify by a course of rigid instruction for the privilege of baptism.

I have already referred to the crowded conditions of the compound in which the negroes were stocked on disembarkation, and on the squalor and misery which was the result of the infectious diseases from which many of them were suffering. There are many white men who cannot stand the odour of a healthy negro. The stink of sick negroes, confined in a limited space, often proved insupportable to Father Claver's negro interpreters. It was in this noxious and empoisoned air that Peter Claver's greatest work was achieved.

Before the day's work began, Father Claver prepared himself by special prayers before the Blessed Sacrament and by self-inflicted austerities. He then passed through the streets of Cartagena, accompanied by his African interpreters, and bearing a staff crowned by a cross. On his shoulder he carried a bag which contained his stole and surplice, the necessities for the arrangement of an altar, and his little store of comforts and delicacies. Heavily loaded though he was, his companions found it difficult to keep up with this eager little man who dived through the crowded streets with an enthusiasm which suggested a lover hurrying to a trysting place.

On arrival, his first care was for the sick. He had a delicacy of touch in the cleansing and dressing of sores which was a true expression of his personality. After he had made the sick comfortable on their couches and given them a little wine and brandy and refreshed them with scented water, he then proceeded to collect the healthier negroes into an open space.

In his work of instruction Claver relied freely on pictures. This method appealed effectively to the simple African mind, and was, moreover, in accordance with the teachings of his Order, for, as we have seen, St. Ignatius in his Spiritual Exercises was constant in urging the exercitant to picture to himself sensibly the subject-matter of his meditations. His favourite picture was in the form of a triptych, in the centre Christ on the Cross, his precious blood flowing from each wound into a vase, below the Cross a priest collecting this blood to baptize a faithful negro. On the right side of the triptych a naively dramatic group of negroes, glorious and splendidly arrayed; on the left side the wicked negroes, hideous and deformed, surrounded by unlovely monsters.

Claver was particularly careful to make every possible arrangement for the comfort of his catechumens. He himself remained standing, even in the heat of the day, and the slave-masters, who sometimes attended these edifying ceremonies, often remonstrated with the slaves for remaining seated while their instructor stood. But Father Claver always intervened, and explained with great earnestness to the slave-masters that the slaves were the really important people at this particular performance, and that he himself was a mere cypher who was there for their convenience. Sometimes, if a negro was so putrescent with sores as to be revolting to his neighbours, and worse still, to prevent them from concentrating their thoughts on Father Claver's instruction, he would throw his cloak over him as a screen. Again, he would often use his cloak as a cushion for the infirm. On such occasions the cloak was often withdrawn so infected and filthy as to require most drastic cleansing. Father Claver, however, was so engrossed in his work, that he would have resumed his cloak immediately had not his interpreters forcibly prevented him.

This cloak was to serve many purposes during his ministry: as a veil to disguise repulsive wounds, as a shield for leprous negroes, as a pall for those who had died, as a pillow for the sick. The cloak was soon to acquire a legendary fame. Its very touch cured the sick and revived the dying. Men fought to come into contact with it, to tear fragments from it as relics. Indeed, before long its edge was ragged with torn shreds.

Claver's work was not confined to Cartagena. Cartagena was a slave mart, and very few slaves whom Father Claver baptized in Cartagena remained there. Now, Father Claver was determined not to lose his converts, and it was therefore his practice to conduct a series of country missions after Easter. He went from village to village, crossing mountain ranges, traversing swamps and bogs, making his way through forests. On arriving in a village he would plant a cross in the market place, and there he would

await the sunset and the return from the fields of the slaves
whom he had first met—it might be some weeks, it might be some
years—before in Cartagena. The ecstatic welcome which marked
these scenes of reunion were a royal recompense for the hardships of the missionary journey.

Father Claver never lost his ascendancy over the men whom
he had baptized. On one occasion a mere message from him was
sufficient to arrest the flight of a panic-stricken negro population
retreating in disorder from a volcano in eruption. Father Claver's
messenger stopped the rout, and Father Claver's bodily presence
next day transformed a terror-infected mob into a calm and
orderly procession which followed him without fear round the
very edge of the still active crater, on the crest of which Father
Claver planted a triumphant cross.

Though Father Claver's activities were not confined to the
negroes, the "slave of the slaves" regarded himself as, above all,
consecrated to their service. Proud Spaniards who sought him out
had to be content with such time as he could spare from the
ministrations of the negroes. This attitude did not meet with
universal approval. Spanish ladies complained that the smell of
the negroes who had attended Father Claver's daybreak Mass
clung tenaciously to the church, and rendered its interior insupportable to sensitive nostrils for the remainder of the day. How
could they possibly be expected to confess to Father Claver in a
confessional used by negroes and impregnated with their presence? "I quite agree," replied Father Claver, with the disarming
simplicity of the saint. "I am not the proper confessor for fine
ladies. You should go to some other confessor. My confessional
was never meant for ladies of quality. It is too narrow for their
gowns. It is only suited to poor negresses."

But were his Spanish ladies satisfied with this reply? Not a bit.
It was Father Claver to whom they wished to confess, and if the
worst had come to the worst, they were prepared to use the same
confessional as the negresses. "Very well, then," replied Father
Claver, meekly, "but I am afraid you must wait until all my
negresses have been absolved."

In the sight of God the white man and the negro may be equal, but in the sight of Father Claver the negro had precedence every time.

MADRE DE DIOS

by Thomas McGovern

A sick call, a walk in the night—these are the simple ingredients of Father McGovern's story. Yet through the art of words, pictures are created that will be long remembered.

He knew that the rain would be coming soon, perhaps tonight. The sky was a sullen leaden grey and there was a stillness, an expectant hush in the air. He watched the clouds, tattered grey streamers, drift away from him to be lost in the darkness behind the mountains. Even the way they trailed along seemed strange. They were trying to hurry, anxious to be off somewhere—anywhere for the rain was coming.

He was about to turn back into the church when he saw Miguel and his flock come stumbling up the road—the sheep a wavering, bobbing sea of grey, almost the color of the sky, and Miguel, thin and quick, prodding them on with a long stick.

He liked Miguel, the thin quiet shepherd boy who took care of his invalid father. Miguel, with the straight black hair, parting in the middle, long nose and eyes much too large for his face. There was a strange, almost comic seriousness about the boy. The way he spoke—how his lips would form each syllable and then when he had tasted the word carefully, how he would speak in his high pitched voice. He liked Miguel and so he waited to greet him.

"Buenos tardes, Padrecito," Miguel called. He weeded a path through the stumbling sheep and came to Fr. Nolan.

"Hello Miguel, buenos tardes."

Miguel's lips widened to a smile. "She look like the rain will come," he said, pointing with his thumb to the sky. And then as an afterthought, "tonight, maybe."

"She—it does, Miguel. And how are you?"

"Very good, Padre."

"And your father? Is he better?"

"No, Padre, if anything he is worse. The doctor was to see him today and he was not happy about him."

"I'm sorry to hear that. I was hoping he'd be feeling better."

Miguel said nothing so Fr. Nolan continued, "I'll be down to see him Saturday with Holy Communion. Of course, if he gets any worse, come for me."

"May God repay you," Miguel said softly and then they bade each other goodbye and the boy turned and followed after his flock.

Fr. Nolan watched the boy and his sheep until the road turned and they were hidden by the mountains. For a few more seconds he could hear the bleating of the sheep and then only silence and the mountains. He turned back into the church. . . .

He was right. He and Miguel and the birds that stayed in their mountain nests and the clouds that hurried over the mountain range. The rain came. A fierce hissing rain, shattering the expectant hush of the air—streaming down in the thick sheets of water—drumming an incessant hollow boom upon the tin roof—smashing the hardened dirt of the road into soft, slippery mud. The rain came and Fr. Nolan pitied the traveler and thanked God for shelter. He lit the kerosene lamp and sat down before the fire and began to read his office.

He finished his office and began to doze off before the warm glowing fire. His limbs had grown heavy—his head had begun to nod. . . . And then this sound! It must be the rain. But it was not the rain. The door, the door—someone is there. Fr. Nolan roused himself from the chair. He hurried to the door.

"Buenos noches, Padrecito."

How could he say that—the poor, half drowned boy? His hair was pasted down against his forehead. His face was white—a chalky, sick white in the darkness and he shivered.

Fr. Nolan grabbed his arm. The boy's shoes sucked noisily, greedily as he led him over to the fire.

Fr. Nolan rummaged in his closet and found some clothes. "Get those wet things off and try these on." Miguel changed clothes. A little color began to seep back into his face. "My father is dying," he whispered.

Fr. Nolan did not want him to go back with him. He had too much of the rain already. But it was his father. And so the both of them set off into the rain and dark down the mountain road. There was no moon, no light, only darkness and the rain lashing through the trees and cascading down the mountain sides. They picked their way down carefully. . . .

There was a light in the house and long distorted shadows could be seen through the window moving back and forth on the ceiling. The dying man was in the corner breathing heavily.

He was an old man, wizened and stunted with sickness. An ugly dwarf with grey rumpled hair and a grey mustache. There were deep lines in his forehead and a network of fine cracks across his leathery sunken cheeks. His breath came heavily and rasping and on every exhale, he made a noise that sounded like "Madre de Dios"—Mother of God. Slowly was he dying. Each breath coming slower. He was breathing his life away, slowly, slowly, slowly—while the candle beside his bed threw distorted shadows upon the ceiling. "Madre de Dios." Fr. Nolan bent over him and gave him the last sacraments. His face glowed for a second or two and then the dying man died.

Now that the man's heavy breathing had ceased, there was no sound in the little room. No sound at all, only a stillness that cried out louder than any sound. Only the stillness and the shuffling of feet. Only the stillness and live men breathing. Only the stillness and Miguel crying.

Fr. Nolan put his arm around Miguel trying to choke back the tears. He listened to Miguel's breathing. He heard the sound, the same sound that Miguel's father had made. The sound that was so much like "Madre de Dios."

PAUL KEPT HIS HEAD

by Patrick J. Byrne

Bishop Byrne, victim of the Communists in Korea, was a man of great humor. He was also a teller of tales. Here is one of his best.

Paul Kim, devout and serene Christian gentleman, is surely in some way related to the great Saint Denis of Paris, of whom 'tis said that, being beheaded, he did pick up his head and bear it some twenty paces. Not being so thoroughly decapitated, however, Paul carried on for seven miles. It all happened thusly:

He was making a journey afoot, in midwinter, through Manchurian parts that were distant and strange to him, and made more desolate still by the vast reaches of snow that left him alone in the whole wide world. But subzero weather spurred protesting feet, and in good time Paul was cheered by the sight of a wayside inn. He entered, to find two other guests already cozy at tea.

Close acquaintance made Paul sorry he had dropped in. Rash judgment is a wicked thing, but the rashness in this case, said Paul to himself, would be to suppose they were not thugs. And so, though sorely fatigued, he tarried for only the briefest sup. Once more in the clear, Paul trudged on to recapture the loneliness that now appeared a blessing. "Safe at last!" sang he, amid short but contented pants, as he looked back. Bliss fled in terror. There they were, not a hundred yards behind!

Paul started to run. The pursuers resented the implication and in no time at all overtook and seized him. The few appropriate remarks with which Paul rose to the occasion were interrupted by a blow on the head that completely stunned him. Sometime later he recovered sufficiently to be aware of their going through his clothes. "I'll pretend I'm dead," thought he, "and perhaps they'll let me be."

Vanity of vanities! Just then one of the thugs found Paul's penknife. "Very nice!" quoth he. "Just the thing to cut a throat!" The which he at once proceeded to do—his pal holding Paul.

Long ages later, Paul's spirit came back for the second time, but very feebly now. The world was dark. The bandits were gone. He was all alone, and he was dying! Sudden fear stirred Paul, against all his inclination to lie there in that frozen numbness, and it was the wholesome fear of dying without the Last Sacraments.

Every day for years and years, he had said a special three *Hail Marys* for the grace of a happy death. "Surely," he now told himself, "after all the years I've asked her for that, our Blessed Lady won't fail me. Surely she will keep me alive till I get to a priest!"

Desperately he struggled to his feet and staggered along, quite lost to all direction yet barely aware of the road. And as he went, Paul discovered why he was not yet dead. He couldn't turn his head. The whole front of his body was a solid mass of crimson ice, where the subzero air had frozen the blood pouring from his throat and had finally clotted the mortal hemorrage.

After a few yards, Paul was down again, so grievously had the loss of blood enfeebled him. Again the almost-irresistible temptation to humor the dying body and lie there at rest; again the resolve of the undying soul to try once more, "for the Blessed Mother always keeps her promises"; and so once again the tortuous rising.

How many times he repeated this process during that awful

journey, Paul has no clear recollection. He looks back upon it as an interminable hell. But there was promise of heaven at the end of it, so he kept doggedly on, refusing surrender; until at last, when the long litany of falls had drained the very last of his strength, came our Fair Lady to reward her gallant knight with the vision of a friendly light in a dwelling close at hand.

Paul stumbled towards it and managed to arouse the household. But when he tried to beg them for a priest, he found to his astonishment that he could utter no word at all—only a hiss through his severed windpipe.

However, the sole treasure the robbers had left him, his rosary, supplied, with gestures, to convey his need. The farmer understood, hurried off on his horse, and soon brought the Padre who lived but few miles beyond. And he brought a doctor as well, who stitched Paul's head back on again.

"So I didn't die," says Paul, "but I should have, only for my confidence in the Blessed Virgin. She will never fail to help," he adds, "provided we do our part, too!"

Paul is now retired, after being our catechist for many fruitful years. He is calmly awaiting the second coming of the Angel of Death, peacefully assured that this time, too, our Blessed Lady will vindicate his confidence.

CHRIST LOVETH ALL

What matter if the flesh be white,
  Or black or brown?
The dying Saviour wore for all
  The thorny crown:
What matter if the poor abode be in
  Far lands unblest?
The Heart of Jesus covers North,
  South, East, and West.

—MARY ALLEGRA GALLAGHER

THE DEATH MARCH

by *William R. Booth*

Father Booth was secretary to Bishop Patrick J. Byrne,
Papal Delegate in Korea, when the Reds overran Seoul.
This tragic story is excerpted from articles he wrote for
International News Service following his release.

I will never forget the day we met The Tiger.

You could tell he was tough by looking at him. And if you
looked closely at his eyes you could see a trace of madness there.
He was a North Korean major—a small, slim man about thirty-
five years old. He was bitter at the Americans who had thwarted
North Korean ambitions. The North Koreans had the war won
when the Americans intervened. Now the North Koreans in turn
had been thrown back and suffered a catastrophic defeat. The
Tiger could never forgive the Americans. He was insane with
rage and prepared to take out his fury on us.

"From now on you are in my charge," he roared when he had
lined us all up before him, "and under strict military discipline.
We are going to make a march to Chungan-jin. No one is to
fall out of line without my permission. If they do I will deal
severely with them."

That afternoon we started the march that was to become
known as the Death March. We only went a short distance out
of town when we camped for the night. Bishop Byrne lent his
blanket to Dr. Kristian Jensen, a Methodist missionary from New
Jersey, who had lost his own. Dr. Jensen was also having a great

deal of trouble with his feet, so Bishop Byrne borrowed a pair of socks from a soldier for him. Later he was to help Dr. Jensen many times on the march because this good man found it very difficult to walk after his many hard experiences.

Bishop Byrne and I shared my blanket. But the coldness of the ground and air gave us little sleep. The next day we started off in earnest. It was a pitiful sight. Everybody was sick and weak, and we had to drag ourselves along. I remember poor old Father Paul Villemot, 83 years old. He had gone through quite a bit to get this far. Now Monsignor Thomas Quinlan supported him on one side and two other French priests took turns on the other. The march was one continuous act of heroism on the part of everyone on it.

Not long after starting the march the second day a couple of exhausted American soldiers fell out of line. The Tiger was immediately incensed. He rushed back shouting that he would shoot five of the officers. Commissioner Lord, an Englishman in charge of the Salvation Army in Korea, was a heroic man and pleaded with The Tiger not to do this terrible thing.

"I have given an order, and it was not obeyed," screamed The Tiger. "Somebody will have to pay for it."

A Lieutenant Thornton stepped forward.

"I was in charge of the column," said the Lieutenant.

Actually he was not in charge, but he knew the rage of The Tiger and he took the responsibility.

The Tiger led Lieutenant Thornton up to a hilltop where we could all see what was about to happen. He tied the Lieutenant's hands behind his back and blindfolded him. Then The Tiger stepped back two paces, drew his revolver and fired point-blank. The Lieutenant died immediately, and all of us knew from that time on what kind of a man we had to deal with. Lieutenant Thornton deserves the Medal of Honor. He freely gave his life to save his brother officers.

The third day of the march was an unending purgatory. We had to make our way up to and across a mountain pass. The wind roared about us. Snow fell in thick squalls. The trail was a trail of blood. Many of the G.I.'s were barefooted, their shoes

having been taken shortly after their capture. Their feet were
bruised and bleeding. The Carmelite Sisters had bare feet and
little sandals, and it was not long before they too were leaving
a trail of blood on the frozen snowy earth.

That day agony snowballed. Everyone knew that to fall out
of line meant death, so neighbor helped neighbor. Two prisoners
would support a third, but finally they would become so weak
they would have to drop him and be supported in turn.

At five o'clock in the morning we began marching that day.
All we had been given to eat was some dried, powdered rice. Few
of us could get it down, so we had to march without food.

Twenty-one American soldiers fell out of line that day and
were shot. Sister Beatrice, the Superior of St. Paul Chartres convent in Seoul, dropped out and was shot. So was a White Russian woman. Someone would fall out of line, then we would
hear the explosion of a gun, and the guards would start laughing and joking. The body would be rolled off the side of the trail
and go bouncing into the ravine below. It was terrible.

Four nights we slept outdoors, although one night we were
herded into a school building. The room was crowded with
two hundred people, but The Tiger drove us civilians into
the room, then the diplomats, and finally about 600 G.I.'s.
We were packed in so tightly no one could move. No subway
crush was ever so bad. They tried to get another hundred soldiers
in but it was impossible, and they had to let them sleep outdoors.
We had to stand all night without being able to move a muscle.
You can imagine the agony that room contained all night when
you remember the terrible days we had been going through,
and the fact we were all suffering from diarrhea. Some soldiers
died that night standing up, and no one knew they were dead
until we were let out the next morning.

Many of us were now without blankets. Quite a few of the
soldiers had thrown away the cotton quilts that had been issued
to them because they became too heavy to be carried. This probably sounds strange but I can confirm it from my own experience.

I threw away my own blanket. I carried it as long as I could.
But mile after mile it became heavier and heavier on my back.

Finally, it became a matter of saving the blanket or myself. I threw it away. I knew that I ran a good chance of dying from cold during the night, but it was a question of immediate survival.

During the terrible eight days of the march 98 G.I.'s died. On two occasions when we stopped to eat Bishop Byrne gave general absolution to all the civilians and soldiers. No one knew who would be next.

During the latter half of the march I left the main body to travel with a newly created group of sick and wounded. The North Koreans wanted an interpreter and I volunteered, thinking that I could do something for the American boys.

Although this group was allowed to travel at a slower pace, the same rule applied that if anyone fell out he would be shot. We lost a number of boys this way. You can't imagine the state of mind we were in as we trudged along.

The guards kept snapping at us, "*Bali! Bali!* Quickly! Quickly!"

It was pitiful to see the attempts of these sick soldiers to keep going and thus remain alive. The guards kept us in a state of mental turmoil and physical exhaustion.

There was a boy from Texas, named Jimmy, in our group. And he had his birthday during the march. I asked him what he would like for his birthday.

"Peanuts," was the amazing reply.

I had a little money left of what had been given me, and I resolved that I would try to get some peanuts in the next village we passed through. When we did reach a village the guards hurried us through, and I was unable to get any. I have felt sorry ever since that I wasn't able to get Jimmy some peanuts for his birthday. But Jimmy did survive the march and was in good health the last time I saw him.

After eight days we reached Chungan-jin, far up the Yalu River, on the Manchurian-Korean border. Over a hundred people had died on the march. Yet its effects were not over. Many who had completely exhausted themselves on this march died shortly after reaching Chungan. Old Father Villemot, who never once complained under all the hardships, passed away in his sleep the next day. The next day the elder Father Gombert died. His 74 year old "little" brother Julien, gave him the last rites.

"I will soon be with you," Julien told his dying brother.

Just twenty-four hours later the younger brother died. These two brothers had spent the entire fifty years of their priesthood in Korea. They were buried side by side in a little ravine.

Sister Mary Clare, an English Anglican Sister, died the day she arrived. And it was here that my own superior, Bishop Byrne caught pneumonia. One more victim to The Tiger's insensate rage.

Bishop Patrick J. Byrne, a Maryknoll Missioner from Washington, D. C., could have escaped from Seoul before the Reds came. As diplomatic representative of the Vatican, he could have claimed diplomatic immunity and received better treatment than he did. But he chose to remain with the Korean people he loved, and when it came time to suffer he chose to remain with his priests.

"I consider it the greatest privilege of my life," he said shortly before his death, "to have suffered together with you."

That is what he said. But all of us felt that it was the other way around.

Bishop Byrne was the first priest to join Maryknoll, shortly after the Society was founded. He held many responsible jobs in the United States before being sent to Korea in 1923 to begin Maryknoll's work there. In 1935 when Maryknoll planned to open work in Japan, he was the man chosen to head up the new mission.

When war with Japan appeared imminent, Bishop Byrne resigned his post as head of the Kyoto territory in favor of a Japanese priest. He remained in Japan all during the war, and because of his extensive charitable activities was not interned. When the surrender was announced, he took to the Japanese radio to assure the people that the Americans would not harm them in any way. He was credited with much of the success of our peaceful occupation of that country.

General MacArthur said of him, "In the early days of the Japanese occupation when everything was in confusion, Bishop

Byrne was of great help to us. He was resourceful and courageous. He was looked up to by everybody."

In 1947 Bishop Byrne returned to the United States to lecture in defense of General MacArthur's policies which were then under attack. He returned to the Orient that same year, having been appointed first Apostolic Delegate to Korea. His first official act was to denounce the arrest and imprisonment of clergy by the Reds in North Korea. The Pyongyang radio frequently referred to him as "Number One Enemy" of the People's Republic. Bishop Byrne knew all this when he decided to remain in Seoul.

Despite his 62 years and frail constitution, Bishop Byrne bore up well under his sufferings. He was a tower of strength to those about him. He helped many on the Death March, despite his own weakness. He was continually giving words of encouragement and hope.

On the last day of the Death March, Bishop Byrne caught cold. This was not too serious and he might have easily thrown it off, if The Tiger had not ordered everyone out at seven o'clock in the morning in ten degree below freezing temperature to exercise. At The Tiger's orders he had to strip down to his shirt and do calisthenics.

When the exercise was over Bishop Byrne mentioned that he was very cold. Chungan is one of the coldest places in Korea, and the temperature drops as low as forty degrees below zero. Jumping around in shirt sleeves in this kind of weather is enough to freeze any man. The school building in which we were quartered was unheated, and the Bishop was cold all day. That night he developed pneumonia.

After some days in Chungan we were ordered to new quarters about four miles further away in a smaller village called Hajangri. The order to move was given in typical Communist fashion— suddenly and at midnight. Despite his pneumonia Bishop Byrne had to walk the distance with us, and when we arrived there, had to stand for an hour in the cold until the Reds cleared a house for us.

There was no organization. The Reds simply decided to move

us, and then after we had moved decided what to do with us. They evicted a Korean family and had us move in. This had already happened many times. Poor people driven from their homes in the dead of night with winter already upon them! No notice was given them, and they were only allowed to take a few personal possessions.

About 20 of us were herded into that house which was about ten by ten feet square. We made Bishop Byrne and Father Canavan, an Irish Columban priest also sick with pneumonia, as comfortable as we could. There was no room for all of us to lie down, so most of us had squat on our haunches all night. The house had one advantage in that it was heated by a Korean stove.

The next night about midnight three guards came to the door. They demanded that Bishop Byrne and Father Coyos, a French priest with tuberculosis, come out and be moved over to a building which had been set aside as a hospital but which we called "The Morgue," because that is what it was. We tried to stall them off, but they insisted that the move had to be made immediately.

Monsignor Quinlan and myself helped the two sick men over the snowy fields to The Morgue. The wind was blowing and it was freezing cold. When I saw the place I was saddened for the Bishop. There was only a little straw on the frozen dirt floor. The house had no heat. The walls did keep out the wind but the interior was as cold as a deep freeze. The house had no windows and so was perpetually dark. A straw mat served as a door.

The Morgue now held four sick people. Bishop Byrne, Fathers Coyos and Canavan, and an American mining engineer named Bill Evans. Bill was born in the Orient of American parents and had never seen the United States. He was now dying for a country he would probably never be able to see.

Miss Helen Rosser, a Methodist missionary from Georgia, was a trained nurse. She did yeoman work among the prisoners. Each day she made a thick bean soup which I carried over to The Morgue. This was the only medicine available for our sick. The Bishop was so weak by this time that I had to feed him. Day and night the sick lay there in the cold each wrapped in his one blanket. For four days Bishop Byrne lay there in a poverty that was like Bethlehem itself. Then he took a turn for the worse. Father Coyos gave the Bishop the last rites on November 24, and shortly after the Bishop passed into delirium. The next morning about nine o'clock Bishop Byrne died. When we went to bury him there was nothing left but skin and bones.

Monsignor Quinlan had his cassock on when he was arrested, and now he insisted that we bury the Bishop in the garment, a silk cassock with red piping. It was the only thing to remind anyone that the shrunken body belonged to a priest, and especially a Bishop.

We took the Bishop out in the fields, and with a pick and shovel hewed a grave out of the frozen ground. The earth was so hard that we were able only to get down about a foot. Here while the guard snarled, "Bali! Bali! Hurry! Hurry!" at us, we laid the Bishop to rest. We covered the grave with stones, and unknown to the guard arranged them in the form of a large cross. The burial party consisted of Bishop Cooper, an Anglican Bishop from England; Monsignor Quinlan; Father Crosby and myself.

Some day I hope to go back to that grave and give the Bishop more decent burial.

In the days that followed more of the party died. Father Canavan. Bill Evans, who asked me to take his last few possessions to his wife. Father Cadars, who died from blood poisoning from an untreated infection he received when he fell on the Death March. Larger and larger our little cemetery grew.

The G.I.'s were buried further away at the foot of the mountains. They were quartered in a little village some distance from us in houses from which the civilians had been evicted in order to make room for the prisoners. The soldiers were dying, sometimes ten a day. We would see their naked bodies carried out on a pole, strung up like a pig going to market. The bodies would be dumped in a snowbank because the ground was too hard to dig.

In the Spring we saw the crows come in flocks, and finish the job.

MY CHINESE PEOPLE

by Francis X. Ford

> When Bishop Ford had to choose an episcopal motto,
> his selection was the word "Condolere"—to suffer with.
> He wanted to identify himself as closely as possible with
> the Chinese in his care.

The Chinese make meals the chief events of the day and enjoy
them as occasions for family reunions. Even in the boarding
house that I am at present running for the students of the various
schools of the city, the kitchen is the focal point in the house.
I doubt whether anywhere outside of China two-score students
ever rally in the kitchen twice a day to give active aid in cooking
the food.

The cook's job appears to be starting the fire before the
students return from school. Once they have returned, the boys
take over in the kitchen—scrubbing pots, washing the rice, cutting
up the vegetables, fanning the three firepots to intense heat,
and scooping up water from the large urns that hold several
hundred gallons. But their main delight seems to be watching
the pots come to a boil.

An American cook might be driven out of her wits by a score
or more of hungry young men in her kitchen, and tempers might
boil faster than the pots. But in China all are good natured and
fond of joking, and they keep their ears and tongues active while

* From *A Stone in the King's Highway* by Raymond A. Lane. Copyright,
The Maryknoll Fathers.

doing the chores. Although only half a dozen can eat at a time or find elbow room at the stoves, the rest seem to enjoy the waiting. The secret lies in not considering it as waiting, but as part of the meal.

The students form a semi-circle around the fire and warm their hands while chatting over the news of the day. They step aside for the moment when a pot needs to be tended, and close in again automatically when the way is once more free. Chinese etiquette requires that meals be eaten in silence, so the time before and after eating is given over to conversation, and the actual eating is of very short duration.

Of course, these students are living as they would were they at home, and similar scenes take place at every fireside throughout the length and breadth of China. At first glance, it seems a disorganized way of preparing meals, ill-suited to Western life, but a moment's thought shows it as not only primitive and natural, but rational and Christian as well.

Right through the Middle Ages down to fairly modern times the huge hearth was the center of family living, with little distinction between dining and kitchen room. Servants and masters ate at the same board and together. In the farming class the world over, there is even today that camaraderie at table that the snobbishness of town life lacks.

If introduced into American life in the cities, the Chinese way might not only solve the "servant problem," but focus the entire household in saner relations. Incidentally, it might be an eye-opener to many a good housewife, showing her how her husband and sons relish preparing the meals themselves. It might also change the gentlemen's attitude from chronic grumbling at the slowness of dinner, since it would give them an insight into the drudgery of the kitchen when this involves isolation from the rest of the family. It would elevate the status of the cook to queen in her special realm, with subjects under her. Although such a system would be hard on the dish towels and crockery, it would make the kitchen more comfortably messy and attractive to menfolk.

In short, making the hearth once more the rallying spot of the family would change the average house from a lodging place, with hasty meals, to a united home. The boys would learn economy and sociology more vividly than when these subjects are taught in school. It might even be claimed that the quality of the meals would change, even if not for the better at first. The best chefs the world over are said to be men.

But the chief attraction of this mode of living is the sharing of enjoyment among all the household. There is no earthly reason why the preparing of food should be considered more burdensome than the eating of it. Nor should marketing to procure the food be considered a dull chore. Most of the enjoyment of a flank of venison is in the hunting of the deer; the successful landing of a wily pickerel is more sport than the bone-picking contest afterwards; and any man would prefer splitting his own logs and feeding his own fire to lighting a gas range.

Man is by nature the provider for the family, and he should be allowed to exercise his right. It is human nature to enjoy the fruit of one's own toil, and the disadvantage of imperfect results is offset by the personal touch of even clumsy efforts.

The curse of city life is its artificiality. Let a housewife resign herself to amateurish meddling, call in the boys of the family to knead the dough and pare the vegetables, gather the entire family in the kitchen to mix the batter and grease the pans, and the household will vote the supper one of the happiest they have enjoyed together. The Chinese have tried this way for centuries, and no other race enjoys meals more humanly than do these citizens of the Orient.

The difference between Western sincerity and Chinese is strikingly exemplified in that phrase, "Keeping up with the Joneses," which so often is the American standard.

In China, dress and house are not merely scaled to income, but are unimportant and no index of the owner's self-esteem or local standing. A few instances to illustrate this may be more striking than a long argument.

A clerk in the mayor's office dropped in today on business. He wore no overcoat although the rain was chilly; his feet were shod in sandals without stockings; his clothes were neat enough but faded by sun and rain; but the impressive fact was that he was unconscious of his appearance and entirely at ease.

Yesterday the principal of a high school called. He also was sockless; he wore the straw footgear, tied with cloth strings, that is common to farmers on these mountain roads. Both of these men would be classed among the notables of the city, but neither felt the need to dress better than his poorer neighbor.

A few doors distant lives a general. On duty he is resplendent in full-dress uniform and is squired by attendants, but at home he wears shorts as he putters, barefooted and mud-stained, in his vegetable patch, in full view of passers-by.

Perhaps the supreme test the world over would be the women-folk. In China, convention does not allow women even in the privacy of the home to be in informal lounging attire, but the wealthiest of Chinese women, as well as the poorer class, dress for comfort more than Westerners do. They wear garments of sturdy, durable stuff, and marketing with a basket is not dis-dained by anyone.

It is in the home life particularly that this sincerity is portrayed. It is not parsimony, or even rugged Spartan living. The Chinese have feasts, as other people have, and they enjoy them thor-oughly. But for feast or fast there is an absence of what, for lack of better term, might be called affectation or assumption of airs. There are frankness and simplicity, devoid of guile, in the genuine gusto of a feast, as well as forthright honesty in ordinary fare—such as the hearty meals of farms in Western countries.

Likewise, in the appointments of a Chinese house, honesty dominates the furnishings. In humbler homes, the unpainted wooden benches stand without apology, in company with cracked washbasin and earthen floor. In homes of better equipment, there is no reservation of "parlors" for formal occasion; the en-tire house is freely used by uninvited neighbors at any time of day, and the always-open door never discriminates against dress or social standing. It is presumed from experience that every-one knows and will practice the elementary rules of etiquette, in his own house or elsewhere; and even the beggar does not presume to intrude beyond the doorstep, no matter how open the door may be. The owner has neither anything to hide nor any pretense beyond the visible; he does not show off his house from vanity. Whatever beauty is present is for use by all.

Such hospitality would perhaps not be possible in Western homes, where many of the furnishings are fragile and easily broken by venturesome hands of children, or are of intricate and delicate material that soils in unwashed hands. Chinese children are much less restrained and even dirtier than Western children, but the treatment of a Chinese house, which builds its beauty into its walls or out of reach of urchins, prevents harmful use of the premises. The furniture is sturdy and solid; there is an absence of gimcrackery; and the result is soothing in its simplicity. In stores, too, there is a simplicity in salesmanship as regards the display, or lack of it, with no advertising. The cash-and-carry basis of sale, without charge accounts, also tends to make transactions commonplace.

Even in a Chinese theater, the audience is as enjoyable to an observer as is the play itself. Faces glisten and beam while friends are greeted; the mere settling into seats, the flurry of wraps, and the comments on the program are enjoyment enough, without orchestral prelude. The Chinese are honestly out to enjoy themselves.

This correspondence of heart and face is carried even into the public busses, with frank interest in fellow passengers and a good-natured tolerance of inconveniences that might easily cost the company a lawsuit in another land. China is probably the only country left in this world where pomp of state is refreshingly absent, where a man may lead his life unhampered by vitiated conventions. It is not that there are no standards, but that the supreme standard is sincerity.

THE GREAT BOLIVIAN
TRAIN WRECK

by John J. Lawler

Father Lawler was a professional newspaperman before
joining Maryknoll. His story of disaster in the Andes
shows the influence of a trained writer.

It was a cold, wintry night. The wind whistled down from its
Andean passes, chilling the warmer air of the Cochabamba
Valley. It was a good night to be in bed, warm under a thick
vicuña or alpaca blanket. Suddenly I became aware of a pounding at the front door.

Rubbing the sleep from my eyes, throwing my cassock on,
I stumbled in the darkness to the front of the house. Pedro,
one of our Catholic Action youths, stood there.

"Padre, something terrible has happened!" he shouted between gasps for breath. "The *fiesta* train went off the track! Many
people were hurt and they're being brought to Cochabamba
in a rescue train. You'd better come to the station."

"What time will the rescue train arrive, Pedro?"

"About one o'clock, Padre."

I told Pedro to go down to the station and tell the officials that
I would be there shortly. Then I returned to my room. My first
thought was to take the sacred oils, stole, and ritual. My second
was that I should need the truck, which was at the Maryknoll
Procure with Father Eugene Higgins.

I reached the Procure after a fifteen-minute run over the darkened roads of Cochabamba. I pounded on the door. After a few moments, which seemed like hours, Father Higgins appeared.

"What's the trouble?" he asked, when he saw my flushed face and heard me gasping for breath.

"There has been a train accident! The injured will be at the station in a half hour. I may need the truck to move the injured."

"I'll go down with you," he said.

In a few moments, we were bounding along in the battered, old mission truck. Our first stop was at the Public First-Aid Station. Cochabamba's whole medical corps, about fifteen doctors, was there. With them was Senor Gabino, head of the railroad. He told us details of the accident.

The train was returning to Cochabamba, crowded with men, women, and children who had gone on an annual pilgrimage to a shrine many miles away. The people were happy and carefree, for it was *fiesta* time. Besides, many of them were enjoying the only outing they could take each year.

As the train was making one of its steep mountainous descents near Araque, the engineer sensed that something was wrong. He stopped the train on the mountainside and stepped out of his cab to investigate. What he saw, froze him with horror. There was but one car attached to the engine—and there should have been six. The coupling between the first and second car had broken. Just then, careening down the mountain, around a curve, came the five cars that had broken away. The runaway coaches crashed into the stopped section.

No one knew yet, how many victims there were. The first group of injured had been taken to Punata, twenty-four miles away. A freight train had been sent out to bring the rest to Cochabamba.

As we started for the station, Father Higgins met one of the members of his newly organized Catholic Women's Club. He asked her to get as many women as she could and take them to the hospital to act as nurses, because there are no professional nurses in Cochabamba.

We arrived at the station just after one o'clock. A half hour later, the rescue train pulled in. Before the train stopped, Father Higgins and I jumped aboard the first car; Father Quiroga, a Bolivian priest, who had come along with us, climbed into the second.

Inside the car I was met with a scene of horror. Shrieks of pain pierced the air. Bodies of men, women, and children were strewn on the floor of the car. It didn't take long to discover that the living were interspersed with the dead.

I went down on one knee beside a woman who was bleeding from mouth and nose. I could feel the blood that covered the floor seeping through my cassock.

"Senora," I said, "I'm the Padre. Make an act of contrition while I give you absolution."

"Thank God! Thank God!" she moaned.

I moved on to the next—a girl about twelve years old, who was whimpering, "Mama, Mama."

I saw that her head was on the lap of an older woman. I bent over further. The mother was dead. I turned back to the girl.

"Padre, my feet!" she cried. "Oh, how my feet hurt!" I glanced down. Her legs were bloody stumps at the places where knees should have been. But there was no time for pity. From all sides came cries: "Padre, I'm dying! I want to confess."

The cold wind that whistled down from the Andes no longer chilled me. I was too numb from shock. I crawled over bruised and broken bodies, anointing and absolving.

Shortly after three in the morning, our work at the station was over. Then we rushed to the hospital. The doctors were working heroically under terrible conditions. The foyer leading into two small operating rooms had been filled with tables, upon which the injured were placed.

"Padre!" called one of the temporary nurses. She pointed to an Indian woman who had just died. "This woman gave birth to a boy about five minutes ago. Will you baptize the baby?"

As I poured the saving waters, there was a cry from the newborn child—a strange contrast in that room of the dying and the dead.

It was seven o'clock when we drove back to my parish. After Mass we returned to the hospital. By that time a count had been made of the casualties. Over three hundred people had perished in the wreck, a total greater than Scotland's Gretna Disaster, which took 227 lives and was the world's deadliest train wreck.

As far as I know, this story of Bolivia's disastrous train wreck was never published in any paper in the United States. Nor is it listed in any accident catalogue. But the Araque tragedy has a lasting memorial in the Cochabamba Valley. Time has fought a losing battle to erase from the minds of the people the ill-fated train ride of four years ago.

The authorities erected a huge cross at the scene, but that failed to satisfy the grieving families. The Indians banded together and approached the bishop with plans of their own. He was quick to give his blessing. For four years, the men spent their free hours fashioning adobe bricks and building walls.

When the work was completed, once again the Indians approached the bishop. The group asked that Padre Morales, a veteran Carmelite missioner, be sent down to open the new church with a mission. Over five hundred families crowded into the new church; every single one received Communion. Every hour on the hour the church bells tolled the sad rhythm of the requiem for the 320 people who had perished in the world's worst train wreck.

COMPENSATION

How dear is now to me that pagan horde,
  The object of thy burning love below!
If Jesus would but me that grace accord,
  Oh, thither with what ardor would I go!
Before Him space and distance fade away,
  This earth is but a plaything on the breeze;
My actions, my small sufferings today,
  May make my Jesus loved beyond the seas.

—SAINT THERESE OF LISIEUX

THE INDIAN AMBUSH

by Sister Blandina Segale

> A wagon train fashioned into a circular ambuscade, a war party of savage Kiowas, and an outbreak of cholera make up the highlights of this true-life story from a pioneer Sister of Charity.

In the fall of 1866, the beloved Bishop Lamy stopped at Mt. St. Vincent and pleaded for an addition to our Sisters already doing mission work in Santa Fe. He wanted to establish some industry by which the native girls might, in time, make a living for themselves. He strongly emphasized "Industry for the Native Girls." He was then on his way to France, where he hoped to find recruits from the seminaries and financial aid from friends. He returned in the spring of 1867 with a reinforcement to help him carry out plans approved by the Holy See for the betterment of the inhabitants of his vast diocese. Twenty-six souls accompanied him.

Rt. Rev. Bishop Lamy wrote from France to have the Sisters meet him in St. Louis. Three Loretto Sisters and our two Sisters proceeded in company with the Rt. Rev. Bishop Lamy and his twenty-six recruits to Leavenworth, Kansas. In Leavenworth, the Rt. Rev. Bishop manned a caravan of about one hundred covered wagons and started on his famous journey on the Santa Fe Trail on the 14th of June. On the 18th, the caravan reached St. Mary's of the Potawatomis. The Jesuit Fathers and students came

* From *At the End of the Santa Fe Trail.* Copyright, Bruce Publishing Co.

several miles to meet the travelers. Sunday was spent at St. Mary's, from which the caravan left June 24th.

On the 29th, the Feast of St. Peter and St. Paul, the caravan camped a few miles from Junction City. At noon four Indians visited the camp. This did not portend any good. After a consultation with some of the experienced drivers, the Bishop gave orders to return to Leavenworth at which place all the mules attached to the caravan were sold and replaced by oxen, as having more endurance.

From Leavenworth the Bishop ordered a detour from the Santa Fe Trail. The Kiowas—the most rapacious Indian tribe of the plains—had sent scouts to visit our travelers when camping near Junction City. The Bishop who understood Indian tactics and Indian warfare, changed the animals and the route, in hopes that the Kiowas would be thrown off the scent. The caravan continued its slow travel until the latter part of July. The eagle eye of the Bishop was constantly on the watch for any sign which might indicate the near approach of Indians. The Comanches and Apaches had also free scope on the plains, but the Kiowas were feared the most. When victorious in their attack on white men, they were most ferocious. The men were first scalped, then killed, the children were also killed; the women were made prisoners—a fate far worse than death.

On the 30th day of July, without any apparent reason the Bishop ordered a corral to be made. Every wagon in the caravan was arranged to form a circle; the oxen were driven inside the circle. The travelers and teamsters ran inside the circle none too soon, for the Kiowas' death whoop preceded the sling of hundreds of arrows which fell harmlessly for some time. This kept up until sunset, when the Indians retired. The order from inside the circle was: "Be on the alert, hands on guns, no fires to be lighted."

The day's travel had been arduous for want of water. All were suffering from thirst, and, though the water of a river could be seen distinctly not more than a few rods from their improvised corral, to attempt to satisfy their thirst, or to water the oxen, would be certain destruction to all. The Sisters prayed their beads and the men kept a vigilant watch, not to be surprised by a night attack from the fierce Kiowas. At daybreak it was discovered that cholera had broken out in the caravan! Soon after the Indians renewed their attack! Word was circulated that one of the Sisters of Loretto had the cholera! Whether it was cholera or fright the victim gave up her soul to God. Meanwhile, the Indians flung their arrows in quick succession. The travelers were well protected by the circle of wagons, from which vantage ground their guns carried death to some of the attacking Indians.

Some kind-hearted messenger came to Sister Augustine and said: "A young man under a wagon on the opposite side of the circle has the cholera and is pitifully calling for his mother." The words were scarcely uttered when Sister Augustine said, "I'll go at once to render what help I can."

Sister Augustine crawled under from one wagon to the next, while arrows were thickly showering above her, and some arrows fell near her, but lost their force by striking either wagon hub or cogs. When speaking of this to me, she said, "I could only compare the flying arrows around me to a disturbed beehive." Sister Augustine reached the dying young man and tried to soothe his last moments as his mother would have done. So he and the dear Sister of Loretto were buried, strangers in every way. Months afterwards, all efforts to find their resting place were unavailing.

Meanwhile, the Indians continued the aggressive fight. The weather was intensely warm, all needed water. The Indians had the advantage. The cholera was doing its work, but no more victims succumbed to death.

It is said that one of the leaders of the party called a few of the men with well balanced minds and gave them his orders: "If the Indians continue the attack for twenty-four hours we are doomed. Make no mistakes in the directions I now give you, but let no man act until I give the order. When I see death is inevitable for us, I will give the signal. Then you, Mr.—— shoot Sister Louise, you, Mr.—— shoot the elder of the Loretto Sisters, and you Mr.—— shoot the younger Sister of Loretto. I will shoot Sister Augustine."

Some people, many hundred miles away, asserted the man

could not morally give such an order. This is true, but knowing the treatment of women prisoners in the Kiowa tribe, I would have prefered to have been shot rather than to have been made a prisoner.

The sun was declining. The Kiowas disappeared. The leader of the party asked: "Are any of you men willing to practice strategy by wading the stream and landing some boxes of provisions and a barrel of liquor on the other side of the stream? Apparently, it is taking your life in your own hands, although I see no danger. My only regret is to use such means to save ourselves." The freight was safely landed on the other side of the stream. As the sun disappeared, the freighters discontinued their work.

The Indians fell into the trap. They suddenly appeared from nowhere and rushed for the barrel of whiskey. They soon chopped off the top of the barrel with a tomahawk, and each, with scooped hands eagerly drank the liquor.

Word was quietly passed to "Start fires an hour later." By this time the Indians had their fill and were dropping off in a dead sleep. Our travelers, like the Arabs, "Stole silently away." The caravan was safe and on its way to Santa Fe. The men and large boys of Santa Fe and surrounding villages formed a cavalcade and met their beloved Bishop about fifteen miles from Santa Fe and escorted him to his adobe cathedral. Meanwhile the Sisters, priests and seminarians arrived in Santa Fe and all proceeded to the cathedral, the *Te Deum* was sung, with what heartfelt gratitude you may imagine. This was the 15th of August. Since our Sisters left Mt. St. Vincent on May 10th, it is evident it took them three months and five days to reach their destination.

PORTRAITS FOR THE FUTURE

by James A. Michener

The author of *South Pacific* gives his recipe for winning the friendship of the people of Asia, with particular emphasis on India where century-old mysticism clashes with today's technology.

The leading resource of Asia, as of all lands, is its people. In the last war when the United States needed bomber bases in China crowds of Chinese peasants lugged wicker baskets filled with rocks and built fields by hand. When Japan decided to make its overnight leap from medieval feudalism to modern nationalism her amazingly skilful people applied their energies and in a brief period of time accomplished the miracle. And when Indonesia determined to be free, from a nation that had been kept in illiteracy sprang men and women capable of establishing a workable government for the sixth largest nation on earth.

But nowhere in Asia are people more important than in India, for here at the traditional crossroads of Asia stands the keystone of the East. India is one of the oldest continuing nations on earth; during long periods it was one of the most highly civilized; it has miraculously preserved the oldest successful religion still being practiced; and it shows every sign of still being able to weather the storms of history.

India is a poetic nation, yet it demands new electrical plants.

It is a mystical nation, yet it wants new roads. It is traditionally a peaceful nation, yet it could, if misled, inflame Asia. It is a nation which has known many conquerors, yet it always clings close to its own soil and in time sees the conquerors vanish. Indians are a cohesive people, yet even after the partition of Pakistan they include many minorities, no common language save English, and numerous divisive forces. Above all, Indians are awakening to the full meaning of both nationalism and social progress at one breathless moment, and their capacity to ignore temporary inconvenience and staggering disaster is enormous.

It would be a great tragedy if America were alienated from this grand reservoir of strength. We have only 151,000,000 people—multiplied in world import by our coefficients of universal education, mechanical skill, and democratic procedure—but India has more than 345,000,000, and when they have created their coefficients of education, good government, and production their force will be immense. America would be very foolish indeed if she permitted either her own petulance or Indian arrogance to separate this vast and surging population from its normal friendship with us.

In the five truncated conversations that follow, various Indians report upon the ideas current in their land today. Although they happen to be Indians they speak for most of Asia, for they represent the kinds of people that comprise the continent. It is essential that we understand them.

Dev Kanta Borooah

He was a brilliant member of Parliament, one of the most persuasive and exciting talkers I've ever heard. He exploded with ideas, bubbled over with energy, and knew a great deal about America. He was a young man with a sense of humor and a determination to see India firmly established.

"I've been in politics for twenty years, because I first went to jail in 1930. Been in prison four times so I understand politics pretty well. Haven't the slightest grudge against the British. Nobody in India hates Britain any more. I never forget they threw me in jail four times but I also never forget they built twenty universities. And organized a decent legal system. And gave us an ideal of how an honest government should be run.

"Then why did we throw them out? Their time was up. Let me explain what I mean. I remember one afternoon when all India agreed that if Britain didn't get out we'd assassinate them all, Lord Mountbatten first. The next day Lord Mountbatten turned the Government over to us. At five-thirty that day we had what we wanted, the right to nominate of our own free will a Governor-General of our own choice. Whom did we nominate? Lord Mountbatten, of course."

Like every responsible man in Asia, Mr. Borooah says, "Oh, if we only have ten years of peace! We do not want war. We do not want to enlarge ourselves or puff ourselves up. We want time to put India on a sound footing. We face enormous problems.

"What are they? First, we must create an adequate food supply. Everything is secondary to that. Second, we must manufacture more things for our people to use. Third, we need lakhs of schools—a lakh is 100,000—for our illiteracy is disgraceful. Fourth, we must battle poverty. Fifth, we must lower the price scale, for we are on the brink of inflation. Sixth, we must continue to break down the caste system. I myself married outside of caste. So did Nehru's daughter. And seventh, we must improve the national health, for our life expectancy is only twenty-six years. Think of that."

Mr. Borooah actually seems impatient to begin his work upon the great tasks that face India. He repeatedly refers to Gandhi and says, "Never underestimate that saintly man. He kindled in us all that was best. He tried to remove all that was worst. I would feel safe if he were living, but we do try to keep his spirit alive. That's why we'll solve our problems."

Mrs. Renuka Ray

One of the people who is working hardest to build a consolidated and modern India is the gracious and powerful housewife who sits in Parliament as the champion of women's rights. She looks nothing at all like an amazon, for she is most attractive and always willing to let the other fellow make his arguments . . . providing she is free to come back and annihilate them.

She says, "I started this fight for women's freedom back in 1927 when I was in college. Since then I've heard every lame old argument put forth by the orthodox Hindu men. They cry, 'Indian womanhood is sacred!' They protest that if these sacred women are given any rights the great mystical life of India will be destroyed. But it all comes down to their not wanting to surrender any of their own privileges.

"These old men cry, 'It's sacrilege to change old customs.' But there used to be a custom in Malabar whereby all land and wealth were vested in women. Believe me, the men changed that law fast enough when they got the chance. And none of them wept about the sacred old customs."

Mrs. Ray has on her side all the enlightened women of India and most of the educated men. She has against her the orthodox Hindu men and about 95 per cent of the women of India, for they cannot read or write.

Socially Mrs. Ray's bill is in no way revolutionary. It forbids a man to have more than one wife. It permits divorce somewhat more sparingly than European countries now permit it. But it does revolutionize Indian life because it permits daughters to share in their father's wealth.

"The old men weep that if our bill passes the farm lands of India will be cut into even smaller parcels. That is a problem about which every Indian should worry, because in a recent survey one region showed 15 per cent of farms supporting an entire family had less than a quarter of an acre each. But the evil will not be removed by keeping women in bondage. What must be done is to work out a better farming system and a better system of freedoms for women. We must ask which is more important: Old land systems that lead to starvation or new systems which will permit land and human beings alike to be free?"

Mrs. Ray is only one thoughtful Indian among thousands who are attacking old problems with fresh vigor. Intelligent, witty, and determined, she is aware that filibusters in Parliament, prejudice outside, and the dead hand of custom are all against her.

Sohan Lal

I am always amazed when my friends ask me, "How did you manage to get along in India? You don't speak their language? Isn't it a dreadful experience?"

At such times I wish I could whisk them to Delhi to spend an evening with my friend Sohan Lal. He's an amazing fellow of forty-four, a brilliant, darting, handsome hummingbird of a man. He stands five-feet one, moves with compulsive energy, and bursts into loud guffaws of laughter.

There for a time he didn't have much to laugh about, for he lived in Lahore, a Hindu on the wrong side of the India-Pakistan border. He lost everything: houses, factories, businesses, even a college in which he was a lay adviser. He fled Lahore and started all over again in Delhi.

"I never worry about it," he laughs. "There's enough work for everyone in Delhi." He runs a printing press and has just issued a vigorous pamphlet at his own expense advising the Government what it ought to do on several important points. "I just decided someone ought to call them to task. I don't suppose I'll sell a dozen, but I'm seeing to it that everyone who should listen gets a copy."

Sohan Lal speaks perfect English, like every educated Indian. It is impossible to go anywhere in India—or, indeed, in most of Asia—without finding someone who speaks English. Of course, Lal sometimes gets so excited that his words seem to tumble out.

Running up to you he thrusts a silver tray at you containing a biting sauce and a towering mound of little brown meat balls. With a swoosh he dips one into the sauce and pops it into your mouth. "Chicken kebabs!" he cries. Then he presses more upon you and laughs, "I always eat eight or nine!"

Then, suddenly, he says, "I've been to America several times." His voice drops, and you realize he has stopped clowning. There is much about America that he did not especially like, but to-night he says, "It's a fairyland. Even the magic lamp of Aladdin could not reproduce the wonders of America. Whenever I am in America I look at your healthy people, your comforts. I want India to be like that."

To be with Sohan Lal is a rare privilege. You find that he is very well informed on a multitude of questions, that he knows better than you what grave problems face India, and that in his own one-man way he is doing something about them. He has helped start schools. He has pioneered in better business practices. And he sends pamphlets to the Government. There are thousands of Indians like Sohan Lal. They are among the most gracious human beings on earth. Fortunately, they understand the West, and it is upon their fundamentally sound friendship that we must rely.

Ram

Men like Sohan Lal and women like Mrs. Ray represent the few. Ram is the many. I met him at a waterhole one afternoon as he took time off from his farming to talk with me. He spoke not a single word of English, had never traveled more than ten miles from his village, rarely had enough to eat and was perpetually in debt.

He scratched his thin nose and said, "My money goes to the zamindar and the baniya."

These were new words to me but he explained them, and if America guesses wrong about these two words we shall meet with tragedy in Asia.

"The zamindar," Ram explained, "owns the land. I pay him taxes. There are many kinds of taxes. Regular taxes. And wedding taxes."

"What are they?" I asked.

"If the zamindar's daughter gets married he gives a big feast. This takes money, so he comes to his tenants and collects a wedding tax. Then there is the automobile tax."

"Have you an automobile?"

"Heavens, no! But the zamindar does."

"So you pay for it?"

"Yes."

"Are such taxes approved by the government?"

"Who knows? All I know is that I have to pay them."

The zamindar is one of the curious mistakes of history. When the British invaded India they had to find some way of making local populations pay just taxes for support of the new government. The temporary expedient was adopted of farming out the taxes to intermediary zamindars who had been doing this job for the Muslim predecessors of the British. Year by year the expedient was extended—always as a temporary measure—until Lord Cornwallis, fresh from Yorktown, decided that the simplest way to settle the whole question was to confirm the zamindars as actual owners of the land. Reasoned Cornwallis, "In case of foreign invasion, it is a matter of the last importance, considering the means by which to keep possession of India, that the proprietors of the lands should be attached to us from motives of self-interest. A landholder who is secured in the quiet enjoyment of a profitable estate could have no conceivable motive for wishing a change."

Today India is trying to buy off its zamindars, just as Rumania, Mexico, and Ireland had to get rid of their absentee and worthless landlords. Wise and just laws have been passed in state legislatures, but so far nothing has happened, for the courts have forestalled expropriation. But if the zamindars and their dead hold on the land are not removed India will go Communist. When Nehru's government passes the necessary federal legislation to end this anachronism—introduced originally by non-Indians—there will be cries in India and no doubt in America of Socialism. But if Nehru doesn't get his laws through in a hurry, if land reforms are not made soon, there will be no need of cries either in India or America. India will have gone Communist.

Ram continues. "To pay the zamindar's taxes is difficult, so I borrow money from the baniya."

"What is a baniya?" I ask.

"A fat man with money. He lends me money whenever I need it."

"Do you pay it back?"

Ram laughs happily. "Pay it back? No! Who would pay it back?"

"You mean he gives you the money?"

This time Ram shouts and tells the neighbors of my question. "The baniya give anyone anything? Oh, no! I pay him interest each month."

We do some figuring and find that Ram pays about 28 per cent interest each year. He is lucky. Many baniyas charge well over 36 per cent. Year after year Ram pays this charge, never escaping his debt, never lowering it.

"Why do you keep borrowing money? This looks like good land."

"Ah, but there are the weddings of my children. And the deaths. And other little things."

Crushed between the zamindar and the baniya, Ram lives out his life. These two fundamental wrongs of village life—and more than 85 per cent of Indians live in small villages—keep rural life unprogressive, unproductive, and economically hopeless. Something has got to be done to eliminate the zamindar and the baniya. And it must be done soon, for Russia keeps telling peasants like Ram that she has a surefire, ready made way to solve these problems. That is why I say that if America guesses wrong about these two words we may well lose India as we lost China.

M. B. Singh

If you want to meet a man who is doing something about the pitiful land system—a man who makes you feel that India has a chance, go out to the dry plains west of Delhi and meet M. B. Singh.

He's a big, bald-headed, happy-go-lucky farmer of forty-five. He's in charge of a government experiment station, and his pregnant experiment consists of having talked 18,000 villagers into combining their meager plots of land into one big farm.

"This is not a collective farm," Singh says promptly. "If anyone living in the area doesn't want to join our programs, he doesn't have to. But when he sees the men around him making money he joins up. I have great respect for the Indian peasant. I ought to, because I'm one myself. Like them I have too many children. Eight."

What revolutionary ideas does Singh have? None. His ideas go back almost to Biblical times. "Look at this plough," he says. "This is the most important thing I've accomplished on the farm. A long section of tree trunk is pierced for yoking oxen. At the other end a simple crossbeam has been lashed. We have no nails. To the crossbeam we attach this tiny steel plough. Total cost $2.10, and it's made our fields wonderfully productive.

"What was my next big idea? Putting fish in the water ponds. We found a hard-flesh carp and from one acre of water get $86 worth of fish. And our diet is improved.

"My next introduction was a new wheat that's been developed up north. Yields 60 per cent more to the acre."

In some ways, however, it is the milk shed that merits first attention. Mr. Singh says he would like me to see this, because it has made the biggest difference in the community.

To reach it we pass through the village walls, and there in a tragic, filthy community we see the untouchables. In huts that almost collapse from the wind swarm the Harijans, as Gandhi named them: the children of God.

Not fifty yards away we come upon the milk shed. It's spotless. "We built it and said we'd buy milk at a premium from anyone who brought his cows here to be milked. The farmers laughed and said why would anyone pay more for milk just because the cow stood in a clean shed. But one man brought his cows, nevertheless, and he did get more for his milk. Now trade is brisk."

"Who keeps the shed immaculate?" I asked.

"Those untouchables. Those filthy, poor, bedeviled people. I can't make them keep themselves clean yet. Perhaps later . . ."

He knows what he is doing. He says, "In these fields you can see India choosing her future. Our village plots have grown so small that they must be combined. Either it will be done co-operatively in this pattern or by force in the Russian way."

The People of America and India

In the immediate future everyone interested in America-Indian friendship must work hard to help these two nations over certain obvious stumbling blocks. Relations may become quite strained, but that is the precise time when we must be most careful to preserve the basic understanding between the American and Indian people. To lose such understanding will be to lose India; losing India means losing Asia; and losing Asia means the creation of an Asia-Europe-Africa coalition encircling the United States and condemning us to such internal pressures that we should probably explode.

The danger spots are these. (1) The logic of Pakistan's claim for Kashmir is so apparent that in supporting that claim against India we could easily become involved in a war of recrimination far more serious than the Kashmir problem warrants. We must not disqualify ourselves in all of Asia simply because we agree with Pakistan on one immediate problem. It is entirely possible that within five years we shall side with India in some claim against Pakistan. We must foreswear the luxury of calling any nation all black or all white.

(2) Our decisions in Asia, made in the furtherance of our protection or national interest—and at the same time perhaps for the maximum good of Asians, too—may run head on into India's decisions on the same problems. This could happen, for example, over the question of seating Red China in the United Nations. When it happens let us remember with the severest intellectual restraint that we are against India's behavior on one problem, that India is against our behavior on one problem, and that when that problem has become ancient history the people of India and the people of America must still remain friends.

(3) It is quite likely that on several points India will vote against us in the United Nations. If this happens shortly after our delivery of wheat there will be a natural condemnation throughout America. But this should not be allowed to crystallize into a long-lasting enmity. That would be stupidity and folly both. We cannot buy India's votes with a few million tons of wheat and we should have no bargain if we did find a country whose honor was for sale so cheaply.

(4) Certain Indians, having won maturity through battling the British, now feel that to maintain their integrity they must

lambaste the United States. Thus we inherit enmities that do not belong to us. Let's not take this too seriously. An Indian newspaperman told me, "Forget the stories you see in our papers. When a nation is number one it's got to get the brickbats. But that very fact proves that we know you're worth it."

(5) As Asian nations—India in particular—attain maturity they are going to ask increasingly embarrassing questions about America's handling of minority groups like the Negro. This is going to infuriate many Americans, but this happens to be a question in which all the colored peoples of the world are interested. Some decades ago the white people united in condemning India for burning widows alive on their husbands' funeral pyres. Quite properly and with no loss of dignity India had to bow to world public opinion. From today on world public opinion, especially Asian opinion, is going to be against certain American practices. Is there any informed American who resents this?

Most educated Indians know that America is essentially their friend. We must retain this friendship with India—as with all the peoples of Asia including the Chinese—for India and Asia are going to be swept by great political movements based on the people, and if we have lost contact with them we could well be engulfed.

PICK-A-BACK RIDE

A university student in desperate straits financially entered our downtown church the other evening, bent on robbery. But he did not count on Father Steinbach. Father ended by giving him cigarettes and a streetcar fare. On the way out the student met an old lady driven in by the heavy rain and offered to carry her home on his back. The old lady returned next day to thank the padre for sending her the nice young man!   —CLEMENT HANSAN

PEARL IN PLEDGE

by Francis Herlihy

> Father Herlihy is a Columban missioner. The following
> account tells of a visit to his confreres in the Philippines,
> one of the prime fields for the fine Columban missionary
> endeavors.

Although the Pacific washes their eastern shores, it is not to
Oceania but to Asia that the Philippines belong. For their lush
green vegetation, fertile soil and breathtaking beauty, these
islands have been titled "Pearl of the Orient." If accuracy were
preferred to euphony, they might be more fitly compared to the
emerald, but that is a detail.

The whole group contains more than three thousand inhabited
islands. Luzon, in the north, has an area of 41,000 square miles,
Mindanao in the south, 36,000. Nine or ten more islands vary in
extent from 1,000 to 10,000 square miles. The population of the
entire archipelago is estimated at sixteen millions.

More priceless than any pearl must the sight of these shores
have seemed to a party of weary sailors in four limping little
ships which came up over the eastern horizon on March 16, 1521,
and groped gingerly through the strait of Suribao, just north of
Mindanao to drop anchor off Cebu. Ferdinand Magellan, although Portuguese, flew the imperial standard of Spain on his

* From *Now Welcome Summer.* Copyright, Clonmore and Reynolds, Ltd.,
Dublin.

ship, the Trinidad. For the first time in the history of ships he had reached the meridian of the Spice Islands, westward. It was sixteen months since he had left Spain to attempt this task with a fleet of five ships in his command. Two of these were of 130 tons, two of 90 and one of 60 tons.

They were well received by the chief and people of Cebu, which is in the inner and lower part of the island group. Six weeks later, Magellan crossed to the neighbouring island of Mactan to claim it for his royal master. There he met his death from the poisoned arrows of the natives. Only one of the ships completed the voyage back to Spain, taking from the Moluccas twenty-six tons of cloves, which amply paid the expenses of this first circumnavigation of the globe.

Many years were to pass before Spain could take hold of the rich fruits of Magellan's voyage. Several expeditions failed in the attempt. In 1564, Miguel Lopez de Legaspi sailed from Mexico and the following year landed at Cebu. Without having to resort to violence he induced the inhabitants to submit to Spanish rule. With him there landed a party of Augustinian friars who then began the work of making the islands Christian.

Seven years later the Spanish colonists went north to Luzon where Legaspi founded the city of Manila. The city was to have a troubled history. Twice it was destroyed by earthquakes. It was sacked, in 1762, by the British who held it for two years. It was the scene of serious revolts of the Filipinos against Spanish rule in 1872 and again in 1896. On the latter occasion it is said that 30,000 Filipinos lost their lives.

Spanish sovereignty came to an end in the islands in 1898. In April of that year the ships of Spain were destroyed in Manila Bay by an American squadron under Admiral Dewey. The city, held by a Spanish garrison against the revolutionists, was captured four months later by American troops.

One result of the passing of Spain from the Philippines was the expulsion from these islands of the men who had made the Filipinos the only Christian nation of the East. Between 1896 and 1899, more than a thousand friars and other religious left or were expelled as a result of the prevailing hatred of everything Spanish.

The friars left, and have not been replaced. Today their memory only remains: the churches which they built, the conventos in which they lived, the schools they established in every Christian village. Earthquakes have toppled some of their church towers, grass and mosses grow in crevice and embrasure; roofs left long untended are open to the sky. The Pearl of the Orient which these *conquistadores* won by toil and sacrifice for Christ is slipping back into the grip of ignorance and superstition.

To land in Manila was to find yourself in a melange to which all corners of the world, it seemed, had given an ingredient. The Orient was here, of course; but not the Orient of hardy Mongols, of tiled, upcurving roofs and temples of stone idols that men try to appease, that they may survive the elements. This is the Orient of the Malays, where Nature has been prodigal with gifts, where heathens worship her in birds and trees and fishes, and her spoiled children need no more shelter than that of the nipa palm.

Europe was here; for everywhere was the handmark of Old Spain: in the facades of baroque churches of Intramuros, in the names of men and places, in women's modest dress and graceful bearing, in mantillas, combs and fans.

And America was here, in marks of modern progress, department stores and frigidaires, radios and boulevards; the huge pier was "the largest in the Orient."

"Put that pen in your inside pocket, Father!" was the parting advice of my friend, the purser. "These birds here can take your photograph without a camera!"

I greeted Father Strong in a manner befitting the occasion. He piloted me to a customs officer, bypassing a lot of people who wanted to be helpful, stored my baggage to await the boat for Kobe, and ushered me finally into a tiny taxi with an open, white-covered seat, upon which I thankfully subsided, mopping my face.

"I heard someone say," I remarked, "it was winter here. What other seasons have you got?"

"There's the hot one," said Father Strong, "and the hot, wet one."

"I am both hot and wet now," I said.

"No doubt!" he chuckled. "But you're out of season. And training," he added judicially.

We were spinning through the Luneta, the great park on the sea-front, with glorious memories of the Eucharistic Congress held here. Making a detour for my benefit, the car turned into the narrow streets of Intramuros where denser throngs and vehicles of many kinds reduced its progress to irregular spurts. Taxis, kindred to our own, honked immoderately. Calesas, two-wheeled pony-carts shaded by large hoods, rattled in and out between slow-moving low drays, pulled by plodding carabao. Long, sleek automobiles waited petulantly for openings in the traffic.

The people, who rambled across the busy streets at will, provided still more variety and novelty. The Filipinos include several distinct races in which are divers tribes and tongues. Pygmy Negritos still wander wild in the forests of Northern Luzon. In the mountain districts, Igorotes, Ifugaos, and others have only slowly relinquished the ancient sport of hunting heads. Such as these do not frequent Manila's streets, but there was a wide assortment of other types: dark and sunburned peons in wide straw hats and *barong Tagalog*—a light jacket, loose at the waist. Sometimes the *barong* is an ordinary shirt, and hangs in artless simplicity down its owner's back. Women in graceful Filipino dress, with wide, stiffened shoulder-pieces and long wide skirt. Lithe young dandies in immaculate white. Immigrants from adjacent countries, Malayans, Chinese, Indo-Chinese, Japanese; and cultured Senors of Manila, possessed of automobiles, university degrees and sumptuous villas.

The *Convento de Nuestra Senora de los Remedios,* headquarters of my confreres in the Philippines, stood beside the grey and battlescarred church of that name in the suburb of Malate. On the hoary facade of the church I saw dinges, made, I learned, by English cannon-balls in 1762.

I spent a very pleasant day there. Some of the priests I had known already, the others I knew, almost as well, by repute. Father Heneghan, the Superior, is still remembered in Ireland as the man beloved by tinkers and the old ladies they call "Shawleens." Father Pat Kelly, the parish priest of Malate, has left a trail of chuckles over a good part of the globe. His huge physique was not made for the tropics, but he was happy here as everywhere else he had been. He advocated that every new arrival in the Philippines should get hit on the head as he came down the gangway, and be thereby adjusted to the Philippine outlook. But he was too big-hearted to make a cynic.

Today, the church and convento of *Nuestra Senora de los Remedios* are piles of war rubble. Father Heneghan and Father Kelly are dead, and where they lie is known to their slayers only and to God. The two other priests I met that day are also dead; one of them has a shallow grave beside Our Lady's grotto in the grounds.

In the cool evening I set out with Father Strong for his parish, Binangonan, twenty miles away in the province of Rizal.

Travel between Filipino towns is a matter of climbing onto a bus, or rather a truck, with straight wooden seats placed closely behind one another, and holding on tightly while it lurches along a narrow winding road. Wedged beside you is a nondescript individual caressing a fightingcock, or a woman nursing a baby, or an old dame puffing at a rank cigar.

The priests in this and in the other towns that I saw—for they handed me along the line—had been my contemporaries in college a few years before. We were little more than boys then—or so we felt. Now each of them had sole charge of parishes with twelve, fifteen or eighteen thousand baptized Catholics. I know many whole dioceses of fewer souls. Statistics I had read had not given me such food for thought as this journey through village after village of friendly, light-brown, civilized people with baptismal names and little, if any, further evidence of the Faith that is their heritage.

Each town had its spacious, age-old church, its huge and crumbling stone convento, with a couple of rooms made habitable for the priest and his "boy." Efforts had been made, one could see, to restore a little beauty to faded sanctuaries, but years of neglect had left indelible marks.

A little church of rough timber, a tiny oasis in some desert of paganism, would be a cheering thing; at least an achievement against odds, a portent of greater things to come. These great empty vaults were saddening reminders merely of an olden glory that has faded; of Faith once throbbing with life and clothed in beauty, now barely saved from the dank fingers of decay.

What a charge my comrades had! Theirs the task of restoring that life; of fanning into flame again this spark that flickers only feebly now amid the dying embers.

"Where do you begin?" I said to one of them. We stood beneath the bells in the tower of his church. At our feet lay the straggling town, white stone and stucco shops and houses and closely packed *nipa* huts. Far away over ricefields, coconut and papaya groves, he pointed out the villages—they call them barrios —which composed his district.

"How can one man cover instructions, baptisms, mission-stations, sick-calls in all those?"

"You can't cover them," he said quietly. "You do your best, and it's mighty little."

I followed the white-cassocked figure of my host as he lowered himself through the manhole in the floor. The successive wooden landings or stagings in the tower were connected by ladders.

"Now, take it easy on these boards," he warned me, "the white ants have a way of eating the insides out of them."

It was a year after this that the next person ascended the belfry, a young priest just arrived from the United States who had been appointed here as an assistant. Being something of a carpenter, he climbed the tower to overhaul the flooring. The white ants had been busy in the meantime; one of the upper stagings gave way beneath his feet and he crashed down the tower to his death.

An army chaplain of Fort McKinley on departing for the States had presented Father Douglas with his car. It was some years beyond its prime, but it was very useful at times. On this occa-sion it was the means of gathering my three fellow-countrymen, Fathers Douglas, Price, and Strong, at the ancient abode of Father Hugh O'Reilly in Morong where I was now staying.

The feast that marked the event was not an elaborate affair, but I realized that it included several items brought from Manila in my honour, such as fresh meat, butter, and baker's bread. The tit-bits of the banquet as far as I was concerned were the commonplace products of the neighbourhood—papayas, fresh-cut bananas, good coffee and marvellous cigars.

In former days, Father O'Reilly had often entertained his brethren with impromptu "pieces" of Dublin, his native city. When we had partially covered times present and times past, for we had topics in riotous abundance, someone said to him: "Tell him, Hughie, about your bats."

Our host proceeded to do so—but I shall not travesty the accent with which he embarked upon any of his stories.

"It is necessary for you to know," he began, "that old Pharaoh himself had never a plague of such dimensions as Morong, this centre of devotion, had to sustain before the arrival of the present incumbent. 'Twas a beast y'understand that flies by night and roosts by day; an' no place'll do the divils to roost but in my dome."

"Meaning your head, Hughie?"

"I mean me church, ye fool. Glory alleluia, I can smell'm yet!"

"We gather that you evicted them?"

"Every mother's son of them; myself and the Reverend Connolly that's now dignifying the University in there. We hit upon the stratagem of training the beasts to use only one entrance and the same exit in their undevotional comings and goings, and ———"

"Take it easy, Hughie! Would you tell the gentleman how you go about training bats?"

"We did not approach them individually, as you might imagine," he replied with patience. "At the risk of my neck I went up yon and put net-wire in every hole an' cranny around the dome, all barrin' one which we left wide open for them all to see. Well, a few of them broke their heads attacking the netting, but the smart boys found the official entrance all right and came trooping out at dusk an' in at dawn—queueing up they were. Well, we left them at it a couple of more nights; then one fine evening the gents are lining up inside to come shooting out as usual, but Tom and myself are up there with a receptacle for them; a bag big enough to hold an elephant, and 'tis the stone-cold end of them. That night, me boy, a whole generation of Morong bats went down the river and haven't been heard of since."

ORDINATION

O Brother, we are mute in face of God's great love and urgency;
O'erawed and dumb, we cannot trace
 The wonders God hath wrought in thee.

The speeding Hands thy gift have caught
 When, virgin-vowed to purity,
The chastened flesh to Christ was brought,
 Espoused for all eternity.

God took thy little and raised
 Thee high above the angel band,
Who bow in awe at thee, amazed,
 For thou art mighty to command.

Another Christ thou art, to lead
 The weary, foot-sore to God's throne,
To call God earthwards and to feed
 Us Bread That giveth life alone.

The pow'r transcending mortal ken,
 Thy chrism'd hands and potent speech,
Beyond the tongue and hands of men,
 To God's own Court insistent reach.

Ah! Brother, use thy boundless strength
 For us and for the blinded East,
That thousands gained for Christ at length
 May praise with thee th'Eternal Priest.

—FRANCIS X. FORD

THE SLAVE OF HIS PEOPLE

by Graham Greene

> Few people who saw it will ever forget the central character of the film *The Fugitive*—a Mexican priest being hunted down by anti-clerical forces. The film was taken from Graham Greene's powerful novel, *The Power and the Glory* in which Mr. Greene depicts a man subject to human frailties but always conscious of his priestly obligations. Here is the dramatic opening of that book.

Mr. Tench went out to look for his other cylinder: out into the blazing Mexican sun and the bleaching dust. A few buzzards looked down from the roof with shabby indifference: he wasn't carrion yet. A faint feeling of rebellion stirred in Mr. Tench's heart, and he wrenched up a piece of the road with splintering finger-nails and tossed it feebly up at them. One of them rose and flapped across the town: over the tiny plaza, over the bust of an ex-president, ex-general, ex-human being, over the two stalls which sold mineral water, towards the river and the sea. It wouldn't find anything there: the sharks looked after the carrion on that side. Mr. Tench went on across the plaza.

He said "Buenos dias" to a man with a gun who sat in a small patch of shade against a wall. But it wasn't like England: the man said nothing at all, just stared malevolently up at Mr. Tench,

* From *The Power and the Glory* (originally published as *The Labyrinthine Ways*). Copyright, The Viking Press.

as if he had never had any dealings with the foreigner, as if Mr.
Tench were not responsible for his two gold biscuspid teeth.
Mr. Tench went sweating by, past the Treasury which had once
been a church, towards the quay. Half-way across he suddenly
forgot what he had come out for—a glass of mineral water? That
was all there was to drink in this prohibition state—except beer,
but that was a government monopoly and too expensive except
on special occasions. An awful feeling of nausea gripped Mr.
Tench in the stomach—it couldn't have been mineral water he
wanted. Of course, his ether cylinder . . . the boat was in. He
had heard its exultant piping while he lay on his bed after lunch.
He passed the barbers' and two dentists' and came out between
a warehouse and the customs onto the river bank.

The river went heavily by towards the sea between the banana
plantations: the General Obregon was tied up to the bank, and
beer was being unloaded—a hundred cases were already stacked
upon the quay. Mr. Tench stood in the shade of the customs
house and thought: What am I here for? Memory drained out
of him in the heat. He gathered his bile together and spat for-
lornly into the sun. Then he sat down on a case and waited.
Nothing to do. Nobody would come to see him before five.

The General Obregon was about thirty yards long. A few feet
of damaged rail, one lifeboat, a bell hanging on a rotten cord,
an oil-lamp in the bow, she looked as if she might weather
two or three more Atlantic years if she didn't strike a norther
in the gulf. That, of course, would be the end of her. It didn't
really matter: everybody was insured when he bought a ticket—
automatically. Half a dozen passengers leant on the rail, among
the hobbled turkeys, and stared at the port: the warehouse, the
empty baked street with the dentists' and the barbers'.

Mr. Tench heard a revolver-holster creak just behind him and
turned his head. A customs officer was watching him angrily. He
said something which Mr. Tench could not catch. "Pardon me,"
Mr. Tench said.

"My teeth," the customs man said indistinctly.

"Oh," Mr. Tench said, "yes, your teeth." The man had none:
that was why he couldn't talk clearly: Mr. Tench had removed

them all. He was shaken with nausea—something was wrong—
worms, dysentery— He said: "The set is nearly finished. Tonight,"
he promised wildly. It was of course, quite impossible; but that
was how one lived, putting off everything. The man was satisfied:
he might forget, and in any case what could he do? He had paid
in advance. That was the whole world to Mr. Tench: the heat
and the forgetting, the putting off till tomorrow, if possible cash
down—for what? He stared out over the slow river: the fin of a
shark moved like a periscope at the mouth. In the course of years
several ships had stranded and they now helped to prop up the
riverside, the smokestacks leaning over like guns pointing at some
distant objective across the banana-trees and the swamps.

Mr. Tench thought: Ether cylinder: I nearly forgot. His mouth
fell open and he began moodily to count the bottles of Cerveza
Montezuma. A hundred and forty cases. Twelve times a hundred
and forty: the heavy phlegm gathered in his mouth: twelve fours
are forty-eight. He said aloud in English: "My God, a pretty one":
twelve hundred, sixteen hundred and eighty: he spat, staring
with vague interest at a girl in the bows of the General Obregon
—a fine thin figure, they were generally so thick, brown eyes, of
course, and the inevitable gleam of the gold tooth, but something
fresh and young. . . . Sixteen hundred and eighty bottles at a
peso a bottle.

Somebody asked in English: "What did you say?"

Mr. Tench swivelled round. "You English?" he said in astonishment, but at the sight of the round and hollow face charred with
a three days' beard, he altered his question: "You speak English?"

Yes, the man said, he spoke English. He stood stiffly in the
shade, a small man dressed in a shabby dark city suit, carrying a
small attache case. He had a novel under his arm: bits of an
amorous scene stuck out, crudely coloured. He said: "Excuse me.
I thought just now you were talking to me." He had protuberant
eyes: he gave an impression of unstable hilarity, as if perhaps he
had been celebrating a birthday . . . alone.

Mr. Tench cleared his mouth of phlegm. "What did I say?"
He couldn't remember a thing.

"You said: 'My God, a pretty one.'"

"Now what could I have meant by that?" He stared up at the merciless sky. A buzzard stood there like an observer. "What? Oh, just the girl, I suppose. You don't often see a pretty piece round here. Just one or two a year worth looking at."

"She is very young."

"Oh, I don't have intentions," Mr. Tench said wearily. "A man may look. I've lived alone for fifteen years."

"Here?"

"Hereabouts."

They fell silent and time passed, the shadow of the customs house shifted a few inches farther towards the river: the buzzard moved a little, like the black hand of a clock.

"You came in her?" Mr. Tench said.

"No."

"Going in her?"

The little man seemed to evade the question, but then as if some explanation were required, "I was just looking," he said. "I suppose she'll be sailing quite soon?"

"To Vera Cruz," Mr. Tench said. "In a few hours."

"Without calling anywhere?"

"Where could she call?" He asked: "How did you get here?"

The stranger said vaguely: "A canoe."

"Got a plantation, eh?"

"No."

"It's good hearing English spoken," Mr. Tench said. "Now you learnt yours in the States?"

The man agreed. He wasn't very garrulous.

"Ah, what wouldn't I give," Mr. Tench said, "to be there now." He said in a low anxious voice: "You don't happen, do you, to have a drink in that case of yours? Some of you people back there—I've known one or two—a little for medical purposes."

"Only medicine," the man said.

"You a doctor?"

The bloodshot eyes looked slyly out of their corners at Mr. Tench. "You would call me perhaps a—quack?"

"Patent medicines? Live and let live," Mr. Tench said.

"Are you sailing?"

"No, I came down here for—for . . . oh, well, it doesn't matter anyway." He put his hand on his stomach and said: "You haven't got any medicine, have you, for—oh, hell. I don't know what. It's just this bloody land. You can't cure me of that. No one can."

"You want to go home?"

"Home," Mr. Tench said: "my home's here. Did you see what the peso stands at in Mexico City? Four to the dollar. Four. Oh, God. Ora pro nobis."

"Are you a Catholic?"

"No, no. Just an expression. I don't believe in anything like that." He said irrelevantly: "It's too hot anyway."

"I think I must find somewhere to sit."

"Come up to my place," Mr. Tench said. "I've got a spare hammock. The boat won't leave for hours—if you want to watch it go."

The stranger said: "I was expecting to see someone. The name was Lopez."

"Oh, they shot him weeks ago," Mr. Tench said.

"Dead?"

"You know how it is round here. Friend of yours?"

"No, no," the man protested hurriedly. "Just a friend of a friend."

"Well, that's how it is," Mr. Tench said. He brought up his bile again and shot it out into the hard sunlight. "They say he used to help . . . oh, undesirables . . . well, to get out. His girl's living with the Chief of Police now."

"His girl? Do you mean his daughter?"

"He wasn't married. I mean the girl he lived with." Mr. Tench was momentarily surprised by an expression on the stranger's face. He said again: "You know how it is." He looked across at the General Obregon. "She's a pretty bit. Of course, in two years she'll be like all the rest. Fat and stupid. Oh, God, I'd like a drink. Ora pro nobis."

"I have a little brandy," the stranger said.

Mr. Tench regarded him sharply. "Where?"

The hollow man put his hand to his hip—he might have been

indicating the source of his odd nervous hilarity. Mr. Tench seized his wrist. "Careful," he said. "Not here." He looked down the carpet of shadow: a sentry sat on an empty crate asleep beside his rifle. "Come to my place," Mr. Tench said.

"I meant," the little man said reluctantly, "just to see her go."

"Oh, it will be hours yet," Mr. Tench assured him again.

"Hours? Are you certain? It's very hot in the sun."

"You'd better come home."

Home: it was a phrase one used to mean four walls behind which one slept. There had never been a home. They moved across the little burnt plaza where the dead general grew green in the damp and the gascosa stalls stood under the palms. It lay like a picture postcard on a pile of other postcards: shuffle the pack and you had Nottingham, a Metroland birthplace, an interlude in Southend. Mr. Tench's father had been a dentist too— his first memory was finding a discarded cast in a waste-paper basket—the rough toothless gaping mouth of clay, like something dug up in Dorset—Neanderthal or Pithecanthropus. It had been his favourite toy: they tried to tempt him with Meccano: but fate had struck. There is always one moment in childhood when the door opens and lets the future in. The hot, wet river-port and the vultures lay in the waste-paper basket, and he picked them out. We should be thankful we cannot see the horrors and degradations lying around our childhood, in cupboards and bookshelves, everywhere.

There was no paving: during the rains the village (it was really no more) slipped into the mud. Now the ground was hard under the feet like stone. The two men walked in silence past barbers' shops and dentists': the buzzards on the roofs looked contented, like domestic fowls: they searched under wide crude dusty wings for parasites. Mr. Tench said: "Excuse me," stopping at a little wooden hut, one story high, with a veranda where a hammock swung. The hut was a little larger than the others in the narrow street, which petered out two hundred yards away in swamp. He said, nervously: "Would you like to take a look around? I don't want to boast, but I'm the best dentist here. It's not a bad place.

As places go." Pride wavered in his voice like a plant with shallow roots.

He led the way inside, locking the door behind him, through a dining-room where two rocking-chairs stood on either side of a bare table: an oil-lamp, some copies of old American papers, a cupboard. He said: "I'll get the glasses out, but first I'd like to show you—you're an educated man . . ." The dentist's operating-room looked out on a yard where a few turkeys moved with shabby nervous pomp: a drill which worked with a pedal, a dentist's chair gaudy in bright red plush, a glass cupboard in which instruments were dustily jumbled. A forceps stood in a cup, a broken spirit-lamp was pushed into a corner, and gags of cotton-wool lay on all the shelves.

"Very fine," the stranger said.

"It's not so bad, is it," Mr. Tench said, "for this town? You can't imagine the difficulties. That drill," he said bitterly, "is made in Japan. I've only had it a month and it's wearing out already. But I can't afford American drills."

"The window," the stranger said, "is very beautiful."

One pane of stained glass had been let in: a Madonna gazed out through the mosquito wire at the turkeys in the yard. "I got it," Mr. Tench said, "when they sacked the church. It didn't feel right—a dentist's room without some stained glass. Not civilized. At home—I mean in England—it was generally the laughing Cavalier—I don't know why—or else a Tudor rose. But one can't pick and choose."

He opened another door and said: "My workroom." The first thing you saw was a bed under a mosquito tent. Mr. Tench said: "You understand—I'm pressed for room." A ewer and basin stood at one end of a carpenter's bench, and a soap-dish: at the other a blow-pipe, a tray of sand, pliers, a little furnace. "I cast in sand," Mr. Tench said. "What else can I do in this place?" He picked up the cast of a lower jaw. "You can't always get them accurate," he said. "Of course, they complain." He laid it down again, and nodded at another object on the bench—something stringy and intestinal in appearance, with two little bladders of rubber. "Congenital fissure," he said. "It's the first time I've tried. The Kingsley case. I doubt if I can do it. But a man must try to keep abreast of things." His mouth fell open: the look of vacancy returned: the heat in the small room was overpowering. He stood there like a man lost in a cavern among the fossils and instruments of an age of which he knows very little. The stranger said: "If we could sit down . . ."

Mr. Tench stared at him—blankly.

"We could open the brandy."

"Oh, yes, the brandy."

Mr. Tench got two glasses out of a cupboard under the bench, and wiped off traces of sand. Then they went and sat in rocking-chairs in the front room. Mr. Tench poured out.

"Water?" the stranger said.

"You can't trust the water," Mr. Tench said. "It's got me here." He put his hand on his stomach and took a long draught. "You don't look too well yourself," he said. He took a longer look. "Your teeth." One canine had gone, and the front teeth were yellow with tartar and carious. He said: "You want to pay attention to them."

"What is the good?" the stranger said. He held a small spot of brandy in his glass warily—as if it were an animal to which he gave shelter, but not trust. He had the air in his hollowness and neglect of somebody of no account who had been beaten up incidentally, by ill-health or restlessness. He sat on the very edge of the rocking-chair, with his small attache case balanced on his knee and the brandy staved off with guilty affection.

"Drink up," Mr. Tench encouraged him (it wasn't his brandy); "it will do you good." The man's dark suit and sloping shoulders reminded him uncomfortably of a coffin: a death was in his carious mouth already. Mr. Tench poured himself out another glass. He said: "It gets lonely here. It's good to talk English, even to a foreigner. I wonder if you'd like to see a picture of my kids." He drew a yellow snapshot out of his notecase and handed it over. Two small children struggled over the handle of a watering-can in a back garden. "Of course," he said, "that was sixteen years ago."

"They are young men now."

"One died."

"Oh, well," the other said gently, "in a Christian country." He took a gulp of his brandy and smiled at Mr. Tench rather foolishly.

"Yes, I suppose so," Mr. Tench said with surprise. He got rid of his phlegm and said: "It doesn't seem to me, of course, to matter much." He fell silent, his thoughts ambling away; his mouth fell open, he looked grey and vacant until he was recalled by a pain in the stomach and helped himself to some more brandy. "Let me see. What was it we were talking about? The kids . . . oh, yes, the kids. It's funny what a man remembers. You know, I can remember that watering-can better than I can remember the kids. It cost three and elevenpence three farthings, green; I could lead you to the shop where I bought it. But as for the kids"—he brooded over his glass into the past—"I can't remember much else but them crying."

"Do you get news?"

"Oh, I gave up writing before I came here. What was the use? I couldn't send any money. It wouldn't surprise me if the wife had married again. Her mother would like it—the old sour bitch: she never cared for me."

The stranger said in a low voice: "It is awful."

Mr. Tench examined his companion again with surprise. He sat there like a black question mark, ready to go, ready to stay, poised on his chair. He looked disreputable in his grey three days' beard, and weak: somebody you could command to do anything. He said: "I mean the world. The way things happen."

"You drink up your brandy."

He sipped at it. It was like an indulgence. He said: "You remember this place before—before the Red Shirts came?"

"I suppose I do."

"How happy it was then."

"Was it? I didn't notice."

"They had at any rate—God."

"There's no difference in the teeth," Mr. Tench said. He gave himself some more of the stranger's brandy. "It was always an awful place. Lonely. My God. People at home would have said romance. I thought: five years here, and then I'll go. There was plenty of work. Gold teeth. But then the peso dropped. And now I can't get out. One day I will," he said: "I'll retire. Go home. Live as a gentleman ought to live. This"—he gestured at the bare base room—"I'll forget all this. Oh, it won't be long now. I'm an optimist," Mr. Tench said.

The stranger said suddenly: "How long will she take to Vera Cruz?"

"Who?"

"The boat."

Mr. Tench said gloomily: "Forty hours from now and we'd be there. The Diligencia. A good hotel. Dance places too. A gay town."

"It makes it seem close," the stranger said. "And a ticket, how much would that be?"

"You'd have to ask Lopez," Mr. Tench said. "He's the agent."

"But Lopez . . ."

"Oh, yes, I forgot. They shot him."

Somebody knocked on the door. The stranger slipped the attache case under his chair, and Mr. Tench went cautiously up towards the window. "Can't be too careful," he said. "Any dentist who's worth the name has enemies."

A faint voice implored them: "A friend," and Mr. Tench opened up. Immediately the sun came in like a white-hot bar.

A child stood in the doorway asking for a doctor. He wore a big hat and had stupid brown eyes. Beyond him two mules stamped and whistled on the hot beaten road. Mr. Tench said he was not a doctor: he was a dentist. Looking round he saw the stranger crouched in the rocking-chair, gazing with an effect of prayer, entreaty. . . . The child said there was a new doctor in town: the old one had fever and wouldn't stir. It was his mother who was sick.

A vague memory stirred in Mr. Tench's brain. He said with an air of discovery: "Why, you're a doctor, aren't you?"

"No, no, I've got to catch that boat."

"I thought you said . . ."

"I've changed my mind."

"Oh, well, it won't leave for hours yet," Mr. Tench said. "They're never on time." He asked the child how far. The child said it was six leagues away.

"Too far," Mr. Tench said. "Go away. Find someone else." He said to the stranger: "How things get around. Everyone must know you are in town."

"I could do no good," the stranger said anxiously: he seemed to be asking Mr. Tench's opinion, humbly.

"Go away," Mr. Tench said. The child did not stir. He stood in the hard sunlight looking in with infinite patience. He said his mother was dying. The brown eyes expressed no emotion: it was a fact. You were born, your parents died, you grew old, you died yourself.

"If she's dying," Mr. Tench said, "there's no point in a doctor seeing her."

But the stranger had got up: unwillingly he had been summoned to an occasion he couldn't pass by. He said sadly: "It always seems to happen. Like this."

"You'll have a job not to miss the boat."

"I shall miss it," he said. "I am meant to miss it." He was shaken by a tiny rage. "Give me my brandy." He took a long pull at it, with his eyes on the impassive child, the baked street, the buzzards moving in the sky like indigestion spots.

"But if she's dying—" Mr. Tench said.

"I know these people. She will be no more dying than I am."

"You can do no good."

The child watched them as if he didn't care. The argument in a foreign language going on in there was something abstract: he wasn't concerned. He would just wait here till the doctor came.

"You know nothing," the stranger said fiercely, "that is what everyone all the time says—you do no good." The brandy had affected him. He said with monstrous bitterness: "I can hear them saying it all over the world."

"Anyway," Mr. Tench said, "there'll be another boat. In a fortnight. Or three weeks. You are lucky. You can get out. You haven't got your capital here." He thought of his capital: the Japanese drill, the dentist's chair, the spirit-lamp and the pliers and the little oven for the gold fillings: a stake in the country.

"Vamos," the man said to the child. He turned back to Mr. Tench and told him that he was grateful for the rest out of the sun. He had the kind of dwarfed dignity Mr. Tench was accustomed to—the dignity of people afraid of a little pain and yet sitting down with some firmness in his chair. Perhaps he didn't care for mule travel. He said with an effect of old-fashioned ways: "I will pray for you."

"You were welcome," Mr. Tench said. The man got up onto the mule, and the child led the way, very slowly under the bright glare, towards the swamp, the interior. It was from there the man had emerged this morning to take a look at the General Obregon: now he was going back. He swayed very slightly in his saddle from the effect of the brandy. He became a minute disappointed figure at the end of the street.

It had been good to talk to a stranger, Mr. Tench thought, going back into his room, locking the door behind him (one never knew). Loneliness faced him there, vacancy. But he was as accustomed to both as to his own face in the glass. He sat down in the rocking-chair and moved up and down, creating a faint breeze in the heavy air. A narrow column of ants moved on in an orderly line to the opposite wall and disappeared. Down in the river the General Obregon whistled twice, he didn't know why.

The stranger had left his book behind. It lay under his rocking-chair: a woman in Edwardian dress crouched sobbing upon a rug embracing a man's brown polished pointed shoes. He stood above her disdainfully with a little waxed moustache. The book was called La Eterna Martyr. After a time Mr. Tench picked it up. When he opened it he was taken aback—what was printed inside didn't seem to belong, it was Latin, Mr. Tench grew thoughtful: he picked the book up and carried it into his workroom. You couldn't burn a book, but it might be as well to hide it if you were not sure—sure, that is, of what it was all about. He put it inside the little oven for gold alloy. Then he stood by the carpenter's bench, his mouth hanging open: he had remembered what had taken him to the quay—the ether cylinder which should have come down-river in the General Obregon. Again the whistle blew from the river, and Mr. Tench ran without his hat into the sun. He had said the boat would not go before morning, but you could never trust those people not to keep to time-table, and sure enough, when he came out onto the bank between the customs and the warehouse, the General Obregon was already ten feet off in the sluggish river, making for the sea. He bellowed after it, but it wasn't any good: there was no sign of a cylinder anywhere on the quay. He shouted once again, and then didn't trouble any more. It didn't matter so much after all: a little additional pain was hardly noticeable in the huge abandonment.

On the General Obregon a faint breeze began to blow; banana plantations on either side, a few wireless aerials on a point, the port slipped behind. When you looked back you could not have told that it had ever existed at all. The wide Atlantic opened up: the great grey cylindrical waves lifted the bows, and the hobbled turkeys shifted on the deck. The captain stood in the tiny deck-house with a toothpick in his hair. The land went backward at a slow even roll, and the dark came quite suddenly, with a sky of low and brilliant stars. One oil-lamp was lit in the bows, and the girl whom Mr. Tench had spotted from the bank began to sing gently—a melancholy, sentimental, and contented song about a rose which had been stained with true love's blood. There was an enormous sense of freedom and air upon the gulf, with the low tropical shore-line buried in darkness as deeply as any mummy in a tomb. I am happy, the young girl said to herself without considering why, I am happy.

Far back inside the darkness the mules plodded on. The effect of the brandy had long ago worn off, and the man bore in his brain along the marshy tract—which, when the rains came, would be quite impassable—the sound of the General Obregon's siren. He knew what it meant; the ship had kept to time-table: he was abandoned. He felt an unwilling hatred of the child ahead of him and the sick woman—he was unworthy of what he carried. A smell of damp came up all round him; it was as if this part of the world had never been dried in the flame when the world was sent spinning off into space: it had absorbed only the mist and cloud of those awful spaces. He began to pray, bouncing up and down to the lurching, slithering mule's stride, with his brandied tongue: "Let me be caught soon. . . . Let me be caught." He had tried to escape, but he was like the King of a West African tribe, the slave of his people, who may not even lie down in case the winds should fail.

IN MEMORIAM

Father McShane, of Maryknoll
Who died at Loting, China, June 4, 1927.

No pennants droop; no muffle drumbeats roll;
  No pomp's processional of pageant gloss.
Unheralded the passing of a soul
  With earthly glamor. Silence seals the loss.
No brilliancy of glory earth bestows,
Absorbing self-complacency it shows,
But mortal stillness reigns the vacant air,
As incense, floating, swell the silent prayer.
Unsought, unneedful to the valiant soul
  Of shepherd consecrated to the fold,
The gilded epitaph of sculptured scroll,
  Or gorgeous casket beautified by gold.
Immortal guerdon gained by labors done
Is not of earthly splendor shed or spun
But He, Who sanctified him for the fold,
Bestows supernal meed, surpassing gold.
Yea, he who worketh mercy in His name
  Fans ardently the ever-zealous soul,
Shall fortify himself with vivid flame,
  And blaze his path to heaven's pearly goal.
No tinsel'd urn requireth he for rest,
Reposeth he in sweetness on the breast
Of Him Who wills diurnal planets roll
And breathes His Majesty unto the soul.

—ROBERT J. FRENCH

AUGUST 15, 1913

by Raymond A. Lane

> Bishop Lane reviews the events which led him to Mary-
> knoll, and gives some nostalgic recollections of the baby
> days of the new mission society.

Sixty-five minutes from the Grand Central, the Hudson River
local shot out of a short dark tunnel and screeched to a halt.
Through my window I read "Ossining." This was my stop. With
other passengers I got off and started across the station plaza. A
trolley car would be there in a minute, I was told, to bring me on
towards my journey's end.

It was August 15th, 1913. Like August 15th of nearly every
year, the day was hot. The new black suit made me warm and
uncomfortable. With the tip of my finger I tested the high stiff
collar to gauge the degree of the wilting process. I took my handkerchief and mopped around the ears and neck and brow, wondering whence came the superstition that hard straw sailor hats are
cool. It was Lady Day, and all good Christians were at the seaside, lakes, or riverside. I thought of the cool waters of the
Spicket and the Merrimack, but consoled myself that I, too, was
on a pilgrimage, on a big errand for Our Lady.

I picked up my bags and started again in the direction of the
trolley tracks. A huge white horse, harnessed to a shiny carriage
with brass and nickel fittings and clean linen seat covers, was
hitched in front of Rigney's Hotel. Entrance to the hotel from

the station street was made through swinging doors, flanked on either side by rich glass plaques which carried the comforting news that Budweiser's was best for you, and Old Scotch was aged in the wood, or something like that. I saw that the hotel could be entered also at the rear from a road that ran along the side of the hill propped up by a heavy masonry wall. Entering from that direction the visitor would find himself on the fifth floor.

Thus I learned that Ossining rises abruptly from the waters of the Hudson and I calculated the odds in making the ascent and continuing my journey aboard the Toonerville Trolley which was now rolling to a stop at the end of the line. The car was hardly big enough to display the elaborate title, "The Hudson River and Eastern Traction Company."

If you can imagine yourself sitting in an old-time rocking chair which has been mounted on a roller skate, you may experience somewhat the sensation I had as the trolley car started up through the town and on to higher places. Up Secor Road, on and up through the shops of Main Street. We passed Young's hardware store, Kipp's furniture shop, the Bank, Secor's Grocery Store, and all the rest. I noticed a couple of churches too. We coasted along a very brief stretch of the Albany Post Road and then zoomed again up Croton Avenue, up and up, swaying and rocking all the time.

The trolley line had been started with the best of intentions of continuing on to Pleasantville, six miles away. A mile or two from the river's edge, however, after climbing several hundred feet, it seemed to lose heart and made a sudden spur off to the left. This led it past the Camp Meeting Woods where business was good, especially during the summer months. The tracks ended abruptly half way down an incline, like a man alerted in the midst of a doodle. The motorman got off to swing the trolley pole around. I pulled my bags together and disembarked on terra firma.

A horse and wagon stood in the shade at the side of the road. What a contrast with the high-stepping steed and the elegant carriage I had just left hitched in front of Rigney's Hotel. This horse showed long wear and harder fare. Mentally I noted sev-

eral safe places to hang my straw hat where his skeleton protruded prominently. The carriage was a high-wheeled open-air
rig, neither a buckboard nor a droshky, but a sort of combination
of both. The driver was looking at me: "Are you Mr. Lane?" I
identified myself and climbed aboard and we started.

Brother Frederick had been sent down to fetch me. He had
heard I was coming, Father Walsh had said something about it
that morning. Father Walsh was back again, had been away for
a few days, an awfully busy man. Father Price was home. The
place was not quite settled, Brother Fred said, and he hoped I
wouldn't mind roughing it a bit. The house needed some repairs,
there was lots of work to do, everyone seemed happy though.
"You're from Lawrence? I'm from Newton," he said. "Giddap,
Billy!"

Brother Fred's words were few, chiefly brief replies to my questions. His fingers were black with printer's ink. "Have a little
press up there," he explained. "Do some leaflets and things for
Father Walsh." He turned to look me over once again as he
spoke. His glasses were perched down below the bridge of his
nose.

The carriage rolled noisily down the hill from the Camp Meeting Woods, rattled over the planks that bridged a beautiful little
brook. Then we started up the hill. It was a dirt road climbing
abruptly and laboriously up the side of Sunset Hill. I found myself leaning forward and holding my breath as Billy slipped on
the loose gravel, strained at the lines, and made the leather creak
against the shafts. Finally, the road leveled off and made a partial turn. I looked back and got my first glimpse of a view which
I have never tired of seeing.

The hill dropped steeply to the green knolls at the edge of the
village. Clumps of foliage were bunched here and there on the
landscape. A white colonial homestead stood out clearly, and
here and there a steeple. Two or three miles to the west, the
Hudson, wide and beautiful and majestic, filled the panorama
north and south for thirty miles, beginning at a bend below Bear
Mountain and disappearing in the Palisades near Yonkers. The
rocky cliffs on the far side of the river stood out sharply, and

beyond them the forests and hills of the Hudson Highlands rolled away as far as the eye could see.

When I came back to the world about me, Brother Frederick was turning the carriage through a grove of evergreens and into what looked like an abandoned farm. I had tried many times to visualize Maryknoll. Here it was now before my eyes, an old wooden farm-house with a new name, "Seminary." The entire student body was on the front porch; all six members were there to welcome the new arrival.

Father Walsh shook my hand and brought me in. I cannot remember now what he said. Then I was turned over to the students. It was almost time for supper. I had my first meal at Maryknoll and thereupon became a member of the family. The dining room was extremely simple; to me, it seemed bare. There were three tables and no table cloths. The tables were arranged like a U, with Father Walsh sitting at the head, Fathers Price and Lane at either side of him, and the rest of us on the outside edge of the two side tables, so that everyone was practically facing everyone else; at least, you looked at no one's back.

That first night I learned my fellow students' names and learned much more about them during the days that followed. They were Daniel McShane, James Walsh, Francis Ford, Alphonse Vogel, William O'Shea and William Lambert. After Night Prayers everyone seemed to keep quiet, and I was told that the "Great Silence" would continue until after breakfast the next morning.

There was a scarcity of everything about the farmhouse. Packing boxes served in some of the rooms as desks and bookcases. There was no electricity. Someone told me to pick up a kerosene lamp and carry it to my room. I started to undress and then knelt down to say a few prayers, I tried to think what they would be doing at home just at that moment. One thing was certain: they didn't have to keep quiet with any "Great Silence." I guess maybe I was homesick; though I was nineteen years old. Something gave way inside, and I broke down like a baby and cried for I don't know how long. It had been harder leaving than I had expected.

As I knelt and dozed, my mind traveled back over the years and I thought of my many childhood dreams and the varied incidents which led to my coming to Maryknoll.

Seven years before, in 1906, when I was in the seventh grade at St. Mary's School, I had seen Father James Anthony Walsh for the first time. He told us about Blessed Theophane Venard, a young priest of the Paris Foreign Missions who had been martyred for the Faith in Indo-China. Father Venard was a classmate of Father Hogan who was a professor at the Brighton Seminary in Boston when Father Walsh was there as a student. The Xaverian Brothers who taught us bigger boys at St. Mary's, wanted us to know about the missions. Three years later, when I was at St. John's in Danvers, Mass., the Brothers were still my teachers, and there I again heard Father Walsh speak.

I thought of the good old days in Lawrence. All the things that had happened at St. Mary's: the day I threw the apple at Pee Wee Barry, missed and hit Brother Robert. It was during morning classes. Brother was at the blackboard, and the apple hit him square between the shoulders. I could still see him turning and demanding that the culprit come forward. I was ready to obey, but John Shine, the gang boss, told me to keep quiet—he'd break every bone in my body if I confessed. Hours of agony followed and I'll never forget the look of astonishment on Brother's face when, at four-thirty p.m., I went up to plead guilty.

The baseball teams, with our victories and defeats, all came back. I thought of the night my brother and myself challenged my father to a race, how he took off his shoes, ran with us and beat us, and how my mother upbraided the three of us for putting on such an undignified show for the neighbors. Then there was the old swimming hole in the Spicket above the mills, always delightfully cool and refreshing.

One day Father Conrady who had been a helper of Father Damien at Molokai came to our school and talked about lepers. He was a Belgian Father, a little man with a long white beard, and he showed us a map of the world and pointed to an island in the West River in South China where he now lived with his lepers.

The *Annals of the Propagation of the Faith* used to come to our home. I found myself computing the numbers of the various missionary orders in foreign fields, trying to figure out what chance I should have of getting overseas if I joined one of them. I was really greatly interested, and almost afraid to admit it even to myself. I toyed with the idea of getting a job on a transatlantic liner and then in London or Paris joining one of these orders. There were no foreign mission societies in America.

My daydreams brought me pictures of myself as a missioner, a great missioner, of course, another Xavier, leading thousands and thousands into the fold. Doctors had been my heroes for a time. I thought of myself as a surgeon, a great surgeon, naturally, and pictured myself after saving someone's life in the operating room. There I was in my spotless white smock, standing in the hospital corridor, while I chatted with the grateful relatives, twiddling the stethoscope or perhaps trimming my nails with a scalpel. Our boyhood dreams usually give us the stage front and center under the spotlight. It is only later, when we grow up a little and begin to get sense, that we back off and grow small and yield the leading role to God.

Once the Dominican Fathers gave a mission in our parish. After that I thought of becoming a great preacher. I saw myself in my white habit, leaning from the pulpit, holding the people spellbound with my dramatic gestures and eloquence.

At an earlier age policemen and firemen had their attractions. From my father I learned that, when just beginning to talk, I had been so carried off by the shiny red hose cart and the galloping horses that one day, sitting in my high chair, I repeated snatches of the charm words I had heard Jerry O'Leary, the driver, heap on his fiery steeds. My poor mother was so shocked, she could have fainted. She told all to my father when he arrived from work that night, and after a council of war, he, in practical wisdom, decreed: "We won't say anything now because he might think he was smart. But, if he ever says it again, then knock the blazes out of him!"

So, the idea of the missions, rather than coming as a lightning flash, grew upon me gradually. One day in my senior year at

St. John's, Danvers, I was browsing around the library and picked up the Boston *Pilot*. My heart gave a hop, skip and a jump, when my eye caught a heading on the editorial page: "American Priests to Start Foreign Mission Seminary." I tried to read the whole article in one glance, and then from start to finish I read it slowly over and over again. Breaking the rules of the library, I cut out the article and carried it in my pocket for a long time. The society had not yet been organized, the word, "Maryknoll," was still to be thought of; the work was just a blueprint and no more, and still I felt I was to be there. I did not even consider the possibility of being rejected. I began to read *The Field Afar*, read every line of it, and then one day without a word to anyone at home, I wrote to Father Walsh and told him what was in my mind.

At St. Mark's Church, in Dorchester, I met Father John I. Lane. When Father Walsh answered my letter he had told me to see Father Lane, who was joining the new foreign mission seminary. Father Lane, a star in sports at Holy Cross in the early eighties, was a big man, handsome, with a smile and a way about him that made you feel good. Too bad the movie producer who likes to show the world that "Priests are People" didn't know Father John Lane. A combination of Father O'Malley and Joe DiMaggio, this big boys' hero in flesh and blood would have put the box offices on easy street for months and years. When I walked out of St. Mark's and started back to Lawrence, I was saying to myself: "If he's going to be there, and any more like him, then—Boys! Count me in!"

Next came the job of telling my pastor. This was going to be hard. There was an old pastor near Boston who used to tell about the time, some few years back, when he caught a youngster high in the limbs of a tree that stood in the yard of the Sacred Heart Rectory, looking down into the priest's house. "What were you doing up there?" he asked with all the severity of his position, when he got the little ape back on the sidewalk. "I had a date with Father Tom," he explained. "He didn't show up and when I whistled he didn't come, so I climbed up the tree to see if he was up yet."

My pastor, Father O'Reilly, an Augustinian, was too venerable in my eyes to be this kind of friend, but there was real affection between us. He was the biggest man in Lawrence, and yet he would take time out to listen to me, a very small person. Even as a youngster I could go into the priest's house, knock at his door, be asked in, sit down and talk. He would listen with attention and sympathy and ponder my words carefully as if I really had something important to say. He was my hero.

In those days, if a boy in Lawrence wanted to be a priest, the usual procedure was to go to Villanova College and then study to be an Augustinian. Now I had to go and tell him that I wanted to be a priest, but I wasn't going to be an Augustinian; in fact, I was signing up with an outfit that just barely existed and wasn't even heard of. I wondered what he was going to say. Honestly, my chief fear was that I might hurt him, not what he might say to me.

"Good, good, my boy. I'm glad that St. Mary's is going to have a boy at the new mission seminary. God bless you!" You could have bowled me over with a toothpick. I had underestimated Father O'Reilly. He knew more about the new seminary than I did. He was pleased, because he himself was an apostle.

Looking back now, I suppose there was hardly any time in my boyhood life that really deep down I didn't feel I ought to be a priest. At times, I thought of other things—doctor, policeman, baseball star, but being so close to priests made me follow along naturally with them. When I served Mass, when I went to the First Mass of one of the Lawrence boys, when I went with the priest on a sick call and minded the horses for him, when I saw the priest at a wake, I imagined myself doing all this some day. Of course, I liked to think of myself too, dressed neatly in black suit and straw hat, strolling out to see my altar boys practicing on the sand lot, stepping up to the plate and walloping the ball out of sight over the tops of the houses. We're all that way, I think: hero in our childhood musings.

Yet, if we were actually cornered and pressed to give the real reason why we wanted to be priests, I think the answer would be about the same: "I want to get to Heaven and I want to help other people get to Heaven."

When you talked about going to the missions in those days, the reaction was not always flattering. People would look at you with a sort of pity, wondering whether you were intellectually immature, emotionally unstable, or whether you just couldn't make it in the seminary at home and had to get in out of the rain by going to a place where all they asked was that you observe the Ten Commandments and be able to write your baptismal name without too many mistakes. He's not too smart, poor boy, he would never do in our parishes here; but he'll be all right away off in some heathen land. That was the idea.

Sooner or later I had to tell my mother and father. My mother began to notice letters coming with strange postmarks, "Ossining, N.Y." Finally, one day I told her all. There was a big lump in my throat and tightening in my chest. I felt mean. All she said was: "Why do you want to go so far away?"

The biggest hurdle would be to get permission from my Dad, I thought. Time was getting short. Father Walsh's letter said that I should come to Maryknoll on August 15th. My father had asked me to work for two years, after leaving High School. A few weeks more and that time would be up. Finally, when only two weeks separated us from the fifteenth, I came back from work one night and found my Dad as usual in the garden reading the newspaper. I told myself it was now or never. I said a prayer, sat down beside him and said: "Dad, I'm going away soon."

"Where?"

"To New York to enter a seminary for the foreign missions."

"That's good. God bless you, son."

My parents' generosity and faith made me feel small. I had expected an argument; yet here they were—so much bigger and better than I had thought. How much better it would have been not to have held back from my parents, but to have opened up to them immediately. It would have been easier for me and would have been an expression of confidence which they well deserved.

The time came to say good-bye. It was going to be hard, I

knew, and I had hoped to get it all over within our own home. My mother was brave and was as always the valiant woman of faith, but anyone could see that for her it was a heartbreaking farewell. My sister and brother, both younger, were unusually quiet.

My father insisted on coming with me as far as Boston. The ride on the Boston and Maine takes about an hour. It seemed a terribly long ride that day. Hardly a word was spoken. My father looked out one window; I looked out the opposite one. At the South Station we parted. He had some words of farewell ready, but they were choked in his throat. I couldn't do any better.

Pictures of home kept coming back to my mind during the ride to New York. It seemed so happy and attractive now that I was leaving it forever. I figured that it would take about seven years to complete my training. Then I would be ordained, return home for a brief visit and then depart for far away places. Thoughts of home began to alternate with images of what lay ahead—New York, the Hudson, Maryknoll, China. . . .

I jumped up from beside the bed where I had been kneeling and dreaming and dozing I don't know how long. I was choking with smoke. The kerosene lamp had burnt itself out, the wick was smoldering, and the room was filled with acrid smoke. It was after midnight. I should have had the light out and been in bed hours ago. The frightening thought struck me that I might be expelled for this grave infraction of the rule, on the very first night after my arrival! I rubbed out the smoking wick and jumped into bed, hoping and praying that I had not been detected. First of all, I had left my light burning long after the time allowed, and then, too, I had been careless and might have started a serious fire. Actually, vocations were coming so slowly in those days that, as we used to joke later, hardly anything short of murder or highway robbery would be considered sufficient reason for sending a student home. When I opened my eyes again, it was daylight. There was a rooster crowing near by, and a bell somewhere about the house was making a terribly unpleasant noise.

MERCY FLIGHT

by Paul Schulte

> The famous World War I ace who later became an
> Oblate of Mary Immaculate tells of the value of the
> airplane in mission work in the Far North.

A chance visit to Eskimo Point, two hundred miles north of
Churchill, enabled me to save the life of a four-day-old child,
for whom there seemed to be no hope. I went up there with a
message from Bishop Turquetil to Father Dionne, who had told
me on an earlier visit that if I did not see the mission ship anchored at Eskimo Point on my next flight, I might assume that
he was away on a walrus hunt, for he had to lay in winter supplies for himself and his dogs.

There was no ship in the harbor when I came in sight of the
mission station. Still I was not sure that Father Dionne had left,
so I flew around the buildings in a circle, according to our pre-
arranged plan. If the missionary were at home he was to come
out and wave. Otherwise I would not land, for the spot is unfavorable. I saw some Eskimo children, but there was no sign of
the priest. Later I learned that he was at home, but had not
heard the noise of the plane at first, and by the time he got outdoors and began to signal with his arms, I had already headed
straight north and away from him.

Meanwhile, firmly believing that he had left to hunt walrus,

* From *Flying Priest Over the Arctic.* Copyright, Harper and Brothers Publishers.

I looked for him along the coast. Spying a few boats between Eskimo Point and Mistake Bay I came down close to them on the water. When a nearer approach made it certain that Father Dionne was not there, I did not anchor, but with a wave of friendly greeting to the Eskimos, was off again, flying north.

On arriving over Mistake Bay I noticed a small ship in the harbor, and a motorboat with two occupants just leaving. When I circled it in salute the boat turned and headed back toward the harbor. Feeling sure that Father Dionne had been found, I landed. My guess was wrong again. He was not in the boat, but one of its occupants, Mr. Voisy, of the Hudson Bay Company, said to me: "Father Dionne is not here, nor do we know where he is. But you, Father Schulte, are a savior in the hour of need. A four-day-old child is at the point of death. His mother is beside herself with grief. Only last year she lost her first child and now her second baby is in grave danger. Nobody knows what to do. Please help us."

I replied: "You are asking for medical aid, but I am not a physician—I am a missionary. What can I do?"

He answered: "You missionaries are skilled in so many ways that you surely can help in a case like this."

I did not imagine for a moment that I could cure this desperately sick child, but I agreed to do what I could to get the only available physician. The Arctic is not like a civilized country, where one can get fast medical aid and hospitalization for the sick. In that territory of more than a million square miles, there is only one physician and one hospital.

I had an indescribable feeling of sympathy for the poor Eskimo mother and her sick baby when I reached them. I saw the little creature but could do nothing to help him, so I gave them both my blessing and hurried off to find Dr. Melling, and to bring him to their aid as quickly as possible. The hospital at Chesterfield Inlet was not far away by plane—only one hundred and fifteen miles. Flying there and landing on Hudson Bay, I jumped into a canoe and paddled hurriedly ashore. Almost out of breath on reaching the hospital I was also out of luck. Dr. Melling had left two days earlier on the *M. F. Therese* for Baker

Lake, two hundred miles west of Chesterfield Inlet, to look after some patients there. I consulted Father Lionel Ducharme, the Superior of the mission, who is authorized by the Canadian Government to operate a small amateur radio station. He agreed to make every possible effort to get in touch with the *M. F. Therese.*

At last the operator on the boat responded. Dr. Melling was called to the microphone. Questions and answers flew back and forth. He tried to tell me how to treat the child until he could come himself, but I insisted that I didn't want instructions. He must come personally and at once. There was no other alternative. Speed was absolutely necessary, for the child was dying.

When he argued that it would take at least two days and two nights to get back to Chesterfield by boat, I said: "Never mind. I shall come by plane tonight to get you."

Still he argued, saying that he had never flown in an airplane, that the waves there were very high, that he doubted if it would be wise for him to go.

I answered: "The high waves cannot keep me from trying everything within my power to save a human life. Are you ready to fly with me, when I come?"

He agreed at last, so I decided to take off that evening to meet him. I had never before flown to Baker Lake, and knew nothing of that region. When I asked Brother Beaudoin if he would fly with me, he answered, beaming with eagerness: "I'll fly anywhere with you."

In order to have aboard somebody familiar with the territory I asked Father Ducharme to accompany us, since he could render invaluable service as our navigator. It was his first venture in the air but he gladly joined us on our rescue expedition. We rowed out to our plane and warmed up the motor. I said a short prayer and made the sign of the cross on my forehead. We waved good-by and were on the wing.

The ship roared westward into the night, following the inlet. After ten minutes in the air I experienced my first engine trouble in the Arctic. One of the magnetos was out of order. For five minutes I tested and checked them. The magneto on my right missed regularly. Since it would have been inexcusable to attempt a night flight over unknown country with only one functioning, I turned back, sad at heart.

Soon we were at Chesterfield again. When we struck the water, night had already overtaken us. Our setback depressed me greatly, but half an hour later, when the darkness had grown so dense that I could not see my hand before my eyes, I began to think that perhaps the failure of the magneto was a hint by Providence that I should not risk my plane, my life, and the lives of my two faithful companions, by flying through such pitch darkness.

I put in a restless night, however, for I kept thinking continually about the child and his mother, and was tortured by the idea of being too late. I wondered why the magneto had failed just at the moment when I needed it, to help save a child's life and bring happiness to his mother. But that night Brother Beaudoin repaired the magneto. At dawn next morning Father Ducharme, Brother Beaudoin, and I were again in the air. We had to buck strong head winds and fly through many fogs.

The last news from the *M. F. Therese* was that it was heading back at full steam to meet us. In about two and a half hours we sighted her on Baker Lake. While circling her to effect a good landing, I fastened my safety belt securely, for the waves were high, though not so high as to threaten disaster. I landed at right angles to the ship, which had stopped. A boat was quickly lowered and rowed alongside the plane. Dr. Melling was on the mission ship. So was his wife. It was heroically unselfish on her part to let her husband make his first airplane trip under those conditions, and her prayers must have gone with us. Two attempts to rise from the water were failures. The waves were so high that we had to taxi into quieter water near the shore before we were able to take off. The wind was now behind us. In less than two hours we reached Chesterfield.

While Dr. Melling ran to the hospital to fetch the instruments he thought he would need in case an operation was called for, we filled our tanks with gas. I was waiting in the pilot's seat when he returned. In a few minutes we were in the air again.

The motor ran beautifully, but the weather looked threatening. Heavy banks of fog drifted past us. Four thunderstorms, through which we passed, impeded the way to our goal. I flew an entirely new inland route, for I could not follow the coast of Hudson Bay in such stormy weather. The rain poured down in torrents. I flew low because I could see practically nothing ahead. Lightning and thunder followed each other continuously as if hell itself were let loose. Thanks be to God, however, I kept on the right course, and suddenly was whirring along above the buildings of the Hudson Bay Company at Mistake Bay. But the rain and fog were so heavy that I immediately lost sight of the ground, although not my sense of direction. Looking down on the harbor I had to admit that it was impossible to see or to recognize its surface because of the heavy downpour. Turning around I flew once more over the buildings of the Hudson Bay Company, guessed my height from the ground, gave my engine a little more gas, held my plane at absolute level, and came down blindly on the water.

It was a perfect landing. I don't believe that I ever came down more softly. The wind was strong, and its direction just right. Heading into it made an easy landing possible. Mr. Voisy rowed out to us and said with a smile: "Father Schulte, you have landed in the worst weather we have had for many weeks."

I asked immediately: "Is the child still living?"

"Yes," was the reply.

This was the happiest moment of my trip, for I felt certain that good Dr. Melling would do the rest. I had borne my share of the responsibility. Taking him by the arm, I said: "Hurry up, doctor; now it's up to you."

He jumped into the boat with his surgical kit, hastened to the dying child and his mother, and speedily performed the necessary operation, with Father Ducharme as his assistant.

Meanwhile Brother Beaudoin and I busied ourselves with the plane, and anchored it. When we reached the Eskimo's tent everything was over. The child lay peacefully at his mother's breast. The mother wept tears of joy, and the happy father squeezed my hand heartily. Everybody seemed to be truly happy and the parents asked me if I would baptize the child. The parents were pagans.

With Father Ducharme's help, I baptized the child, giving him my own baptismal name. The little Eskimo Paul is the first Catholic of Mistake Bay. He is to me also a proof that I made no mistake in my first landing at Mistake Bay.

By means of wireless telegraphy and an airplane, creations of the human mind, a life and a soul had been saved. I felt as if I were the happiest of all those who rejoiced that day, and I hoped that little Paul would grow up to be strong, healthy, and a good huntsman of his tribe. I should be even more pleased could I make him a good flying mechanic, or perhaps a pilot so that he might help his tribesmen as I had been able to help him. When, some time later, I met Father Dionne again and received his congratulations on my rescue flight, he said to me: "I had always hoped to give my own Christian name to the first convert at Mistake Bay."

I asked: "What is your Christian name?"

He answered: "My name is Paul."

When in turn I said: "That is also my name," he threw his arms around me and said: "Really, this is a welcome surprise. May the little Eskimo Paul lead them to the true faith and the true love of God!"

I find it easy to read God's providence in my rescue flight of six hundred and thirty miles. I had intended to land at Eskimo Point, not at Mistake Bay. Had Father Dionne come out of the house in time I would have landed there and would never have thought of Mistake Bay. The child undoubtedly would have died. This whole experience affected me deeply.

In the tent of reindeer skin in which Paul underwent his operation, lived a second mother with a sick child—a beautiful nine-year-old girl with soft dark eyes and coal-black hair. I have forgotten her name, but I called her Little Snowbird.

For a year this girl had been sick with an infected knee. No doctor had ever been summoned to find out what was wrong. The leg was bent stiff at right angles, and the knee was one large sore. The good mother had tried everything in her power to relieve the little sufferer. She had made poultices and used Eskimo medicines, but without result. Instead of improving, Little Snowbird's health had become steadily worse. The infection had spread; the knee had swollen badly, and was so painful that the child often groaned and almost fainted from agony. Meanwhile, the mother had watched her child with an ever increasing fear that she would lose her. She called her many pet names and bestowed on her the most tender caresses. The child's father did what he could to give her help and comfort by promising to catch a fine, big, fresh fish for her when he went hunting, but they were heartbroken to see her sufferings increase, and her strength consumed by fevers.

Dr. Melling examined the girl, who cried bitterly as he removed the bandages from her knee. He shook his head, saying, "This child is very sick and will have to be taken to the hospital immediately. I believe it is a streptococcus infection. She must have an operation soon or she will die. The pus will have to be drained out of that knee. Only in the hospital can the operation be performed safely and only the hospital Sisters can give her the special nursing she will need."

I volunteered immediately to bring her with us in our airplane to the hospital. Father Ducharme explained our plans to the child's parents with kindly tact, and obtained their consent. I shall never forget how the father carried the girl in his arms to the water's edge, the mother walking beside them; how the canoe was paddled to the plane, and how we prepared a comfortable resting place for the child. Dr. Melling took the seat beside me. Father Ducharme sat behind, looking after the little one. Brother Beaudoin loosened the landing ropes from the buoy and gave the sign "All clear."

With a wave of greeting to the Eskimos, and a last smile from our patient to her parents, we were aloft. Little Snowbird made her first flight—toward recovery and new health. She was carried to the operating room as soon as we reached the hospital, well on toward evening. It was much later when the operation was finished, fresh bandages were on her knee and she was at rest in bed.

The exertions of those two days and the sleepless night between them had fatigued me a great deal, but for all that I waited until everything was over. Then I walked softly into the children's room, and looked at the beautiful Eskimo child asleep. Her black hair stood out against the white pillow, and there seemed to be a smile on her face. I stood there watching her, knowing that for the first time in her life she was sleeping in a real bed. Making the sign of the cross over her, I wished her a speedy and complete recovery. Meanwhile, my heart was filled with deep joy to see the lovely child sleeping so tranquilly. The look of pain had completely vanished, and one of deep peace now rested on her face, mirroring in some degree the calm of her innocent soul. Softly I whispered the prayer: "God bless you, Little Snowbird, and God keep you."

TO MARYKNOLL

In Memory of Bishop Walsh

"Why stand you, looking up to Heaven?"

Why stand in darkening twilight sad and wan?
The westering sun, which your reluctant eyes
Had prayed to keep forever gold the skies,
Shed constant sunrise as the earth rolls on.
Recount his days that with showered riches shone;
Sweep his horizons lit for enterprise;
Know that with death love's sunshine never dies
But finds in gratefulness unending dawn.
The clouds which the ascending Lord concealed,
Grew bright in Pentecostal tongues of fire,
Apostle hearts with ardor to console,
Departing to God's garnered harvest field,
Your father, brother, guide shall still inspire—
Your missioner in Heaven's Maryknoll!

—FRANCIS P. DONNELLY, S.J.

ANGEL IN THE CLOUD

by Albert J. Nevins

> God had another plan than martyrdom for Paul Ri, a
> veteran Korean catechist, who for fifty years taught
> Christianity until finally he stood before a Communist
> firing squad.

The Red commandant of Mokpo was angry. For days he had
felt the anger swelling up inside him. And now it broke, with
first a rumble and then a roar, just like the thunderheads that
roll in on Korea from the Yellow Sea.

"It is impossible for people to simply disappear!" the commandant screamed. "I saw Paik yesterday with my own eyes. Today when I send you to arrest him, you tell me he has gone. Who
warned him? How did he get away?"

"All I know is that he has gone," answered the lieutenant,
flushing and full of uneasiness.

"You are stupid!" snarled the commandant. "You never know
anything. For weeks now, the people we have listed for arrest
have been disappearing. Someone is warning them. Someone is
helping them get away. And I intend to find out!"

It was several days before the commandant summoned his
lieutenant again. On this occasion, the Communist official was
all smiles.

"What do you know of Paul Ri?" he asked.

The younger man thought for a moment, and then replied:
"He is the old man who worked for the Columban missioners
before we arrested them. He was a teacher, I think."

"Do you consider him dangerous to the People's Government?"
"No," answered the lieutenant. "He is an old man. What can
he do to harm us?"

"I will tell you what he has done!" shouted the senior Red
official. "He is the man who has been smuggling away the people
we intended to arrest. I don't know how he gets the names, but I
do know that he does. Then he goes to the person, warns him,
and after darkness leads him through the hills to safety. Besides
that, he has been going among the Catholics and encouraging
them to resist us. He is the one man who has organized all the
opposition to us here in Mokpo!"

The commandant pulled a portfolio from his desk. "Here is
the whole history of the criminal Ri," he continued. "Ri was born
seventy-two years ago on an island in the harbor here. He was
married at sixteen, and four years later joined the Catholic
Church. He converted his wife, parents, and grandmother to the
foreign religion. Shortly afterwards, he moved to the mainland
and became a teacher, for the foreign priests. In 1936, he came
here to Mokpo to work for the Columban Fathers. His first son
became a priest, but is now dead. Another of his sons is studying
to be a priest. For over fifty years, this Paul Ri has been teaching
the foreign religion. He is the most dangerous man in Mokpo!"

"I'll arrest him immediately," said the crestfallen lieutenant.

"No! I will arrest him," said the commandant, with a cruel grin.
"Then I shall have the pleasure of personally shooting him!"

The commandant left his office, escorted by some of his soldiers. The group went to the Mokpo church and found Paul Ri
teaching some of the children. When the children saw the Red
commandant, they screamed and ran, because that man was
much feared for his many cruelties.

Paul Ri was taken into custody. The commandant ordered
that the old man be led to a hill beyond the town, where his
execution would take place. The commandant ordered, also, that
every known Catholic should be rounded up, to witness the
"traitor's" death. When the hilltop was reached, Paul Ri prayed
in silence.

The commandant sneered: "This is the day of your sacrifice,

traitor! On the anniversary of this day in years to come, your children will offer sacrifice to your spirit."

The Christians wept, but the Red soldiers laughed at this jest. The commandant lifted his arm to give the signal to fire. Then suddenly an airplane roared out of a cloud. It was a United Nations plane, and it opened fire on the soldiers. The commandant fell dead, his body riddled by bullets. In the confusion, Paul Ri escaped and made his way to safety behind the American lines.

The Red commandant was so hated that no one buried his body, and after nightfall the dogs ate it. When the lieutenant heard of this, he ordered that all the dogs of Mokpo be killed. Not long afterwards, the Reds were driven from the area, and Paul Ri was able to return home.

THE ROSES OF PADRE ZAVALLA

by Francis X. Lyons

"Joseph's Coat" is still blooming but the tall Ecuadorian priest is no longer around to tend it. Father Lyons paints a sensitive portrait of a lonely man of the Andean highlands.

When I first met Padre Zavalla, he was the pastor of a small town in the mountains. Like most of the old priests in the inland villages of Ecuador, he led a lonely life. His parishioners were chiefly the colorfully clad Indians of the highlands. To the old adobe church, with its crumbling tower and its clear-sounding bell, they went for baptisms, marriages, and funerals; but their other contacts with their spiritual father were few.

Padre Zavalla was a tall, heavy-set man. Although well over sixty, he did not need glasses to aid his kind brown eyes. It was evident that the deep lines around his large mouth came from laughing much. His jowls had begun to sag after a serious illness, and this condition, combined with his unruly shock of hair, gave him the appearance of a big St. Bernard dog. Like all the priests of Latin America, he wore his cassock in the streets, even when a sick call took him out on his rawboned horse. On those occasions, he would turn his cassock up, secure it at his waist, and go jogging along with his trousers tucked inside his woolen socks. In the evenings, when he felt the chill of the night air, he would wear a light coat that reached to his ankles. "Shaggy" was the word for Padre Zavalla.

The padre lived in a two-story mud house next to the church. It had been built by some predecessor of his, and it had not been kept in repair. But in spite of poor surroundings, this lonely priest retained a sense of beauty.

I soon learned that my friend had two passions: one was photography, and the other was rose growing. How he ever became interested in cameras remains a mystery to me; perhaps, like many another young cleric, he had needed some interest to help fill the long days and longer evenings in some forsaken town. He became as good as any professional, as the years went by. When I made his acquaintance, he was the proud possessor of a battered old plate camera with a mediocre lens, which he kept upstairs in his bedroom, away from prying eyes and meddlesome hands.

The walls of the little room that was his office, just inside the door of the house, were lined with all manner of photographs. Each one was in a frame, and each was exquisitely colored—for as time went on, the stark reality of an unretouched photograph annoyed Padre Zavalla.

With true artistic ability, and an eye for color that could have come only from keen observation of nature in all her moods, he was accustomed to sit for hours at his little desk, with his photographs and his water colors. I think he was happiest when thus relaxed, and he never felt any need of other recreation.

No matter how many times I entered that little office, my artist friend would want me to look at all those pictures on the wall again and exclaim over each in turn, as he explained to me the locale, the lighting, and all other details, which the true enthusiast finds more absorbing than the resulting picture. I never objected, for I could have studied those magnificent enlargements for hours. There was one in particular that held me entranced, and I tried every art in my attempts to wheedle it away from the owner, but he always frustrated me. His photographs were really part of him—tangible products of his hands and mind.

The picture that I admired so much was a scene in the high sierra, fifteen thousand feet above sea level. No more beautiful scenery exists in the world, than that of those serrated, snow-covered mountains that rise majestically at the end of a seemingly endless expanse of flat plateau. This particular photograph was of a group of wild vicuñas, standing still and apprehensive in the middle of a vast snow-covered plain, surrounded by the towering ice-clad mountains. There was not a human being in the picture, not a rock, not a blade of grass, nothing but those beautiful fawn-like animals in a great expanse of white.

Every time I looked at that wonderful photograph, I could feel the awesome solitude of those heights and recall the sharp pain in my chest from the rarefied air. I could remember the mornings when I had passed over those great plains, seeing the frost still on the stubby ichu grass, hearing the rush of the cold mountain streams, and watching the glint of the early morning sun reflected from the snowy mountains. I had to tear myself away from that scene, every time. No one, I believe, has ever taken photographs to equal those of Padre Zavalla!

His other passion, rose growing, was carried on in the small garden in front of the house. There was only one big bush, but that seemed to bear every type of rose known to the neighborhood. The priest was tireless in begging shoots from anyone he found in possession of a rare and uncommon species. Those shoots he grafted onto his big bush, and there always were several different sizes and colors of roses represented, so that the priest-gardener called his big bush the "Joseph's Coat plant."

• Padre Zavalla was not a great man. He never erected a cathedral; he never made converts by the thousands; he was not even especially learned in advanced studies. But he was typical of most of his brother priests who work out their salvation in the many little towns below the Rio Grande. Like them, he lived a lonely life far from priestly company; he worked zealously for his Indians in so far as he could; and to guard against old age, he tried to save a few pennies from the pitiful stipends he received. Like his fellow priests, he had no sense of comfort. A bowl of rice, or a turkey—an easy chair, or an old box—anything was welcome, and inconvenience made no difference to him. He found his pleasures in the simple, lovely things of life; his pictures and his roses. A simple man, Padre Zavalla!

I was far away when Padre Zavalla fell sick. A friend wrote to tell me that one evening the aging priest had suffered a heart attack and had been carried to the nearest big town and placed in a hospital. His parishioners expected his death, and that evening they entered his poor house and carried away his moldy camera and the pictures from his wall. The next morning he died.

I suppose the roses are still blooming on his "Joseph's Coat plant"!

A   CHALLENGE   ANSWERED

"How can it be that Napoleon found millions of men ready to sacrifice their lives to ravage a nation while I cannot find a handful of devoted men to aid in extending the reign of God?" asked Father Charles Nerinckx, apostle of Kentucky, in an address in Belgium a century ago. His question was answered when DeSmet, later to become a great missioner among the Indians in our far West, and others volunteered to follow Father Nerinckx to America.

Unto Every Creature

by Mark Churchill

Maryknoll Missioner
in South China.

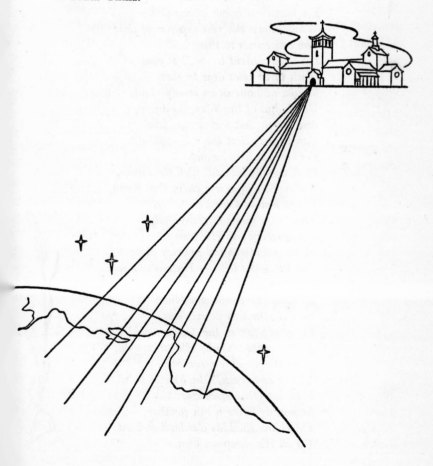

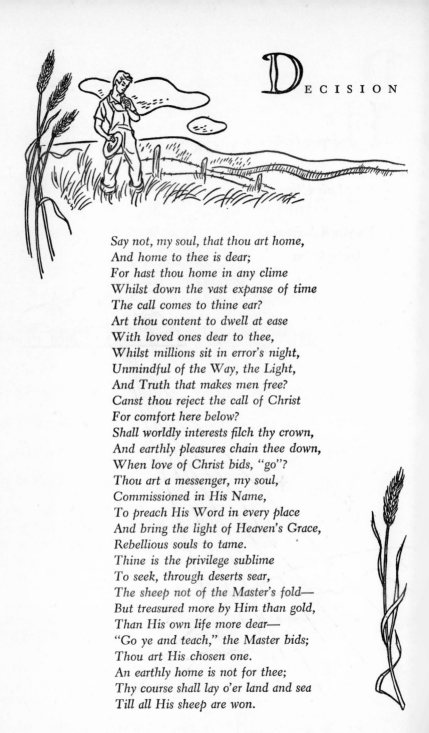

DECISION

Say not, my soul, that thou art home,
And home to thee is dear;
For hast thou home in any clime
Whilst down the vast expanse of time
The call comes to thine ear?
Art thou content to dwell at ease
With loved ones dear to thee,
Whilst millions sit in error's night,
Unmindful of the Way, the Light,
And Truth that makes men free?
Canst thou reject the call of Christ
For comfort here below?
Shall worldly interests filch thy crown,
And earthly pleasures chain thee down,
When love of Christ bids, "go"?
Thou art a messenger, my soul,
Commissioned in His Name,
To preach His Word in every place
And bring the light of Heaven's Grace,
Rebellious souls to tame.
Thine is the privilege sublime
To seek, through deserts sear,
The sheep not of the Master's fold—
But treasured more by Him than gold,
Than His own life more dear—
"Go ye and teach," the Master bids;
Thou art His chosen one.
An earthly home is not for thee;
Thy course shall lay o'er land and sea
Till all His sheep are won.

DEPARTURE

The stars look down on Mary's Knoll
And silent vigil keep.
The peace that inundates my soul
Is silent, too, and deep;
And nearness of the long-sought goal
Has set a ban on sleep.

Tomorrow is Departure Day:
The ancient temple bell,
That hangs within the cloister bay,
Its strident tone shall swell,
With warning to be on my way
And bid the Knoll farewell.

I walk the last time 'neath the pines
Be-silvered by the moon,
And hearken as their murm'rous spines
The vagrant night winds tune,
And love the more since God designs
That I must leave it soon.

I love the Knoll, but leave it still
Toward foreign fields to hie,
And herald far God's Holy Will
Beneath an alien sky;
Yet hope to stand on Mary's hill
Again before I die.

The stars that look on Maryknoll
Their wistful vigil keep;
The peace, that inundates my soul,
Is pensive, too, and deep.
Can I, who near my life-long goal
Resign myself to sleep?

DESTINATION

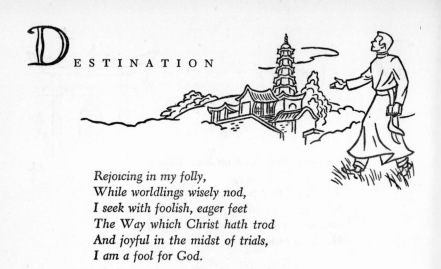

Rejoicing in my folly,
While worldlings wisely nod,
I seek with foolish, eager feet
The Way which Christ hath trod
And joyful in the midst of trials,
I am a fool for God.

I preach the folly of the Cross
In hamlets far and near,
Enticing men to folly's ways
And teaching all who hear
To trust the foolishness of God,
His folly to revere.
The riches which the prudent seek
Shall not be theirs for long,
For earthly life is very brief
And earthly prudence wrong,
And weak and foolish things, at length,
Confound the wise and strong.

A-wandering in sordid lanes,
I seek a priceless prize
Which folly ever cherisheth
And wisdom doth despise:
The souls of dying pagan babes
As "Thieves of Paradise."

I have not where to lay my head,
Yet all the world is mine;
For all is Christ's and Christ, my all,
Benignly doth resign
Himself to me as guerdon of
My foolishness divine.

I hold Him in my trembling hands—
The Bread and Wine of Life—
And carry Him to foreign lands
Where Satan's wiles are rife
And myriads of human souls
Are hazard in the strife.

Rejoicing in my folly,
While worldlings wisely nod,
I seek with foolish, eager feet,
The Way which Christ hath trod
And, joyful in the midst of trials,
I am a fool for God.

DEDICATION

In union with Thy sufferings
On Calvary's blest Tree,
O Christ, through Mary's stainless hands,
I offer unto Thee
Myself for those redeemed souls,
Which Thou preparest for me.

O, sanctify me for their need
And for Thy Glory's sake;
My daily life more like to Thine
In every aspect make,
That others from my blameless life
May good example take.

In all my daily actions, Lord,
Grant me heroic grace;
In sorrows, teach me by Thy love
My Calvary to face,
And, in humiliation's midst,
My trust in Thee to place.

Work freely in my soul, O God,
(For self-will I resign)
And of Thy labors let the fruits,
So plentiful, be mine;
But ever, in Thy justice, Lord,
The glory all be Thine.

HOPE

Say not the struggle nought availeth,
  The labor and the wounds are vain,
The enemy faints not nor faileth,
  And as things have been they remain.

If hopes were dupes, fears may be liars;
  It may be in yon smoke concealed,
Your comrades chase e'en now the fliers.
  And, but for you, possess the field.

For while the tired waves, vainly breaking,
  Seem here no painful inch to gain,
Far back, through creeks and inlets making,
  Comes silent, flooding, the main.

And not by Eastern windows only,
  When daylight comes, pours in the light:
In front the Sun climbs slow . . . how slowly!
  But Westward, look, the land is bright.

—A. H. CLOUGH

SAINT TORIBIO

by Donald Attwater

A celebrated British writer tells of an American saint who is little known outside Lima, Peru, and who was a layman when he was appointed archbishop of the New World's most important diocese.

I wonder how many people outside of South America have ever heard of St. Toribio. And yet he is, equally with St. Rose of Lima, the first known saint of the New World. It is true that he was not born on the American continent, and not canonized by the Church until fifty-five years after her, but they lived in the same place at the same time. Toribio died first, and it was he who conferred the sacrament of confirmation on Rose.

Toribio Alfonso Mogrobejo was born in Spain in 1538. His childhood and youth were notably religious, but he had no intention of becoming a priest and was, in fact, educated for the law. He was so brilliant a scholar that he became professor of law in the famous university of Salamanca. While there he attracted the notice of King Philip II of Spain (widower of Queen Mary I of England), and eventually the king made him chief judge of the ecclesiastical court of the Inquisition at Granada. This was a surprising position for a layman to hold, and it was not a pleasant or easy post for anyone, layman or cleric. But it led to something even more surprising. After some years the archbishopric of Lima, in the Spanish colony of Peru, became vacant.

* From *Saints Westward*. Copyright, P. J. Kenedy and Sons.

Toribio had carried out his judge's duties so well, and displayed such a fine missionary spirit, that it was decided to send him to Peru as archbishop.

Toribio was shocked at this decision, and wrote to the royal council pointing out that he was entirely unfitted for the office, and that anyway it was against canon law to appoint a layman to ecclesiastical dignities. The council replied that they were better judges of his fitness than he was, and as for his second objection, that would easily be gotten over: he would have to be ordained priest and bishop. So Toribio submitted. He was consecrated bishop, and in 1581 landed in Peru. He was then forty-three years old.

Like similar enterprises by other nations elsewhere, the immediate effects of Spanish conquest and colonization in South America were not all evil, and were very far from being all good. With the Europeans came Christianity, and the Church's missionaries achieved much—in some places more than in others—for the spiritual and temporal welfare of the native Indians; they would have done even more but for the tight control of the Spanish civil authorities. But a worse handicap was the behavior of so many of the conquerors. With whatever individual exceptions, they were filled with a lust for wealth, exploiting and pillaging the country, enslaving the people and making them work in the mines for the benefit of their oppressors.

St. Toribio arrived in Peru not quite fifty years after Pizarro's conquest, and he was indeed faced with a tough proposition. Not only was religion in decay among the officials, the military and the colonists; but also, it must be sadly admitted, some of the clergy who had come out from Spain to spread the good news of Christ had failed to withstand the dangers and temptations of their new surroundings. The Archbishop decided at once to make a visitation of his whole territory, which was huge. It stretched 400 miles or more along the Pacific Coast and many miles inland among the spurs of the Andes, some 18,000 square miles in all; with no means of transportation except horses and mules, and often not even these. That first visitation, which he was to repeat twice more, took him seven years to complete.

It was not only the wilderness and roughness of the country, and the rigors of the climate bringing on sickness, that made progress slow. "Time is not our own: we shall have to give a strict account of it," was a favorite saying of St. Toribio. This meant that he must not hurry unduly, for the work that he had to do needed care and patience; were he to hurry through it, and then rush off to somewhere else, he would be wasting his time.

Among the things that took time was the study of the Indian languages and dialects. It was one of the troubles in Peru (and elsewhere) that Indians were often baptized who had hardly any knowledge of the Christian faith and its obligations. One reason for this was that many missionaries had very little knowledge of the Indian languages. St. Toribio at once saw the difficulty and tried to remedy it, beginning with himself.

Naturally enough their new archbishop was not popular among many of the Spaniards, the wickedness of whose lives he reproved and whose oppression of the Indians he opposed; they did all they could to hamper him. And they could do a lot, for St. Toribio was no respecter of persons and was as quick to condemn an influential citizen as an unimportant one; so he had opponents in high places. When he wanted to stop a public abuse he did not simply say from the pulpit, "It is wrong to do so-and-so." He would say, "Don X. Y. Z. persists in doing so-and-so. This is wicked; and if he does not know why, I will tell him." Then as now, offenders tried to wriggle out of it. "What's the harm?" they would say. "Everybody does it." And Toribio would reply with a quotation from one of the early defenders of the Church, Tertullian: "Our Lord said, 'I am the truth.' He did not say, 'I am the custom.'"

In spite of opposition, St. Toribio's twenty-five years as archbishop of Lima were full of achievements. In 1591 he founded the first seminary in the New World, at Lima. He established churches, religious houses, hospitals, and schools, and in civil affairs he gave special encouragement to the making of roads— he, more than anybody, knew how much they were needed. Every two years he assembled his clergy round him in council, and the difficulties of travel were sometimes made an excuse for not attending.

As a missionary he was no less successful, and he is said to have baptized and confirmed half a million souls. Figures like that are completely unreliable and almost certainly exaggerated, but we may be sure it was a large number. Among those he confirmed, as well as St. Rose, are said to have been Blessed Martin de Porres and Blessed John Massias. From 1590 he had the help of another great missionary, the Franciscan St. Francis Solano, whose denunciations of the wickedness of Lima so alarmed the people that the viceroy had to call on St. Toribio to calm them.

Toribio made so strong an appeal to the Indians partly because of his knowledge of their languages, which he kept on studying almost up to his death. But even more it was because of his shining goodness and his obvious concern for their welfare. In order to have time to instruct them properly he would stay for days in villages where he could hardly get food, much less a bed. When he heard of Indians lost in the mountains he would himself brave the hardships and dangers of the rescue parties searching for them; and always he did all he could to lighten their burden of poverty and oppression. On his most arduous journeys he would celebrate Mass every day, and daily confess to his chaplain. For St. Toribio love of God and love of his spiritual children always went hand in hand, and he did not forget that their bodies were the dwelling place of their souls.

He was no less selfless in caring for his Spanish flock. In Lima he was a frequent visitor to the hospitals, taking comfort and the sacraments to the patients; he helped the victims of epidemics at great cost to himself; and he encouraged public processions of penitence—a common feature of Spanish religious life—walking in them himself. He had feeling for the sensitive pride of his people. He knew that many are shy about making their poverty or their other needs known; they do not like to accept public charity or help from their acquaintances. So he did all he could to assist them privately, without their knowing from whom their benefactions came.

St. Toribio's last sickness attacked him when he was away from

Lima, at Pacasmayo, far to the north. Working to the last, he struggled as far as Santa, where he knew the end was at hand. He made his will, giving his personal belongings to his servants and all the rest of his property for the benefit of the poor. He asked to be carried to the church to receive viaticum there, and was then brought back to bed and anointed. While those about him sang the psalm, "I was glad when they said unto me, We will go into the house of the Lord," St. Toribio died, on March 23, 1606. He was sixty-eight years old.

It has been said of him that he renewed the face of the Church in Peru. His influence was felt beyond those borders, so that his feast is now kept all over South America. St. Rose of Lima, on the other hand, is the patron saint of the continent, and her feast is kept in all parts of the world. Perhaps that is why she is so much better known than St. Toribio. But in remembering the one, we ought not to forget the other.

NARROW ESCAPE

by Mark Tennien

> Father Tennien tells of a desperate chance he took to
> deceive the Communists and how by sheer nerve he was
> able to carry it through to success.

Time was running out for me as a prisoner of the Communists when October, 1951, was torn from the calendar. The village sickles hacked at the tufts of rice to gather the autumn harvest. Fields were dotted with farm folk swinging bunches of grain

---

* From *No Secret is Safe*. Copyright, Farrar, Straus and Cudahy.

against the inside of threshing boxes. The thump, thump, thump of farmers beating off the kernels of grain boomed through the valley like signal drums to herald the coming of winter. The straw was stacked, the sun was yellow and summer had gone. Lazy oxen were lashed and cursed as they dragged plows to turn the soil for winter wheat.

November was passing, and I grew impatient with the Communists' delay in letting me go. When I gave them the letter requesting an exit travel permit in July, they assured me it would be cleared in a few weeks. Two years under Communism, one of them as convict and prisoner, were wearing me down. Now I was worried at the delay in release. Perhaps they would not make the mistake of letting me go, for they had already made many mistakes.

It was a mistake to let us stay in China after the Communists took over. It was a mistake to put me under house arrest where I could see and hear the Communist meetings in the church; a mistake to leave me as eyewitness to the land-reform meetings, the public trials and public beatings held in the church; a mistake to sentence and shoot the landlords in plain sight of the "foreign spy." After months of eyewitness observations from the house prison, it was another mistake to put me in jail with five hundred prisoners, where I saw too much for their pleasure. It was a mistake to give me the indoctrination course, but they found out too late. It was a mistake to let me have my fountain pen in jail, for I kept a written diary of what I saw and heard. It was a mistake to let me smuggle the prison diary out of jail. It was a mistake to leave me my typewriter at the mission. Under house arrest after the jail term, I could type out my prison diary in double copy for a book to expose them.

After all these blunders I began to wonder if they would make the final mistake of letting me get out of China. If they arranged to have me conveniently die, it would correct all their mistakes. I was more worried as time slipped by. On November 15 a friendly police officer visited me. I asked him to press the Chief of Police to get an answer from Provincial Headquarters on my exit. They had had nearly five months now to look into my case.

Next day the officer told me an official letter had been sent in to urge for action.

Later in the afternoon, November 23, the police officer came in smiling. He announced they had received clearance from Provincial Headquarters to release me. Tomorrow I would be escorted to have pictures taken for a travel permit and fill out the necessary papers. But he warned that I must leave the day after, for travel orders were restricted to the four days necessary to get out of China. It would not be my fault if I did not get across the border by November 28, I assured him.

He came for me early next morning. There are no secrets in China, and Christians were already stealing in to say farewell. The officer abruptly ordered them away. We started the procedure so as to be ready to set out next day. I was bolder now and sent word to the military asking for payment or return of the mission telephone, gasoline, and other things they had taken from the mission while I was in jail. The Chief of Police was requested to pay for the drum of gasoline he had taken. My requests and protests brought no results.

A big decision faced me as I packed my foot locker that night. I picked up the copy of my prison diary and wondered if it was foolhardy to try and bring it out. During the recent months in house jail after my prison term, I had been revising and typing it. Many daring chances had already been taken to try and get a copy out to Hong Kong. Although the manuscript had been smuggled into the outgoing bag, my letters might still be caught when the mail went through the big centers like Wuchow and Canton. And so I lived in fear and expected a jail sentence or something worse if my letters were caught. But my luck held and nothing had happened up to now. Tomorrow I was to start the journey toward freedom. Perhaps it was crowding my luck too far to carry the dangerous material with me.

But no word was received from Hong Kong to say that the manuscript had arrived. All incoming letters were seized and kept by the police censor in Shumkai. Brother Francis wrote from Hong Kong in riddles which would give the desired answers if letters could reach me. But they were all stopped.

I decided on a big gamble, to take the manuscript with me. It represented many months' work and contained statistics, translations of documents, songs, and other things that could not be reconstructed outside. The long ledger sheets, typed on both sides to reduce bulk, were clipped together with wire staples. Elastic yarn was slipped under the staples to tie the sheets tight, half around each leg. A string inside my belt held each pack from slipping down. Documents concealed on the person were sure to condemn me as a spy if they were discovered. I thought I could get by without discovery. Concealing the script was my mistake, not the Communists'.

In the morning five police came to take me to the bus station. My cook, Martin Neep, had stuck by me through all the Communists' ridicule and ugly epithets. He helped carry my baggage to the bus station for inspection.

"We start with a search of your person," announced a police officer. "Let's see what you have in your pockets."

My heart jumped with fright and sent a sharp pain through my chest. Now was the time for quick thinking. I spread the contents of each pocket on the foot lockers, and at the same time pulled the pockets inside out. The police searched through everything; they even pulled cigarettes and fountain pen apart to look inside. As I pushed my pockets back in place the Secretary to the Police Chief slipped his hand into my pants pocket. His fingers felt the top edge of the manuscript sheets, though it was hardly higher than a seam.

"What is that under your pocket?"

"My underpants, of course!" and with that I dropped to one knee and fumbled with the keys to open the foot locker. This put his hand out of danger. Now I had to try and talk myself out of a tight corner.

"Open up the small bag first," ordered one of the police.

"No, no, search this one first; it is open now."

Communists insist on having their orders followed, so I started a heated argument, while dumping things out for their inspection. The Secretary was distracted in trying to settle the argument and he seemed to forget about my pocket. I stayed down on the one knee for nearly an hour watching the baggage search. When they took my camera and pictures, it gave me an opportunity for violent protest. Fortunately I had smuggled out many pictures beforehand. In my own mind the argument was a secret plea for freedom and perhaps for life, so I turned on the heat. I was not angry, but I was scared enough to put on a good act. The argument and ceaseless talk kept them on the defensive. It distracted them and stopped any more dangerous questions.

Finally the search was over and I was left to repack my baggage. The Police Secretary had completely forgotten about the crease under my pocket. I stayed down on one knee and dallied with the packing until the police wandered across to the bus station. Then we quickly loaded the baggage on the roof rack of the bus, and I climbed inside to stay away from frisking hands.

THE NEW MEM-SAHIBS

by James A. Michener

A warning to American women going abroad not to repeat mistakes made by the women of other Western nations. Michener, while famed for his stage and film successes, is a serious student of Far Eastern problems.

Noel Coward, who can be extremely cruel when in the mood, made the wry comment after meeting the British matrons of Singapore that now he understood why it was so difficult to hire upstairs maids in London.

I could not agree to this libel, for I found the matrons of

* From *The Voice of Asia.* Copyright, James A. Michener, Random House.

Singapore both intelligent and attractive, and one night at the super-posh Tanglin Club I saw several who were downright beautiful.

But I would agree heartily with the French cavalry officer who said that in his lifetime only three things had really terrified him, a tiger in the Malay jungles, a cobra in Mysore and almost any Englishwoman in the tropics.

What happens to perfectly decent women after they live in India or Java or Malaya is impossible to explain. At home they were not the sort to lord it over servants, for most of them had none. Nor were they self-appointed paragons of social virtue, for many English towns have an enviable freedom in social relations. But once put them in the tropics, and these same gentle girls become unbearable.

It would be unreasonable to expect women suddenly surrounded by twenty servants, when they had none before, to retain their balance, and few do. Quickly they succumb to delusions of grandeur and consider it inevitable that white women should order about almost any of the 1,500,000,000 yellow and brown and black men of Asia. As one French priest-sociologist explained it, only the lowest-caste natives would hire out as servants because the others bitterly resented being kicked by white women.

It would also be unreasonable to expect that white women in the tropics should remember much about the democracy they knew at home. Almost alone and submerged in an alien sea of strange colors, strange foods and strange inhabitants, it is instinctive for them to clutch at the silliest rules for protecting their cherished social life. For real, archaic and oppressive social patterns you have got to go to the tropics and watch white societies protecting themselves from brown.

But it is not unreasonable to demand that from now on the mem-sahibs accept the citizens of Asia as human beings or stop coming to Asia. Proud Indians and Indonesians and Filipinos will no longer tolerate the social nonsense of past generations, for they know that the white man and his mem-sahib are no longer gods.

It must be quickly admitted that Englishwomen were not the

only offenders in establishing insufferable social systems which ridiculed and insulted Asians. The Dutch in Java were as bad. Australians in Rabaul were worse. And although the French behaved a little better, they made up for it by excessively harsh economic exploitation. All the Europeans were alike.

But it was reserved for the Englishwomen to lead the pack. All across Asia you meet local citizens who speak with venomous hatred of the British social system as it affected them. Today many Indians frankly acknowledge the debt they owe to England, but they add that the social persecutions they experienced in English society were unbearable. Usually they place the blame for this upon the women, holding that Englishmen were often prepared to accept Asians as human beings, but that their women would never relent.

The desire for revenge that such behavior generated in Asia is incalculable, yet it must be taken into consideration when judging Asia's future. There is a memory of social ignominy that this crop of political leaders will never forgive, and many of their actions are obviously motivated by a desire to prove that Asian society will no longer accept white domination in any particular.

Although Englishwomen were largely responsible for the hateful policy of arrogant supremacy, it was left to their men to express this policy in its most ridiculous form. A recent letter from such a gentleman has had wide circulation in Asia, always to the accompaniment of hoots of ribald laughter. A last-gasp Englishman explains to the public how white people should govern Asia. The letter was written, believe it or not, in 1951.

"Psychological propaganda and an outward show of authority are worth dozens of committee meetings. Leading officials should wear colorful uniforms as often as possible.

"When the High Commissioner leaves King's House in his Rolls-Royce, fine example of the world's finest motor car, he should be preceded and followed by traffic police outriders on motorcycles.

"The traffic police all over town should be warned of his journey and should control and direct traffic accordingly to allow him free and swift passage.

"His convoy should be ostentatious so that people will know when it passes that it is the High Commissioner.

"All major officials should conduct themselves in the same way, so as to impress the population. A suitable uniform should also be designed for soldiers who are on leave, so that their presence will invariably be noted.

"Lesser officials should be officials. When the secretariat empties itself at tiffin time you cannot tell if the people coming out are officials or junior assistants in a commercial undertaking.

"Newspapers, too, should give prominent display to the photographs of highly respected citizens and accompany the photographs with suitable captions.

"High officials should also address the population frequently by radio to remind the country that it is being well governed."

Such a letter, accompanied by the mem-sahib point of view, represents such a discredited theory of colonial government as to be tragic in the light of today's events. One might grudgingly admit that in governing a totally ignorant and savage land such pompous nonsense might be necessary for a few decades. But the poison of such empty forms is that they remain as pleasant games long after their usefulness is past. And into the emptiness someone like Ho-Chi Minh or Sukarno or Mao Tse-tung injects a real, life-size revolution.

Contrast this bankruptcy of ideas with what Russia offers Asian people today. Leadership of their own lands. Increased crops. More food. Ownership by local people of local industries. It is true that most of the Russian promises are not fulfilled, but when opposed to Rolls-Royces and uniforms and police on motorcycles the Russian theory is going to win everytime.

It is disturbing, therefore, to find that today in the first flush of America's world responsibilities, many American women fresh from two-room apartments have picked up the mem-sahib racket right where the Englishwomen left off. I have heard half a dozen American women sipping tea and saying, in self-pity, "If we Americans pulled out of here tomorrow, within six months these characters would be back in trees."

I am sure Englishwomen thought the same way right up to the

minute they were being kicked out of one establishment after another. Surely the Dutchwomen were convinced that without them Java would collapse. And if Americans persist in such ideas, if they persist in playing the role of great white father and mem-sahib, our efforts to win Asia to our side are absolutely doomed.

All American firms sending employees to Asia, all governmental agencies having business there, and all friends seeing vacationists off should see to it that the women who go along are given a pamphlet explaining what happened to the English and Dutch and French and Australian societies that were built upon the tacit assumption that all people who are not white are feeble-minded.

There is much that is wrong with Asia. Some things are terribly wrong. And by and large sensible Asians want our help in correcting them. But they will not tolerate our ridicule.

It is good, therefore, to remark that in numerous instances white women have done great things in creating friendly respect between Americans and Asians. I think they have done a better job, sometimes, than their husbands, and it is such women that should represent America.

This is terribly important because Red China and Communist Russia are sending extremely powerful and impressive women to other parts of Asia. The results are impressive, for they are un-doing the damages done by the mem-sahib. We must not leave the field of social victories entirely to the enemy. Let some other nation become the new mem-sahibs. Let us be the nation of democratic equality.

When I think of India I think of the Kashmiri Gate. It stands in the western wall of Delhi and through it has passed con-querors, new religions, old beggars and the princely viceroys of British India.

But I remember the Kashmiri Gate because of a somewhat different traveler. There was a young woman who haunted this gate and in some ways she spoke for India. I could pass through the gate to Sohan Lal's for a fine evening and I could think that India was a land of brilliant philosophy. I passed through the gate for dinner at the expensive hotels and I could imagine that India was a center of great wealth. And I drove in the countryside where the prolific growth of the soil impressed me, but when I came back through the Kashmiri Gate I would see this strange woman and I could never forget that she was India, too.

For she was naked. She was completely naked and once I saw a policeman gently advise her that she really must go home and put some clothes on. She pulled away and walked on through the Kashmiri Gate where the conquerors had marched.

She was about twenty-two, most attractive in appearance, very wild-eyed. She carried a few filthy belongings in a rotting cloth and was either a madwoman or someone protesting the bitterly high price of cloth. We looked at each other whenever we passed and she seemed to be a living protest. Actually she was merely a naked woman walking through the Kashmiri Gate. No one thought to arrest her.

There is much in India that no American can understand. It is a different land requiring different approaches. We hear about the cities, but it is a land of tiny villages. We develop high regard for Indians of superior education, but India is a land of illiteracy. We hear of princes and maharajahs, but here is a land of gnawing poverty. Most important, we hear of India's temporary problems, but fundamentally this is a land of immense stability with a permanent urge toward self-preservation and projection into the future.

I had in India the oppressive sense of history that has frightened many Western visitors traveling there: What happens in the next few decades is of almost no consequence to India. It will go on pretty much as before. Land reforms will take place. Strange new conquerors may march through the Kashmiri Gate, but India will remain. Its population will multiply and a thousand years from now India will be there, timelessly struggling with such new problems as will have arisen.

But for America the next few decades are of immense importance. We are clinging to a less fundamental perch, and that is why I have felt that it is more important for us to hold India's friendship than it is for India to worry too much about America. This may not seem obvious now, but as we go on I think it will become apparent.

I wish that some way could have been worked out for India, Great Britain and America to have combined as a team. That was impossible, so now I hope that America and India will co-operate on common problems. If that proves impossible—as evil-intentioned people in both America and India seem determined to prove—then all we can do is retreat to a tenuous friendship with Japan and pray to God that the rest of Asia does not blow up in our face.

I do not believe that Indian-American friendship has been lost. It has, however, reached the testing stage. Our handling of wheat for India was ridiculous and calculated to do us the most possible harm. Perhaps we should not have said at first that we would give them the wheat free. Involved are economic problems which I do not understand; but once having said we would, we were then committed, and our subsequent backing and filling and debating dissipated whatever good will we might originally have created.

The people of Asia are not stupid. One day they will stand in the world as our absolute equals. At that time they must be able to look back at a long history of constructive American-Asian relations. We started a good history with China. We continued with the Philippines and Japan. Right now the crucial chapters are being written in India.

FATHER RICCI EXPLAINS

Father Matteo Ricci, the Jesuit who opened China to the Faith, was asked how he could leave his home, his homeland and his loved ones and spend his life in distant China. His reply has become a classic. "There is no problem," he said. "We missioners have God for our Father, all mankind for brothers, and the world for a home."

CLOSE CALL IN THE JUNGLE

by Gorden N. Fritz

An airplane crash is only the beginning of trouble for these two Maryknollers traveling in the land of the Amazon's headwaters. Yet through it all a sense of humor is never lost.

It was a beautiful, bright morning when the big cargo plane lifted itself from the La Paz airport into the rarefied atmosphere of the Bolivian Andes. The plane was destined for the jungles of the Beni River, in the far interior. Monsignor Thomas J. Danehy and I were the only passengers aboard, and most of the cargo was for our Cavinas Mission.

After a while the plane wound out of the mountains, and down over the jungle and the Beni headwaters. Soon our first destination, the little town of Rurrenabaque, came into sight. We settled down on the airstrip, a perfect landing—but only for the first few seconds!

Then one of the wheels locked, and the C-54 skidded off the runway, into a series of big ditches at the far end of the field, crumpling the undercarriage and ripping off one of the wings. Fortunately, neither of the motors caught fire, so there was no damage to the pilot, to Monsignor, or to me, other than a rather violent shaking up of ourselves and the cargo—and, of course, the long walk to the other end of the airfield.

During the next week we found that the airplane crash was a

mild beginning for a series of troubles. We lost a day waiting for our cargo to be dragged from the wreckage. On the second day I bought a pair of big, dugout canoes, weighing about four tons, and lashed them together with ropes and vines. Monsignor hired the town's only tractor and began hauling cargo from airport to river. By the next morning, our canoes were all loaded, well supplied with pots, pans, and food, plus gas and oil for our five-horsepower outboard motor, which we had put on one canoe.

At eight o'clock we said good-by to Rurrenabaque and the crumpled plane, which still lay at the end of the jungle, abandoned, and not worth being salvaged. The day was bright and pleasant. Our destination, Cavinas Mission, 500 miles away, seemed near and easy of access.

Everything began well. We skillfully passed through the twenty-odd miles of logs and rapids that form the first part of the river. At nightfall, we stopped our motor, cooked and ate, and settled down in the canoes for a good sleep, letting the canoes drift on unguided. We had decided to travel at night in order to reach Cavinas for the big Indian fiesta. That was our first mistake. It doesn't pay to rush in the jungle.

At two o'clock the next morning, Monsignor and I awoke with a start. Right in front of us, a huge log stood upright in the river. The water was roaring as it split around the log. Seconds later we crashed, the collision forcing the canoes almost to stand on end. Cargo and missioners were thrown into the river. I grabbed a few boxes and packages that came floating by.

"Let them alone!" Monsignor called. "Get the canoes, or we'll never get out of here."

By this time the canoes had slipped off the log and were slowly sinking. After a struggle we managed to get them to shore. Then we tried to locate any cargo that might be near. Fortunately the brief case we had saved contained matches and a flashlight, so we were able to build a small fire. We stood shivering over that, slightly disturbed as some wild jungle beast paced back and forth on the bank above us, until morning.

Taking stock by daylight, we found that fortunately we still had our motor, gas, and oil. But our food, cooking utensils, and so forth, were gone. I had lost my personal possessions, and some crocodile is probably now wearing Monsignor's red robes.

With one small tin we had salvaged, we bailed out the canoes. Then we took off again on the river. At three that afternoon, we came to a thatched hut, where we obtained some food. Then on again until nightfall. That night we did not try to travel. But this did us no good. The river went down during the night, and morning found us high and dry on a mudbank. We had to dig ourselves out with our one salvaged "shovel."

At noon a submerged log knocked the motor off the canoe. Fortunately we had tied it with rope, so it was still with us. But the rest of the day was needed for cleaning and drying the motor. We went to bed without supper that night because of mosquitos.

The next day our bad luck continued. A strong wind prevented us from moving until almost nightfall; then the pump on the motor went out of commission. For the following day and a half, we had to paddle. Finally we concocted a Rube Goldberg contraption, and we were able to run the motor as long as one of us remained at it, pouring water into it. But soon afterwards, we became stranded on a sandbar.

The last day was not too bad. We sighted Cavinas Mission at noon. Just then we hit the worst underwater log of the trip, and completely smashed the motor. For the next hour and a half, we had to paddle in the heat of the midday sun. We arrived at the mission looking like barbarians, sunburned, dirty and unshaven, and clothed in tattered garments.

While we were "fighting" our way down the river, Bolivia's worst revolution had broken out. So instead of being able to tell about our heroic exploits when we got home, we were silenced by everyone else's tales of the revolution.

JOHNNY

by Sister Maria del Rey

> The young Igorot tribesman had a battle to fight all by
> himself. Although he never learned the outcome, his
> victory was complete. This is a true story by a talented
> Maryknoll Sister.

This is the story of Johnny, the Brave One—of Johnny the Strong One, and of Kitma, his bride.

The story of Sister Fidelis, as well.

Johnny got his title the hard way. Many times on the mountain trails of northern Luzon he had stood before Japanese sentries utterly impassive as the searching hands felt through his vegetable basket for the paper he had hidden in the core of a cabbage. Many times his stocky half-clad figure with the stolid legs and muscular toes had covered the distance from Bukod, to Tuba, Tubao, to Asin, bringing packets of quinine from the Sisters on the hill near Baguio to the Americano Captain, bearded to cover his gauntness, hiding with his wretched band of guerrillas who shivered and sweated by turns with malaria, as they lay stretched out on the grass.

Small wonder, then, that after the war Johnny was feted as canyao after canyao was given in the Igorot mountain villages to celebrate the victory of '45. Deep in the wooded mountains, the native drums sent the invitation for miles around. "There is a canyao in Lakad tonight; and tomorrow we dance at Asin."

Johnny and the young blades went to them all, resplendent in genuine olive-drab G.I. fatigue suits and jungle boots. Sometimes they brought G.I. friends as well and were just a bit self-conscious about it all. At first, they were content to sit around the clearing watching the dancers as they slowly circled the fire. But the slow clang of the gongs of native copper, mined and beaten as they did in prehistoric ages, and the thrum of heavy fingers on hollow wood, warmed Johnny's blood. Then the wrinkled chieftain came toward him holding out the long white dancing blanket, an invitation to dance next; every bit of Igorot in him surged forward with pride that this honor had come to him.

"And who shall take the woman's robe?" asked Atab, the old man.

There was no sign of preference in Johnny's face as he pointed almost contemptuously to a girl squatting with the other young women across the clearing from him. "That Kitma, there," he said. He threw the white blanket over his shoulders so that the two ends hung down his back and the cowl-effect draped across his chest. Atab was also impassive as he crossed the open place, skirting the fire, and presented the big sheetlike cloth to his daughter, Kitma. It was really a white seersucker bedspread from some foreigner's house in Baguio.

The drums at one side of the clearing mumbled and then swung into a steady rhythm. Johnny stepped forth to lead the dance; behind him, after a space, followed a man dressed only in a ragged felt hat, a flannel shirt of khaki, and a G-string around his loins, the long narrow tails of which flapped between his legs almost to his knees. He carried a copper gong, bonging it in slow time as he walked after Johnny, round and round the fire. Two other musicians followed him, similarly dressed; one struck two iron railroad spikes together in dull jubilation; the other ting-ting-ed on a real orchestral triangle.

The four men merely walked around the fire for several circuits in slow rhythm. Then Kitma joined them, slipping into the space behind Johnny. Johnny started the long strides of the male dancer; his head bent forward and his straight arms as far back as he could reach them. Then one arm came forward above his head and the hand twisted at the wrist; the gesture was repeated with the other arm. That was all there was to Johnny's dance; the visiting American soldiers thought it ridiculously simple, even inane.

But Kitma really danced. She wrapped the cloth around her and draped the end over one shoulder. She raised her hands, palms up, to shoulder height, and kept them immovable in this position. Teetering on her bare toes over the rough, pebbly ground, she swayed at the waist from side to side. At times she made bird-like swoops forward; at others, the men behind her slowed to let her lag behind Johnny. The grace of her head with its lank, black hair falling first over one shoulder and then over the other as her body bent to right and left, the unsteady light of the fire, the teetering feet and rigid arms and hands—it seemed to the tribesmen sitting on their heels in the great circle, that she was dignity and beauty and art incarnate.

They were tired at last. The jungle boots and unaccustomed clothes were heavy and hot, and Johnny stepped out of the clearing quite abruptly without a backward glance at Kitma. Indeed, he had not so much as recognized her presence behind him at all. Kitma, too, when she had danced around to the group of girls again, quite suddenly slipped off the bedspread, threw it over her father's arm and walked with her ordinary heavy Igorot tread to her place.

But it was after that dance, that both Johnny and Kitma knew what they knew, and knew that both knew it.

That was in May, 1945. It was June when Atab formally gave his daughter in pagan marriage to Johnny at a canyao of such proportions that even Atab, owner of three carabaos though he was, went into debt for it. But Johnny was not quite as happy as he expected to be at the canyao. The very sound of his name disturbed him as it was spoken again and again in toasts when the gourd of tuba, the native coconut wine, passed from old man, to young man, to old women, and around the circle once more.

For Johnny had no Igorot name. Or rather, no one remembered what he was called before his mother had taken him and his brother Joseph to the Maryknoll Convent near Baguio to be baptized. It was Sister Matthew then who had taught the doctrine to his mother, but she left a few years afterwards. Sister Fidelis was his friend, in the early days before the war. Sister Fidelis— her strong face and deep mannish voice, her flash of big white teeth in sudden humor, her sharp cleavage of "Right!" and "Wrong!," her rapid stride from village to village, teaching, cajoling, correcting, winning by kindness and retaining by righteousness.

But four years of upset and war is a long time to a young man. His mother was dead, now; Joseph went off to the lowlands when the Japanese were after him. Sister Fidelis was taken to the concentration camp in 1942. The Japanese officers occupied the convent on the hill for a while then; and dug deep tunnels and caves to hide themselves from American planes. Now it stood, half-ruined and empty, on the road to Baguio, an abandoned tank in the driveway and a big gun crouching uselessly under the pine trees at the side. Johnny had passed it many times, and always he thought of Sunday mornings when he and his mother and brother walked the long trail for Sunday Mass and catechism lessons afterward.

So Johnny frowned a bit at his wedding canyao, and Kitma pouted at him for it.

"Later, I will straighten this out," he promised himself, and took Kitma to his new house in the rice fields.

It was perhaps two months later that he met Sister Fidelis on the road. Life was beginning to stir again in Baguio after the near-annihilation of carpet bombings. He hoped to sell a few extra cabbages and camotes to folks who had thrown up rusty tin shelters on the ruins of their burned houses.

He was honestly glad to see her although he knew what was coming.

"I hear you are married to Kitma, daughter of Atab, Johnny," Sister Fidelis fired the first shot.

"You have heard right, Sister."

"That was a pagan marriage. Now you will come before the priest for the Sacrament of Matrimony, won't you?"

Johnny looked at his toes for some time.

"Kitma does not like," he said.

Then the judgment came, as he knew it would.

"It is wrong for you to live with her, Johnny, unless you are first married before the priest."

"Kitma is very beautiful, Sister. She is good, too. You know her well."

"It is wrong, Johnny."

"Atab is quite rich. He has given us, recently, a fine carabao."

"Still, it is wrong, Johnny."

"Already, we have good hopes for a child, Sister."

"Provide for the child, Johnny. But it is wrong to live with her until you are married."

And he got no further than that with her. At last, he said:

"You will come to my house, Sister, and talk to Kitma. She says she likes you. Perhaps then, she will consent."

But Sister Fidelis shook her head and flashed her broad smile.

"This is your battle for right, Johnny. Win it for yourself."

In the year that followed, Sister Fidelis heard news of Johnny from time to time. He left Kitma right after the rice harvest—left her with the sacks piled high in the main room, piled high under the house, stuffed into the granary shed alongside. Kitma would not have to work for many months to come. Then he went off to work in the mines away up north.

Sister stopped sometimes in the neat palm-thatched hut as she went around visiting the villages. Kitma was always polite. She offered her dog meat and soup and a bag of sweet potatoes to take home, but there was no disguising her self-confidence.

"Johnny will come to see the baby, Sister. He will come and then he will stay with me."

Johnny did come when the baby was born; he came, stayed for a few hours, and went off again. Kitma, in anger, went to her father for a tribal divorce.

Seven old men, each a chieftain in his village, sat on their heels in a circle on the clean swept earth underneath Kitma's house. They were chieftains, but wore G.I. shirts and trousers, now quite old, quite dirty, quite ill-fitting. Some few had jungle boots as well, but most would rather grip the ground with their toes in the good old-fashioned way. However, there was no doubt of the infiltration of America among the children; bright plastic hair pins, little dresses and shirts made of army toweling, and the inevitable bubble-gum were everywhere.

But jungle boots, toweling and bubble-gum were immaterial to the business of the moment. The old men were awaiting the appearance of Johnny to present his side of the current divorce case.

Johnny had stopped to see Sister Fidelis on the way. She had gone out to the villages, the other Sisters told him. But he met her on the road, with Acop and Hensa, the Catholics.

"I am not the Strong One, now, Sister," he told her. "I am weak. I will go to meet the elders, but I cannot rely on myself. You must pray."

"We will pray together, Johnny. Take my crucifix with you," she had said. "Then I will go to the village of Atab with you although I cannot take part in the council. You must fight them all yourself."

Sister stayed at Acop's house in the village and prayed. Johnny went on to take his place in the council, opposite Atab. The seven old chieftains shifted a little to make room for him, and he, too, squatted on his heels in silence. Kitma stood behind her father, nursing her baby. Her black eyes slanted resentment and humiliation, but there was deep questioning, too. She knew, she *knew* that he loved her. Every device of bamboo wireless had failed to find another woman in the case. The love which drew him from even her, then, was for a Thing, or perhaps a Person with greater right to him than she had.

There was silence for an unbearable five minutes. Then Atab pulled his pipe from his mouth.

"That Johnny there and my Kitma, they are married by our custom. Yet Johnny lives far away . . ." Atab told the story fairly and evenly. "It is his God who does this," he ended.

The old men twisted their eyes and pipes to look at Johnny. "That is true," he said simply.

"My Kitma is beautiful?"

"That is true," said Johnny.

"I have given you much with her?"

"That is true," said Johnny.

"You have no other wife?"

Johnny winced; dear God, how could he ever love any other woman? Stop looking at me, Kitma! He pressed the hard little crucific into his palm.

"No other," he said.

Atab shrugged his shoulders. Lots of people do queer things to please their gods. He himself had grown his hair for ten years because he had vowed to do so.

"I say, then, let these two be no more man and wife. Each will be free," he suggested to the council.

No one demurred. A nod went round the circle.

"Wait a minute!"

It was Kitma who spoke. The old men frowned quickly and several stood up in surprise. A woman, even a married woman, does not often speak in the tribal council.

Kitma was hot and ashamed. She hardly knew why she had cried out. And now they were all looking at her. Then her thoughts cleared; this Person that Johnny loved so much, loved with a gem-like hardness, she must know too. "I have his warmth," she thought, "but He has his fire. I have his strength, but He makes him a man of steel."

She stepped forward into the circle.

"I will do what my husband says," she murmured with bent head. "I will marry Johnny as his God wants."

Atab and his councillors paused a little. Then they shrugged. Atab laughed at his daughter. "Kitma, first you want; then you don't want; now you want again. That's the woman in you." But he was not mad.

For nearly six weeks, then, Kitma trudged the mountain trails through pine trees, to the Maryknoll Convent near Baguio. Three times a week she and Sister Fidelis pulled the Igorot meaning out of Spanish derivatives. Misa, gracia, santa ecclesia, religio— things for which there was no proper word for. God brought to

Kitma's mind only the crude lumps of stone set up in the rice fields. The modern Igorot did not quite believe in these as divinities, but there was enough tradition in him to be a bit wary of removing them, or treating them contemptuously.

Then, it happened.

The fog settles thick in the valleys of northern Luzon's mountains, seeping, penetrating into every crevice like a blanket of fire-foam. It settles thick and stays long. If a man is to get a day's work in the rice field done before sundown, he can't afford to mind a little fog.

Kitma could hardly make out Johnny's figure as he stopped by on his way to the field. She was blinded by the smoke from her household fire, for one thing. But even when she rubbed her sleeve across her eyes and stood away from the smoking pile of faggots on the earthern floor, he seemed a wraith in the white fog which drifted into the crude wooden cabin through the open door. It was only when he folded her in his arms that she felt how living he was.

"When did Sister say?" he asked.

"Just three more lessons, Johnny. We'll be married Saturday week. You'll have your Catholic wife!"

He gave her an extra hug and stood away, looking at her. Suddenly, he reached for the rifle which stood in the corner. It was a heavy, crude affair, one which he had salvaged from alongside a Japanese body as it lay beside the blasted gun a bomber had spotted and wiped out. A good rifle—not equipped with safety catches and a bit rusted on the outside of the barrel, to be sure, but good enough for shooting mountain cats or brandishing at folks who come prowling around your carabao at night.

He smiled his slow Igorot smile as he fiddled with the rifle trigger. And Kitma thought, "How much our baby looks like him!"

"Time to start shooting for the wedding canyao, then! It will be clear up on the mountain tops, soon," he said, and ran out into the fog.

Scarcely a moment later, a shot rang out. Kitma looked out the door and laughed at herself for thinking she could hope to see anything. She turned back to the fire, the pot of rice, the baby, feeling warm and happy. These things within the house, and a good man shooting outside; indeed, the Good God of Sister Fidelis' talks had given her everything.

But by mid-morning, the fog had lifted. Kitma piled sweet potatoes into her woven basket and slung it behind her. A harness of braided leather suspended it from her head, so that she walked with neck outthrust and shoulders stiff, as all tribal women do. But it was the simplest means of carrying loads on the up-hill mountain trails.

"I'll sell these camotes in town and get something pretty for me and the baby," she thought, "something for Saturday week."

Johnny, Jr., was slung around her hip on a comfy hammock of ragged cloth, and Kitma set out on the five mile hike to Baguio glowing with deep content.

It wasn't far away, that she found Johnny—just where her cabin path met the dirt road. She found him sprawled in the thick mountain fern, with his foot still against the stone which had tripped him, and his face a mass of blood. The bullet had gone through his eye and out the top of his head. The explanation was plain: he had fallen and the rifle went off as he fell.

The Japanese rifle had revenged the nation that made it, and the corpse he stole it from.

"This is the end of things for Kitma," Sister Fidelis said to herself as she watched her pass among the guests at the funeral feast the next day. "She won't be able to stand Atab's reasoning. 'If you had let Johnny and his God alone, you wouldn't have brought this bad luck on yourself.' They'll tell her this shows only one thing. 'The tribal gods have their ways of getting back at Catholics.'"

"I must say," she admitted to herself, "he has a wonderful example to point out here."

But Kitma was at the convent for the next lesson-day. She had very little to say.

"Johnny loved his God. I do, too."

And on Saturday as planned, she and the baby were baptized. And now begins the pay-off in this story.

Other young tribesmen were not slow in coming to Kitma's door. They brought their fighting cocks and tried to make her admire the glossy feathers and proud combs. They offered to dig her sweet potatoes and plant her rice.

But to their propositions she had only one answer.

"You no Catholic, I no marry." And that was that.

Apo was not so easily put off. He knew a good woman when he saw one, and knew where to put pressure to get her. He went to Atab, her father.

Atab pulled at his pipe as he listened and watched, with a distant eye, his two best pigs rooting in the dusty cabin yard.

"It's woman-foolishness," Apo was saying. "All right for Johnny to tell his wife what god to go after—but no man takes his orders from a woman. You tell Kitma, Atab; you're her father. She'll listen to you. Besides, as chief, you owe it to the tribe to keep to our ancient beliefs.

"It isn't as if I come empty-handed, either, Honorable Chief. You don't need to be told that Kitma could do worse. And Kitma—well, I've got to have her, Atab, that's all. There's nobody else can match her."

The hot, half-choked voice stopped. Yet Atab merely pulled out his pipe stem and rubbed it meditatively through his hair. Then he put it back into his mouth, rose and turned to go inside.

"Well, what do you say, Atab?" Apo pressed forward.

"I say this, young man," and the blurred old eyes looked straight ahead. "Kitma knows her own mind. If you want to marry Kitma, do what Kitma says." With that he went inside.

And Apo did!

A PRIEST AMONG BANDITS

by Mark Tennien

As Chungking correspondent for NCWC News Service, Father Tennien came across many good stories. This one about a Maryknoller who hid out with bandits is as refreshing as sunshine after rain.

When a telegram told us in Chungking that Japanese army and puppet troops had attacked Chekkai on a foraging raid, none of us worried. We knew Father Donat Chatigny could hide out in some bandit lair where he had been called in the past to cure the sick. A week later we learned he was back at his ransacked mission, with nothing but good to say about the friends who had harbored him in the hills, and nothing bad to say about the enemy who had despoiled his mission. Like St. Francis, who befriended a wolf, Father Donat found some good in everybody.

Father Donat Chatigny was a smallish, bald man, just turning forty, so gentle of mien that one of his flock once said, "He is just like St. Joseph." But though soft of speech, this priest had iron in his courage. And he needed it, for he carried on his labor of mercy right under the guns of the enemy. He was one of those missioners who worked in the front line, in perpetual danger of surprise and capture.

The China Sea runs in and out of a jagged coast line for about two hundred miles between the Canton Delta and French

* From *Chungking Listening Post*. Creative Age Press. Copyright, The Maryknoll Fathers.

Kwanchowan. That is the seafront of the Maryknoll mission, precariously facing enemy-held islands just off the coast. From time to time the Japanese poured a blast of shells into these towns and landed on foraging raids.

Perhaps the most dangerous and nerve-wracking place in that mission field was the peninsula of Chekkai, which stuck out like a finger to taunt the ships that sailed menacingly up and down the coast. This hot assignment needed a man with a clear mind, a cool head and a brave heart. His bishop found these qualities and many more in Father Chatigny, an imperturbable little gentleman who comes from the gentle folk of Acadia and speaks in soft words like "the murmuring pines and the hemlocks."

I first came to know Father Donat during his arts course. The students noted his seraphic smile, soft voice and rapture at prayer, and laughingly called him "Cure of Ars," after the famous St. Jean Vianney. The faculty found that, though his head was in the stars, his feet were on the ground, and he established himself as a leader in studies or in labor tasks assigned. He himself was never ruffled and he never ruffled another by a sharp word.

Chekkai is a mountainous little country where the people speak the Hakka dialect, a language that is strange to the neighboring districts. These Chinese hillbillies are for the most part hard-working farmers and fishermen, but guns hang on the wall of almost every home, and these rough gun-toters have feuds that would startle the Tennessee mountaineers out of their home-made boots.

Catholicism in Chekkai is generations old. The Christians there are not hallelujah-shoutin' revivalists but firm believers, though rough and tough like the mountains and people around them. Once converted, they have little time for those who do not see the light. They are not exactly spiritual snobs, but rather inclined to the attitude of "let the devil keep his own." When the priest went around to help sick pagans, his Catholics sometimes told him he would do better to keep his pills and energies for the faithful of the fold. The little pastor was an enigma to the unlettered working folk of Chekkai. Religion for them was something very necessary to save their own souls, and that was about all. Their religion was tied to the earth, not hitched to a cloud, and it puzzled them to see the good padre helping the Catholic, the pagan, the rich or the poor, the official or the bandit.

For almost a decade the pint-sized missioner with the disarming look about him tramped the bandit-infested mountain paths as if strolling in fields of lilies. He went unmolested, for the bandits respected the man who had love for all and malice toward no one.

On his trips through the country, Father Chatigny carries his Mass kit and a medicine kit, for he is a great healer of bodies as well as souls. His remedies range from old-fashioned ones, dating back to Evangeline's grandmother, to the latest sulfa drugs. He crosses the hills, winds his way through the rice paddies and wades the streams to visit his scattered flock in the distant villages. When others of us fume and sweat in the season of prickly heat, he always seems cool and unbothered and walks along briskly, as if born to the tropics rather than to the snows of Quebec.

Just before the war I made a pilgrimage trip across the water with him to Sancian Island, where St. Francis Xavier died in 1552. When a stiff wind filled the sail, the boatmen swore at having too much wind while they reefed the sails and swung the rudder. Then when the wind died and the boatmen whistled to call up a breeze, between breaths they cursed the devils that had stopped the wind. I myself was worried as the boat tipped and leaped in the high wind and galloping waves, and was impatient with the calm an hour later, which left us in the middle of nowhere. But Father Chatigny took it all with the composure of the rocky coast of his parish.

During the calm they gave us a meal of rice and fish on the boat. Grace before meals is for many of us a perfunctory thing, with a wave of the hand for the sign of the cross. But before this frugal meal Father Chatigny's sign of the cross was a solemn rite, his grace a devotional ceremony such as might precede a Christmas dinner.

But not always is he mild, if always meek. In a sermon at one of his mountain mission stations he was scourging his people, for he heard they had been aiding bandits in a recent raid. The people were squirming and worried and kept staring with horror toward one of the low windows. He looked that way and saw framed in the window the faces of four of the bandits themselves. But while they leaned on their rifles, the fearless priest told his people that banditry was wrong, bad and unjust, and that they should have nothing to do with the bandits. Even bandits admire courage and respect a just man, so there was no shooting.

Tramping through the mountains, Father Chatigny digs up strange flowers and plants and orchids. For besides his orphanage and his dispensary at the home mission, he has a third love—his garden. When he goes to visit a fellow missioner he brings seeds and slips of flowering shrubs and plants. The Flame of the Forest which overspread his church or the pink bougainvillea which climbs the tower has offspring in all the near-by missions.

Father Chatigny's letters best show the man. A great part of a letter of his often sounds like St. Francis of Sales or the author of the Imitation of Christ; another part will be practical and pedestrian. People turn up at neighboring missions with letters from Father Donat which end like this: "This boy's father is a bandit; keep him away from home, give him a job and work him hard. I am sure he'll turn out all right." Or, "This man is very poor, I can't cure his sickness. Have the doctor do his best and please feed him up." Or again, "This woman was thrown out of her village; ask the Sisters to put her to work in your orphanage so we can rehabilitate the poor woman."

Famines, feuds, bombs, shells and invasions fail to excite the imperturbable little priest. Reassuring words roll out of him in the tensest situations. One day he was visiting Father Sweeney's leper colony in the neighboring county of Toishan. He went to the church in the afternoon to hear confessions. The Japanese across the river started to shell the place. Two shells exploded in front of the church. Father Donat slowly folded his stole and came out of the confessional and calmed the frightened people milling around the church. With the other priests he directed the lepers to the sacristy and back door. Then he helped carry the cripples up an embankment, across a road and down into a gully. In a few moments a shell landed smack on the road, and another in the gully. The priest gave general absolution to prepare the people for death. They then expected Father Donat to pronounce some elevating and spiritual thoughts on eternity. But idealists are, after all, the most practical men, and he calmly sat down, saying, "We are all ready now, and there is no use worrying; if it gets you, it gets you."

Through nearly seven years of war Father Chatigny lived there alone, the only foreigner in the country that looks out on islands held by the Japanese. He saw their warships come close and shell, and his bag was always packed for the time when the enemy threatened to land again. Later he saw the big bombers with the star and bar—the American emblem—patrolling the sea off shore. He also saw two Japanese ships floundering after hits by American bombs. Twenty of the Japanese in a lifeboat were picked up by a big fishing junk and brought to a coastal village of his fishing folk, where they were turned over to the local soldiers.

What bandits and Japanese were unable to do, the Chinese Communists accomplished. Father Chatigny is now at work on Formosa where, I am sure, he still visits neighboring priests with his basket of flower seeds, shrubbery slips and fruits. They will still smile at his foibles and tease him a little, but he will always be sunshine, for he has found the bright road through this world of war and tragedy, where most of mankind seems to have lost its sanity. He is as refreshing as the dew, for though he walks the earth with us, he walks the high road—so high that his world is carpeted with clouds.

THE SECRET

by Paul Horgan

Father Louis was old and spent and about to be retired
as an active missioner. He makes one last journey to his
scattered flock and eventually finds death in a Texas
desert. Here is a memorable highlight from his last
earthly adventure by a Pulitzer Prize winner.

But so was the life hard that he found at the end of each stage
of his travels. He had seen men grow old and die in his visits
here, and their sons with their wives bring new souls to this wilderness in turn. They learned severe lessons in isolation, heat, and
the hostility of the animal and vegetable world. Everyone, the
child, the grandfather, the husband, the wife, the youth, the
horse, the maiden, worked unceasingly against dust, thorn, ignorance, and scarcity from dawn to dark. The great world was but
a rumor here, and, by the time it came to the brush deserts,
mostly wrong. But a world without limits of dimension dwelt
behind the eyes of all those parched, brown people obedient to
the natural terms of their lives. It was the world of the human
soul, in which could live promises so beautiful and satisfactions
so full of ease that the hardships and the betrayals of impersonal
nature could be survived, if only someone came from time to
time with the greatest news in all life.

For Father Louis knew in a simple flatness of fact—fact as hard as rock, as mysterious as water, as dazzling as light—that without God the richest life in the world was more arid than the desert; and with Him the poorest life was after all complete in a harmony that composed all things. To be the agent of such a composition put upon him a duty in the light of which all peril on his journeys became at worst mere inconvenience. Everyone he toiled overland to see needed and deserved that which he, at the moment, under existing circumstances, alone could bring. In a very practical way he was still awed by the mystery of his office. And as a human being he could never deny himself the joy it gave him to see in their faces what his coming meant to his people in the harsh wilderness. They knew what he had come through. They were proud to be thought worth such labor and danger. They loved him.

His mind was active in the solitude through which he crawled day after day mounted on Pancho. One of his favorite fancies was this, that a great triangle existed between God in heaven and any little ranch toward which he rode through the days and himself. It was an always changing triangle, for one of its points was not fixed: his own. As he came nearer and nearer to his goal of the moment, the great hypotenuse between himself and God grew shorter and shorter, until at the last, when he arrived, there was a straight line with all in achieved communion. He smiled over this idea, but he respected it too; and sometimes he would take a piece of charcoal from a fire and draw a series of pictures of what he meant, explaining it to the people he was visiting and they would murmur, and nod, and consult each other, and enjoy the notion with him, marveling.

One day at noon on the present journey he knew he should soon see what would look like a long thin blade of cloud shadow far ahead on the earth that slowly quivered with wafts of light like those in wavering mirrors. But it was not a cloud shadow, as he had found out nearly thirty years ago. It was the distant gash of a long canyon whose yellow rock walls were stained with great stripes of slate blue. It came from the north and far away to the south opened into the rocky trough of the Rio Grande. In its bottom were all the signs of a river but running water. Here and there were shallow pools fed by the underground flow which needed storm water to call it continuously to the surface. Father Louis always paused at such a pool for a bath. There were sores on his body from the catch of thorns through which he rode. Sometimes a needle of the brush would break in his flesh and burrow its way under his skin. For the most part he was unaware of such an affliction, but by its comfort the warm alkaline water of the pool reminded him of the misery he had forgotten to notice. It was usually midafternoon by the time he reached the canyon wall as the sun went lower. The place was like a palace to him, open to the brassy sky. Wrens and hawks came to look at him in their wary turns. To be below the surface of the rolling plain in the canyon was to have for a little while the luxury of privacy, somehow. He bathed, and dozed as he dried, and sat in the shade reading his breviary. He knew when it was just time to gather himself together and resume his ride in order to come by nightfall to the house and the spring of Encarnadino Guerra, where he would spend the night.

This friend was a boy of ten when Father Louis first met him. He was now the father of six children, the husband of a silent, smiling woman named Cipriana, the son of a widowed mother called Dona Luz who on his last visit told Father Louis she would not live to enjoy his next one. He remembered how she sat blinking in the brilliant shade of the desert bowing to him over and over, while a triumph of patience went over her face, eroded by time and trouble and work and pain, as she said, "At night, when everything is quiet, and I am awake and alone, for I cannot sleep much any more, something speaks to me, and tells me to be ready, and not to make any other plans."

She looked at him with hardly any light in her small eyes, and he knew she was right. When he said Mass for them that time, he thought he saw in her face some powerful, direct understanding of the holy sacrifice which during all her pious life had slumbered within her but which at last came clear in her whole, small, withered being.

He wondered whether through any dry, desert-like tenacity she might still be living.

But when he rode up in the arching twilight to the dwelling of the Guerras, almost the first thing they told him after their excited greeting was that Dona Luz had died early in the summer while sitting in the shade on her bench holding her stick of ocotillo wood which her hands had shined so smooth.

In the light of the candle lantern the family looked at him and then at each other. They were shocked by how he had changed since last year. He was stooped and he slowly trembled all the time. He had to peer at them to see them, even though he preserved a smile to make nothing of this. Burned by the wind and sun, his face looked smaller. He breathed shallowly, with his mouth a little open. He seemed to them a very old man, all of a sudden.

It was like a secret they must keep from him. After their first start, they got busy making his supper. The younger children lost their shyness and came from behind chairs and the edges of the table to see him, and at last to climb upon him. He smelled dry and dusty to them, like the earth.

After supper he held lessons in catechism for the younger children, who tomorrow would receive their first communions. The parents and the two older sons listened also.

After that, there was a little time left for gossip. The family's news was all of the seasons. The priest's was boiled down out of letters and newspapers from France. The Guerras already knew that the earthly love of his life was his native country, which he had not seen for over thirty years, but which still spoke in his darting eyes, his cleverness at description, and in the accent with which he spoke Spanish. They listened respectfully while he made picture after picture in his talk of what he loved and missed; but they could not really see with him either the cool green fields, the ancient stone farmhouses, the lanes of poplar trees, the clear rivers, or the proud old towns, or the glorious towering cathedrals, or the silvery web of his dear city of Paris sparkling delicately in daytime, glowing in the long dusk with golden lamps and violet distance.

But they were honored simply to have him here, and stared

before his marvels, and held their breath for tomorrow, when he would give them sacraments.

In the morning he visited the grave of Dona Luz. Everybody went with him. She was buried a little way off from the adobe house. When he saw how little earth she displaced, he nodded and smiled, as though meeting all over again her modest character which he knew so well. Guerra brought some water in an earthen vessel, not much, but enough. Father Louis took the jug and held it in both hands a moment, and gazed into it. They were all reminded of how precious water was on the earth, how it determined by its presence the very presence of life. Then he blessed it, and they all knew what this meant in terms of their daily struggle. Then, reciting prayers for the dead, he walked around the small mound of the grandmother and sprinkled the holy water upon it, and they knew he was keeping once again a promise made between heaven and earth a long time ago.

After that they returned to the house and he took them one by one and heard them confess their sins, of which as they were contrite he relieved them. Then, at an altar improvised against the wall where the old woman used to sit for so many hours, he said Mass, wearing his embroidered French silks, and using the pewter chalice that came out of his saddlebag. The family knelt on the ground in a straight line facing the altar. The famous triangle of Father Louis was brought into a straight line also. God and mankind were made one. As he recited the words during the offertory, "Oh, God, Who has established the nature of man in wondrous dignity and even more wondrously has renewed it . . . ," Father Louis left behind him the bodily presences of that isolated family, and an almost bitter sense of the clearness of each of their souls humbled him at his altar.

When Mass was over, they returned within the house, where, at the raw table polished by countless unnoticed contacts of all the family, Father Louis sat down to fill in certificates of first communion for the younger children. He had a flask of guizache ink and a German steel pen. Sitting as far back from the documents as he could the better to read, he began to write. A look of disgust came over his face as his trembling hand gave him trouble. Exclaiming impatiently, he put his left hand on his right wrist to add strength and steadiness where they were needed; but this did not help much, and when he was done, he pushed the papers toward the head of the family saying, "Nobody ever can read my writing except God."

They all took him seriously, prouder than before of their papers.

"But that is enough, isn't it?" he demanded in comic ferocity.

They had a merry breakfast, when all talked as though they would not soon again have a chance to talk, which was true; all except Guerra, who was going to speak of something as soon as he had built up enough of his own silence. Finally he was ready.

"Father," he said, leaning back a trifle in his chair, and half closing his eyes to disguise deep feelings, "you won't be going on anywhere else, after us, will you?"

"Oh, yes."

"Where will you go, Father?"

"Why, I plan to ride from here over toward the river—I have a couple of families over there—and I may go as far as the town of San Ygnacio, to see if the priests from Mier are making visits there, as they ought to. Why?"

Guerra put his head on one side and shrugged.

He did not want to say that the old man was exhausted and ought not to go so far in the pitiless country under the searing sun. It would not be polite to say the old man was older than his years, and he must be seventy anyway. He might be misunderstood if he said that everybody reached a time after a life of hard work when he must pause and rest and let stronger people do what needed doing. It would hardly do to show outright that he thought Father Louis should give up, and stay here, and rest a few weeks, and then perhaps Encarnadino Guerra might leave everything here in the hands of his two strong, quiet boys, and just ride with Father Louis until he saw him safely back in Brownsville.

Father Louis peered close to his younger friend and saw enough of these thoughts to stir him up.

"Eh?" he cried, rapping hard with his knuckles on Guerra's

skull, "what goes on in there?" He was sharp and angry. What were they all thinking? That he was a feeble old man? He knew all there was to know about that; but if anything was to be said about it, he, not they, or anyone else, was the one to say it. "Mind your manners, you, boy," he said to Guerra, screwing up his small eyes until all that showed of them were two sharp blue points of light. "Eh? You have opinions, have you? Who told you to think anything! Eh? When I want you to think anything about anybody, I'll tell you. Eh? I got here, didn't I? How many times have I managed to come? And what for! Does anybody tell me to come? Or where to go? Or when? Or why? Then you keep your place, and thank God for your blessings, and for your friends, and understand that it is just as bad to hold an impolite thought as it is to say an impolite thing. Eh?" His whole body shook with the passion he failed to control. "Bad. You'd just better be careful, that's all I have to say, do you hear?"

The family were appalled at this burst of feeling. They sat with downcast eyes, fearing that it would be disrespectful to look upon Father Louis in his rage. But they had little glimpses of his unshaven face whitened with anger, and they could hear how pulse-shaken his voice was. Guerra was more Indian than anything else, and his countenance became fixed. He leaned back, let his eyelids cut his gaze in half, and took his dressing-down without response. He was not even hurt by it. He knew why it came to him. He knew how much it proved him right in his concern. He admired the flare of spirit in the old man. He was at peace with himself for trying what he had tried.

The youngest child, not understanding what had taken place, now, belatedly, felt the emotion among all the older ones, and turning up her little clay-doll face she burst into wails of misery and fear, bringing her tiny creature-paws to her howling mouth until she resembled the small sculptured masks of earth buried with the dead centuries ago deep in Mexico.

Father Louis roughly took her upon his lap. He bent his bristly face close to hers, cactus and blossom together, and in barely audible murmurs quieted the child, and himself, which took about five minutes.

This act reclaimed them all for each other. Once again the visitor was kind and smiling, and the family without fear.

"And so, good-bye for this time," said Father Louis putting the child down and standing up. "If you will get my horse for me?"

Guerra spoke to one of the boys, who went to fetch Pancho. They all met him outside. Cipriana brought some tortillas for the saddlebag. Everyone knelt down to be blessed. The hot sunlight smote them. They had lingered long over their breakfast. It was late. Father Louis, mounted and ready, blessed them three times, and then turned and rode off to the south. After a while he looked back. They were still kneeling. The next time he looked back it was hard to see them, for at even a little distance they made the same shadows as the scrubby bushes that grew on the caked earth, and seemed just as eternally rooted there.

A CHRISTMAS HYMN

Bethlehem! City of Bread!
The Bread of Life in thee, this morn,
Is of the Father and of Mary born.
Angels of heaven, your sweet lays upraise;
Sing for the Infant and Ancient of Days.
Here lies no stranger.
The Child in the manger
Smiles as a God.

Prophets rejoice! Prophets rejoice!
Your eyes have held for Israel
Him Who for us is Emmanuel.
What is the splendor that shines in the skies?
Earth's newborn Infant shall have Mary's eyes.
Mourning and sin shall cease;
God sends the Prince of Peace—
Jesus is born.

—JAMES DROUGHT

"EVERYTHING'S ALL RIGHT IN KOKOMO!"

by James Keller

> Father Keller, the Maryknoll founder of The Christophers, gives some of the philosophy behind his successful movement which has no organization, no meetings, no memberships, no dues. The work of The Christophers has been felt in all walks of life.

A few months ago while traveling through Indiana, giving talks in the smaller towns and cities of the state, one thing more than any other impressed itself on me. It was the *quality* of the people who made up the various audiences—farmers and factory workers, small businessmen and housewives—in short, the sound, solid folk who are the backbone of America.

No wild-eyed, irrational, heads-in-the-clouds visionaries were they. On the contrary, on their faces were the calm, down-to-earth expressions of people possessed of an honest sense of values. In their eyes was the quiet confidence born of such knowledge.

If ever a description fitted a group of individuals, it was the phrase, "salt of the earth." And in one talk frankly I told them so.

"If we had people with your plain common sense teaching in our colleges, running our government, our trade unions, writ-

* From *You Can Change the World* by James Keller. Longmans. Copyright, The Christophers.

ing our newspapers, magazines, books, radio programs and movie scenarios," I said, "everything would be pretty much all right with our country . . . and the world."

After the talk one middle-aged gentleman came up to me. He seemed neither angry nor pleased with what I had just observed but, taking my hand, said simply, "I come from Kokomo . . . and everything's all right in Kokomo!"

If he had launched into a tirade of criticism or disagreement, his words would not have startled me half as much as that quiet statement of fact: "I come from Kokomo . . . and everything's all right in Kokomo."

Though he failed to realize it, that one little remark sums up only too well what probably is the chief obstacle to peace in the world. Most *good* people are taking care only of themselves while most *evil* people are taking care of everyone else. Most people with good ideas are thinking in small circles, in terms of a thousand separate "Kokomos" while the people who are out to wreck our civilization are planning and acting on a long-term, daring scale—in terms of centuries and over the span of the world!

To know that everything is all right in Kokomo, however, is encouraging . . . thank God for it. But for us, the refreshing hope in that knowledge is to release into the bloodstream of the whole country and the arteries of the world the confined goodness which makes Kokomo and communities like it what they are. And tens upon tens of thousands of people of every age and in all walks of life are doing just that right now! They are getting out of themselves and into the thick of things. They are exerting their tremendous influence for good and hastening the day when peace will once more come to all mankind.

And that word "tremendous" is not misused.

For instance, still fresh in people's memories is the recent gigantic letter-writing campaign directed by the American people to the people of Italy, telling them what freedom and democracy mean in the United States and what they would mean to Italians if they only appreciated these rights enough to work for them.

Not just hundreds, or even thousands, but literally millions of letters went out from people of Italian descent in every section of this nation to their relatives in the "old country." Yet that campaign didn't just start by itself—somebody started it. And that somebody was *one man*, a barber in Southampton, Long Island, N.Y.

He had left Italy himself in 1913 and had come to the United States, determined to become a living part of our democracy for the rest of his days. He'd married, raised a family, and found life good. As the years went by, however, two things began to bother him. One was the constant stream of criticism from many quarters about what was wrong with our government and with the world in general. The second thing—and which irritated him even more than the first—was that those who did the complaining never seemed to do anything about making conditions any better.

Following World War II when news of millions of Italians flirting with Communism reached the American press, his patience reached the breaking point. He decided to do something about it personally.

First he wrote to his own relatives in St. Catherine, Sicily. Next he wrote to his wife's relatives who lived near the same town, telling all of them what the free way of life meant in America. Then he got his oldest boy, a doctor, and his oldest girl, a dietician, to write. He sent letters to the President and to all the newspapers in the New York area, asking for their support. The reaction to the idea was invariably good—but invariably it was accompanied with regrets that the project was too big to handle. Various organizations which he approached personally received him with smiles and wished him well . . . and that was all.

Faced with having the whole idea collapse on the spot, this barber still wouldn't quit. He kept writing and contacting his friends who had relatives in the old country, asking them to lend a hand. Gradually—providentially—the idea began to catch fire. Businessmen, young GI brides, housewives, veterans' groups, civic societies, and religious leaders took up the fight. Soon a steady trickle (that in no time at all became a torrent) of heart-felt letters of thanks started coming back from Italy, promising to push the democratic concept of life. The result: hundreds of thousands of people in America began to do something no other agency or official group could possibly have done—reach the hearts of the Italian people.

People all over the earth are beginning to realize more and more that there is a very intimate connection between truth and freedom. Sobered by the scourge of war, even those opposed to religion are more disposed to admit the inescapable conclusion of what Christ meant when He said: "The Truth shall make you free." Once a sufficient number of people realize that false-hood is nothing more than the absence of truth, just as darkness is the absence of light, hate the absence of love, and disease the absence of health, then there is high hope that this old world of ours will one day come to know the blessing of a real, lasting peace.

Anyone can help in this task. You can. I can. And, naturally, the closer we are to Christ the better Christophers we will be. Yes, no one is so far away from Christ that he or she cannot share in some measure in this tremendous undertaking.

And startling as it may seem, even a pagan in darkest Africa or a Communist in the heart of America who learns even *one* of Christ's Truths—and tries to spread that truth in the lifestream of his land—is beginning to be a Christopher, whether or not he realizes it. The more he does for Christ, the closer he draws to Christ. With each truth-bearer he will have the consolation of knowing that he can be a bearer of that true light "which en-lighteneth every man that cometh into this world." They can be partners with Him Who said: "I am the Way, and the Truth, and the Life." (John 14:16)

Every one of us can be a bearer of Christ—a Christopher.

THE DEAD END PADRE

OF TOISHAN

by Joseph G. Cosgrove

> Some men literally work themselves to death. Father
> Larry Conley was one of them. A classmate of his tells
> Father's story with vividness and sympathy.

Shortly after Easter in 1945, Father Larry Conley was forced to
join China's fifty million refugees. Japanese troops threatened
his part of Kwangtung Province, and he had to leave Hoingan.
With Father Joseph P. Lavin, of Framingham, Massachusetts, he
went first to Yeungkong, and then to Kochow.

Nearly all the personnel of Maryknoll's Kongmoon Vicariate,
in fact, were on the move that spring, as the Japanese invaders
were trying to link up an overland road between Indo-China and
North China. However, the inconvenience was short-lived, since
the Japanese surrendered on August 14, 1945. Thus an end came
to Father Larry's wanderings. Bishop Paschang ordered Father
Francis J. O'Neill, of Woonsocket, Rhode Island, to devote his
full time to organized relief work in the Province of Kwangtung,
and Father Conley was appointed in Father O'Neill's place as
pastor of Toishan City.

Toishan was a city of approximately 250,000 people, with only
a meager Catholic population of 400. "It is heartbreaking to live
in a place like Toishan, crowded with all sorts of people and to

* From *Accent on Laughter*. McMullen Books, Inc.

have only a handful for Mass on Sunday," Father Larry said. "For a priest to get the better class to come to church, is more difficult than for a camel to pass through the eye of a needle!"

Father Larry first became interested in the poor ragamuffins of Toishan City after the end of the World War, in 1945. "It broke my heart," he wrote, "to see these little waifs of skin and bone, with practically no clothes, standing at the doors of the shops in town, waiting for a few grains of rice to be dropped in their rusty tin pails, or rummaging in a garbage heap, or eyeing some fortunate one gnawing a piece of sugar cane and then springing upon the discarded pulp. It all was too much for any Westerner, especially for a priest."

The Kwangtung Relief agency endeavored to alleviate some of the war-caused misery and hunger by distributing rice to the poor. But the committee's funds were limited. Their sphere of operation was so vast, that the best help they could offer only staved off starvation for a while. A new organization, known as the Chinese National Relief Rehabilitation Administration, was to be subsidized by its American counterpart, UNRRA, but was not fully established.

Meanwhile, Father Larry wanted to do something to remedy the bad situation. When the merchants saw him taking the boys off the streets, many were moved to co-operate by giving donations towards the work. The local mandarin threw the weight of his influence behind the missioner's endeavors, and also offered an abandoned temple as a place to house the boys.

Many of the youngsters were in a deplorable condition, and whatever standards they had were low, as a result of poverty and hunger.

"Yesterday," Father Larry wrote, "one poor little fellow, who looks like a skeleton and has tuberculosis, stole rice and fish from an old woman living nearby. It was heartbreaking even to think of reprimanding the thief.

"The kids live in an old temple and sleep on rice straw. We get their rice from the relief agency every day. Along with rice, they have fish or meat that comes in tins from the British Red

Cross. They don't have much, but it is sufficient to keep them alive until times get better."

A little dormitory was improvised in the temple, and Father Larry saw that it was kept in perfect order. Blankets were rolled up neatly after the boys rose in the morning, and the place was swept clean. Any extra clothes that the boys had were placed in rattan bags beside their beds.

Rules to be observed were kept to a minimum. Father Larry felt that boys in general have a deeply rooted revulsion for regulations. However, he did punish mildly the violators of the few rules in his own way. When donated candy arrived, any boys who had broken the rules were passed over; and indeed, the other youngsters helped to make sure that the offenders were overlooked, as is the custom of children.

"We use everything connected with the packages that we receive from the relief agencies," Father Larry added. "The paper cartons are sold, along with the wire. From tin cans, we make cups; and we sell them at a profit. We want not only to clothe and feed the youngsters, but also to teach them to help themselves. So, with the profits from the tin cups, we invest in bamboo for the making of brooms and fans."

On July 27, 1946, Father Larry wrote: "I'm keeping busy these days, taking care of my family—eighty boys and girls who comprise my Dead End Kids. I get them from every place. We do what we can for them, but at times it is not enough.

"If I do not look after them all the time, they are apt to get into trouble. I am afraid that most of them would have been dead long since, if we had not rounded them up. Few persons care whether the youngsters live or die, despite the fact that there is plenty of food in town now, and there is lots of money, too.

"Just the other night, a young fellow sat down in front of our church after being told that we would help him. He had no clothes; he was skinny as a rail; his legs were swollen almost twice their normal size and were covered with sores. The stench was awful. He said he had been walking for days, with hardly a thing to eat.

"We took the poor fellow in, and placed him in the priests'

house. The Sister-Doctor is taking care of his legs, while I take care of his stomach. This morning he told me he's feeling much better; but he still has far to go before he reaches a normal condition. At times I get very angry when I hear certain persons in town say that China should be helped, for I know that those same persons do nothing to help their own needy people."

Father Larry worked day and night, caring for his orphans. "I should like to get away for a couple of days, but I am afraid that, if I do, my Dead End Kids will miss out," he was heard to say more than once.

Father Larry used every imaginable means to get help for his needy youngsters. After the Chinese New Year in 1948, he tried to start a club of foreigners.

"There are about a dozen women from Mexico, here in the district," he said. "For them, living in the country means little opportunity to get together to talk Spanish. If they have some place to meet, they can have a tongue-wagging *fiesta*. I hope to bring them together very soon. They are generous with their help, often sending us cakes and pies. Luxuries of this sort are wonderful, because I have no facilities at present to have our cook make them. I eat with Chinese bowl and chopsticks three times a day, and my food is prepared by the native Sisters."

One of the means Father Larry used to raise money for the work was a raffle. "I had a raffle for the Dead End Kids the other night," he wrote to his mother in August, 1947. "It went off with a bang. We made over twenty million dollars profit! This sum will probably stagger you, Mom, until you know that the native money is hardly worth the paper it's printed on."

In addition to his work for the orphanage, Father Larry conducted soup kitchens at three places in the city. Many of his orphans took turns in helping to distribute food to the lines of hungry people at those places.

The Dead End Kids had a well-planned schedule in the old temple. They rose early and performed light morning chores. Their first meal was at nine o'clock, according to the general native custom. Much of the day was given to mastering the Chinese equivalent of the A B C's and learning some useful trades.

However, it soon became apparent to Father Larry that city life was not the best environment for his young charges. He began inquiring about possibilities for a better location for the orphanage.

Toishan is located on a river, with rolling hill country on the three other sides. A former Hong Kong resident, "Willie" Wu, offered the missioner a small farm located several miles southeast of Toishan. The place had a number of mud-brick buildings that could house the homeless boys sent there to benefit by the fresh air and freedom of the open country.

Because of some business complications, it was impossible to take up "Willie" Wu's offer at once. The Toishan mandarin therefore met the missioner's need again, this time offering him the use of a building that had been a temporary hospital. "The change from the temple to this building was," Father Larry explained, "like moving from Shantytown to the other side of the railroad tracks."

Unique among the primitive facilities at the hospital was a bathtub, which the boys under Father Larry's direction removed from the building. The tub was placed on an embankment, and iron piping was attached to its drain and laid down over the hill. At the end of this pipe, a tin can with punctured holes was attached to serve as a unique shower spray. While a couple of boys showered, those awaiting their turns carried buckets of water from the mission well and dumped the contents into the bathtub. Chic Sales in his prime could hardly have invented anything to excel this useful device.

With some of the profits derived from the sale of the tin articles made by the Dead End Kids, Father Larry bought teaching equipment and inaugurated his own little school. But at once there was a problem in regard to teachers. To his amazement, the priest discovered that, among the ten old people whom he had previously cared for in the temple, there were two who, many years earlier, had taught in a country school.

"However, the Dead End Kids," Father Larry observed, "aren't too keen on book larnin'. They would rather be doing things with their hands."

Those boys who were disinclined to study were put to work in vegetable gardens, or taught how to make brooms and fans to be sold on market day.

Christmas in 1946 was a highlight in Father Larry's life. "It was my best Christmas, so far, in China!" he wrote. The detailed account followed.

"The people sent the Dead End Kids every imaginable gift, and I myself even got two live chickens. Besides, the poor people of the parish donated $2,800 Chinese money in the collection at Christmas Day Mass. This is only a few dollars in U.S. coin but for the Chinese it is really something! The poor in this district are really poor.

"Another incident that helped to make this Christmas a huge success was the baptism of one of the orphans. I had picked him up from the street last year. At that time he was thin, sick, and hungry; but after six months of regular eating and a few good baths, he rounded out into a nice looking boy. The youngster took it upon himself to study Catholic doctrine for two months. At the end of this period, the Sisters told me he knew enough doctrine to receive Baptism, so the happy event took place on Christmas Day.

"The three Chinese Sisters loaned me by the Maryknoll Sisters fixed the chapel with attractive decorations. They used a blue parachute a G.I. once gave me, and made an effective hanging behind the altar. The Dead End Kids scoured the countryside for pine branches with which to decorate the sanctuary. They reminded me of the time long ago when, as a small boy, I ran into trouble with the policeman while looking for similar pine branches to decorate our home during the Christmas holidays."

Father Larry depended greatly upon the Maryknoll Sisters and their collaborators, the local Chinese community known as the Sisters of the Immaculate Heart of Mary. Their main task was conducting a thirty-bed hospital, which was attached to the mission, but they could always be counted upon to assist in his various problems.

"So far, I have baptized ten of the Dead End Kids who died of their ailments shortly after I took them off the streets. Providing for these youngsters demands quite a bit of effort, but the work has its rewards, especially in the matter of baptisms."

The native New Year's Day is always a momentous event, in every part of China.

"Today some of the Dead End Kids asked me if they could go home for the New Year," Father Larry wrote to his mother in 1947. "I have no idea where what they call 'home' can be, but each went off with a big smile and a sprightly step. Each carried a pound of rice and a can of condensed milk—two things that local Chinese treasure dearly.

"I enjoy watching the boys shake with joy when they received such gifts. It reminds me, Mom, of how we used to watch for you to come home from Boston, when we lived in Milton. We would impatiently wait for you to dig down to the bottom of your shopping bag and bring out some candy or big apples for us. Those were happy days, Mom! And I guess children the world over are all the same.

"Chinese New Year's Day, for the Dead End Kids here, will be a big celebration. They will have cuttings of pork, beef and fish; and plenty of greens, cookies, candy, peanuts. Last but not least, each will have a generous serving of rice. The treat will cost a pretty penny, but will be well worth it!"

Later that same month, Father Larry wrote to his mother about the New Year Celebration.

"I used to be able to see the Dead End Kids every day," he said, "but lately that's been out of the question. Today being a big holiday, however, I managed to visit them for a while. Many of them have gone 'home' to the country to spend a few days. Only twenty stayed at the orphanage here.

"They had one big meal. This afternoon, when I went to visit, they were roasting peanuts and eating the cookies and candy I had sent them. They seemed very happy indeed.

"One little lad got up enough courage to ask me if he could go to a movie in the evening. I told him he could. The other boys got the idea that they would like to see a movie, too, so I arranged that as a special treat."

Father Larry said in the same letter: "Another thing the youngsters here enjoy is knowing that I have fifteen tons of rice for them, stored in the attic for the months ahead. The shipment arrived a week ago from Chinese people in Siam, who sent the rice to the Chinese Relief Agency in this area. It's not as fine as some of the UNRRA rice the youngsters have been getting, but it is very good.

"Some bags molded badly, and we use that rice to feed the pigs. The boys have been raising six pigs, which I bought three months ago. Now the Dead End Kids could sell them for ten times what we paid for them! But we won't sell them until two months from now; then they will bring a still greater profit in the market. The other day the boys sold two piglets and received a tidy return. The money will certainly come in handy on holidays, when we give the Dead End Kids and the old folks a special feast.

"I have big plans for the Dead End Kids, if only I can get help. It's not very often I can run a raffle such as I had a short time ago, bringing a return that will keep the boys going for several months. It is good to be able to say that we probably shan't have worries for some time now, particularly since we have our most important staple, rice."

"Father Larry's raffle was unique!" reported Father Paul J. Duchesne, of Cohoes, New York, who was one of Father Larry's neighbors. "He began by raffling off a motor cycle, for which he had paid more than $500 in British Hong Kong currency. I was afraid he might have trouble in the event the money exchange went wild.

"However, I had not reckoned with either the Chinese gambling instinct or Father Larry's popularity. He more than doubled his money on the motor cycle! Contentedly he said to me: 'That was only a teaser! Next I'll raffle a bicycle, and after that a fountain pen, and I'll sell as many chances again. Just warming the crowd up, Father Paul; just warming them up.' "

Father Larry wrote on March 23, 1947: "My friend 'Willie' Wu has again offered me the use of his farm as a home for the boys. The city is no place for them. So I'm thinking of moving the whole gang out to Willie's farm very shortly."

A short while later Father Larry was able to move his Dead End Kids out into the country, to live on Willie Wu's farm. The missioner planned to conduct an industrial school there, where the boys would learn tailoring, shoemaking, and other practical trades, to give them a background for adult life.

"As to crops, I don't know what to do," Father Larry told his nearest neighbor, Father Arthur A. Weber, of Cuba City, Wisconsin. "But you are a farmer, Father Art; you could give me some idea of what I ought to have the boys plant."

From the beginning, the boys started to grow vegetables themselves, according to the universal Chinese agricultural instinct. They also undertook to raise more farm animals.

"The boys now have two fine cows and expect three more," Father Larry wrote to his mother, a short time later. "These cows left their home in Australia at the invitation of UNRRA, and are now raising families here on the outskirts of Toishan City. We expect two calves in a month or two. Who knows—we may be able to start a dairy farm soon!

"In our farm family now are four pigs, a few chickens, four dogs, plenty of pups, and one parrot! Pigs are a good investment, and we expect to raise many of them when we can get more food to feed them.

"The boys just picked 400 pounds of olives and sold them at a good profit. This farm we have has wonderful opportunities for vegetables and livestock. But I, being a city-bred youngster, am entirely ignorant of what and how to plant. My nearest neighbor, Father Arthur Weber comes often to see me and helps very much with my farm problems."

Writing again, Father Larry said: "We sold a big pig yesterday, Mom, at a handsome profit. The way I talk about my business ventures, huh? But China's money is so worthless now, it takes a basketful to buy each thing we need. Carrying on can give one an awful headache!"

On Thanksgiving Day in November of 1947 Father Larry took the keys for the mission's supply room. He wanted to arrange space for extra rice that he expected to store for his refugee boys. Later, after lunch, he asked Sister Maria Corazon, the doctor in the little Toishan Mission Hospital, if he could help her by painting a private room, as he knew that the Maryknoll Sisters would need it for a patient that evening.

The missioner got to work on the room, and painted until about half-past five. Then Sister Dominic Marie of the Maryknoll Sisters who was a nurse in the hospital stepped in and told him that she had cooked a Thanksgiving dinner. Father Larry left to wash and change. But as he started out, he said he didn't feel like eating.

Sister Dominic Marie went back to the convent to finish preparing the meal. She had hardly reached the kitchen, when one of the Chinese nurses, ran in, screaming that Father Larry had fainted. Sister rushed to the hospital and spent an anxious ten minutes working to revive the priest.

He told her that he had suddenly felt dizzy and had fallen unconscious. He complained of a pain in his side. When Sister Dominic Marie asked if he had experienced such a pain previously, he acknowledged that at noon he had lifted and moved two heavy barrels of milk powder, carrying them from the storeroom to an empty space outside. He said that he had not felt any pain then, but had experienced a very tired feeling.

After the Sister nurse examined him, Father Larry said he was much better and ready to eat the Thanksgiving dinner. Before it was served, Sister Dominic Marie was called away to receive a patient who had just been brought to the hospital in a serious condition. By the time Sister returned to the dining room, the priest had finished his Thanksgiving dinner and had gone to the chapel to pray.

Sister felt anxious about Father Larry, however, and she asked one of the Chinese Sisters to accompany her, to see if he was still all right. As they neared the chapel, they heard him calling. When they opened the door, they heard him say, "Quick Sister! I'm going out!"

Sister Dominic Marie reached Father Larry in time to save him from falling off the chair. After she succeeded in bringing him back to consciousness, she told her Chinese companion to prepare a bed in the pharmacy. The two Sisters carried the sick priest downstairs. From that time on, Sister Dominic Marie was in constant attendance until the end.

About eleven o'clock at night, Father Larry's pain was so intense that the Sister nurse called the doctor. Sister Corazon took a blood count. Her diagnosis was that the priest had ruptured his kidneys, and that he was suffering from internal hemorrhage. The Sisters decided to send a telegram to Canton immediately, to get another doctor to assist Sister Corazon in case an operation should be necessary. However, the telegraph office was closed, and there was no other way by which the message could be sent.

In the morning, Father Larry seemed a bit rested. It was then decided to send a Chinese woman to Canton for the additional doctor, as that would be a quicker way than sending a telegram.

In the afternoon, Father Larry's pain became intense again, and he suffered greatly all through the night. At six o'clock in the morning, on November 29, one of the Chinese Sisters entered the sickroom and asked if she might relieve Sister Dominic Marie for a while. But the latter had hardly left the room when the other religious ran after her, to say that the patient was calling for her to return.

"Sister, I am sorry to be such a baby," Father Larry apologized; "but really, the pain is getting worse!"

Sister Corazon was called, and both Sisters worked hard to give the sufferer some relief. An urgent call was made to the mission at Sunchong, asking Father Weber to come and anoint Father Larry at once. Sister Dominic Marie decided to tell her patient that she had sent for Father Weber.

Father Larry was silent for a while. Then he asked, "Is this the end, Sister?"

Father Weber arrived soon and administered the Last Sacraments. But he was obliged to return to his own mission almost at once, as he was expecting a visit from Bishop Fourquet, of Canton, that same day.

Sister Dominic Marie had been reciting the Rosary with Father Larry. After the second decade, he interrupted to say:

"Thank you, Sister, for everything. You have made the going easier for me."

Seeing that the end was close, Sister started to recite ejaculations, telling Father Larry to repeat them after her. The dying missioner did so. His last audible words were: "Jesus, Mary, and Joseph, may I breathe forth my soul in peace, with you!"

This he said three minutes before he died. Sister Dominic Marie started the prayers for the dying, and was finishing the Litany when Father Larry breathed his last.

"It was just a peaceful, gentle going home to God," Sister commented later.

MISSIONER'S PRAYER

Carpenter of Nazareth, who toilest still
At the long task begun in ancient days,
Speak, Son of God, and tell me how I can
Have part with Thee, a humble part and low.

Let me be the hammer to drive the nails
That knit men's souls to Thee. So form me strong,
Shaped to Thy hand, unwearying in toil
To make all one in Thee before Thou come.

Let me be Thy chisel, to shape the rough,
Unseasoned, knotty hearts of men. The blows
Of Thy beloved hand I cannot fear,
So grind me sharp and keen to do Thy will.

Let me be the wood itself, and be for Thee
A cross for thoughtless men to gaze upon.
Let hammer, chisel, adze, and saw and plane
Fit me to Thee; and nails that pierced Thee through
Make me a throne for Thee for evermore.

—DONALD V. CHISHOLM

THE NUN

by W. Somerset Maugham

One of the world's foremost writers tells of a valuable lesson given him in a small convent in China. It is a lesson all of us can remember.

The convent lay white and cool among the trees on the top of a hill; and as I stood at the gateway, waiting to be let in, I looked down at the tawny river glittering in the sunlight and at the rugged mountains beyond. It was the Mother Superior who received me, a placid, sweet-faced lady with a soft voice and an accent which told me that she came from the South of France. She showed me the orphans who were in her charge, busy at the lace-making which the nuns had taught them, smiling shyly; and she showed me the hospital where lay soldiers suffering from dysentery, typhoid, and malaria. They were squalid and dirty. The Mother Superior told me she was a Basque. The mountains that she looked out on from the convent windows reminded her of the Pyrenees. She had been in China for twenty years. She said that it was hard sometimes never to see the sea; here on the great river they were a thousand miles away from it; and because I knew the country where she was born she talked to me a little of the fine roads that led over the mountains—ah, they did not have them here in China—and the vineyards and the pleasant villages with their running streams that nestled at the foot of the hills. But the Chinese were good people. The orphans were very quick with their fingers and they were industrious; the Chinese sought them as wives because they had learnt useful things in the convent, and even after they were married they could earn a little money by their needles. And the soldiers too, they were not so bad as people said; after all *les pauvres petits*, they did not want to be soldiers; they would much sooner be at home working in the fields. Those whom the sisters had nursed through illness were not devoid of gratitude. Sometimes when they were coming along in a chair and overtook two nuns who had been in the town to buy things and were laden with parcels, they would offer to take their parcels in the chair. *Au fond*, they were not bad hearted.

"They do not go so far as to get out and let the nuns ride in their stead?" I asked.

"A nun in their eyes is only a woman," she smiled indulgently. "You must not ask from people more than they are capable of giving."

How true, and yet how hard to remember!

HERICO'S OPERATION

by Andre Dupeyrat

A missioner is called upon for many duties not usually associated with the priesthood. From the pen of a veteran French missioner, author of the best-selling book *Savage Papua*, comes one such instance.

I had been back at Fane-les-Roses barely an hour, when the Papuan bush telephone began to function. The message, relayed from mountaintop to mountaintop, came from Mondo in the north. It said: "Herico, child of the missionary, is dying. He asks his Father to come at once."

Herico (the Fuyughe name for Henry) was a young man of about twenty. Educated at our "college" at Popole, he had shown brilliant promise. But he was the son of a leading chief, and once his "studies" were finished, he had had to return to his village as heir presumptive.

I paused only long enough to put on my heavy boots, still covered with mud, and to collect the viaticum and the oil for giving the last sacrament from the church, and at once set off along the track.

In those days, the village of Mondo was still almost entirely pagan. When I arrived, bathed in sweat, the central clearing was deserted. Then I saw a solitary old man, squatting on the platform in front of his house.

"Where is Herico?" I asked.

"Over there," he said sullenly, nodding toward a brokendown hut.

I walked over to the hut. But even before I crossed the threshold I thought that I was going to faint: from the shadowy, silent interior came a frightful stench. Clutching the small haversack in which I was carrying the consecrated host, I braced myself, and called:

"Herico, are you there?"

A feeble voice floated out from the obscure depths of the wretched hovel.

"Yes, *Babe*, I asked them to call you, because I am dying. . . . I wanted to confess, and receive communion and the body oil."

"Going to die? . . . But what's the matter? Your voice is still clear . . ."

"My leg has gone rotten. The people said that everyone would die because of the smell, and tomorrow they were going to carry me into the forest and leave me there. . . . You know the customs of the 'true men.' So I am going to die. . . ."

Indeed, I knew them well, those "customs": when someone is suffering from a long and tiresome illness, or has grown old and enfeebled, and is thus no longer wanted, his relations, egged on by the other villagers, have him killed, or else take him out into the bush and abandon him there. Sometimes, he is left in a crude shelter, like the old man who waited to be baptized in the Yaloghe country, and sometimes in an old, worn-out sleeping net slung between two trees above a shallow trench. Deprived of food and care, the unfortunate wretch dies in terrible solitude: his body soon decays, and falls together with the rotted net into the trench. Later, if someone passes near this macabre burial place, they may pile a few leaves and twigs over the body. In a short time, the maggots and the insects have stripped the flesh clean down to the bone. After that, the bones are collected and brought back to the village, where a ceremony of mourning is enacted, with dances and feasting, to appease and placate the spirit of the dead man.

I could scarcely breathe in the fetid atmosphere of the hut. Nevertheless, I said to the wretched Herico:

"You are the son of an Outame, you yourself are a powerful chief. . . . How dare your people behave like this?"

Herico said nothing for a moment. Then:

"I am also the son of the missionary. They wanted to practice all sorts of *menghes* (magic rites) over me. I refused. Then my uncle declared solemnly that I was 'a man of no worth.' For the time being, he is the head man, since my father died a long while ago. But he was supposed to give me my full rights as soon as I got married. . . . Perhaps he wants me to die instead? It was he who persuaded the people to take me into the forest."

A feeling of nausea gripped me.

"Herico, my son, I am going outside for a moment. Your words have caused me great grief. I shall come back. As you are not actually dying, I cannot give you the holy oil. But as I have brought the body of Our Lord in the host, I shall give you communion. Prepare yourself for it."

I stepped outside. I was utterly overcome with a combination of fatigue, suffocation, and rage.

The village looked as deserted as ever. But I had already noticed that the communal hut, perched on its tall, slender piles, was full of people. They had doubtless awaited my arrival in the expectation that I would make a scene, which showed that, in spite of everything, their conscience was uneasy.

I took up a stand in front of the *Emone*:

"Listen, the lot of you hiding in there!. . . . Have you no shame, to talk of carrying the son of your Outame away into the forest? . . . . Is it for me to remind you of the honorable customs of your ancestors? Certainly you must put aside their evil customs, like that of taking the sick and the old into the forest. But the honorable customs you must keep. . . . Herico's uncle wants to kill him so that he can rule instead. But who is the true Outame? You know very well that it is Herico, son of your old Outame! . . . . And you want to see him die? Shame upon you all! . . . . Have you forgotten the word of God that says you must not kill your fellow man? It's easy to see you are still pagans and sons of the devil!"

No one stirred. The uncle must have bribed the sorcerers to get them on his side. The people were afraid.

I resumed my philippic: "Herico will not be taken into the forest. I demand that eight strong men step out of the Emone this instant, and that they arrange a *sosofe*—a net litter—to take Herico to Fane. There, I will look after him and, with God's help, will make him well again. . . ."

Still no one budged. I began to see red. Deciding to adopt the role of Samson, I strode beneath the Emone and started to shake the supporting piles, with the result that the whole structure began to sway. At the same time, I began to yell:

"Are you all deaf up there, sons of cockroaches?"

The insult must have cut them to the quick, for several of the Emone's inmates leaped down and scuttled off with the frenzied haste of startled cockroaches. With one prodigious bound from the rear of the edifice, they vanished into the neighboring bush.

There were still a good number left inside. But if I continued with my strong-man act, they would all take to their heels—and I still needed eight bearers. The afternoon was well advanced, and there was no time to be lost. It was then that I resorted to a stratagem that, used by others than missionaries, has sometimes had more fateful consequences.

"Listen, the rest of you, up there, and stay where you are! . . . .
I am going to light a *matsitsi* (match). I shall count up to three.
If, by the time I say 'three,' there are not three plus two men out
here in front of me, I shall set fire to the Emone!"

The threat was heroic—but futile. The supporting piles were
far too damp to be set on fire with a match. Besides, it goes without saying that I had not the slightest real intention of putting
my threat into execution, and the people themselves knew that
as well as I did. But that was the only way to act with those over-
grown children: they could be swayed only by dramatic gestures,
a carefully set scene. Nevertheless, it did not enter my head at
the time that a genuine drama might easily have been enacted
—for, after all, they might easily have killed me.

I did not need to light my match, or even to complete the
count. For scarcely had I said *gegedo* (two) than eight stalwart
young men tumbled out into the central clearing, smiling and
eager, just as if nothing had happened.

"Get the *sosofe* ready," I ordered them, "and quickly. We
leave in a few minutes."

That done, I picked up once more the viaticum, and with it my
courage, and went back into the evil-smelling hut where Herico
lay. A pitiable little figure, he lay screwed up in the darkest corner on a pile of ashes and detritus. Holding a handkerchief over
my nose, I heard his confession and gave him communion. Then,
leaving him briefly alone once more, I went out to draw in some
clean air and see how the bearers were getting on with their
work. They had already completed the *sosofe*—four stout
branches tied with rattan to form a rectangle, and in this space
a native net was being attached.

I went back to Herico.

"My heart is happy," he said. "Thank you for coming, *Babe*.
Now, I can die. . . ."

"There's no question of that, my son. You're coming back to
Fane with me."

I can still see the whites of his eyes shining in that odious dark
corner, raised toward me in astonishment and joy.

Then we got him outside. He presented a frightful spectacle—

Job emerging from his dung heap. The poor boy was so thin that one could count each rib and vertebra; the skin hung in gray folds from his wasted arms and legs. Many parts of his body, and even his face, were caked with a crust of filth, composed of soot and ordure: and he had a number of large, open sores. But the most horrible sight was his left leg, swollen to enormous dimensions, and oozing with yellow matter. This was the source of that terrible stench which, together with his uncle's intrigues, had persuaded the villagers that they must rid themselves of the miserable wretch.

Herico was placed on the net litter. He gave a grimace of pain, then smiled joyfully.

Three hours later, we arrived without mishap at Fane. The bearers, who had taken it in turns to carry the litter, were still quite fresh, and departed singing.

I had Herico installed in a small, clean hut with a stout door, which was occasionally used as a dispensary. As it was already late, I put off examining his leg until the following day, but I gave instructions to Sister Jeanne that she should immediately wash Herico's soiled and wasted body, using a brush if necessary, and give him a nourishing meal.

Sister Jeanne was one of the three native sisters who looked after the Mission station. Born in a village on the plain of Mekeo, and abandoned when she was no more than a baby, she herself had been taken in and cared for by the Mission. Intelligent and devoted, Sister Jeanne was also as quick and diligent as a bee and I knew that I could trust her entirely.

The next day I set about examining poor Herico's leg. It proved to be the most horrible task I had had until then. As he explained the matter to me, he had fallen on some sharp object and had received a wide, deep cut. He had done nothing about it and in a few days, the wound had become infected and enlarged. Thereupon, on the orders of his uncle and the sorcerer, his leg had been bound up in tobacco leaves and a plaster of clay. It was at this point that he had energetically refused to allow the sorcerer to utter incantations over him. Perhaps some poison had been mixed in with the clay plaster. Whether that was so or not, the condition of the leg grew steadily worse from then on. As soon as the oozing matter began to show through the outer wrappings, more were added.

"But Herico, why didn't you ask someone to call me sooner?"

"I asked my uncle to, but he must have decided already that I should die. . . . No one would listen to me. It was only when they were on the point of taking me into the forest that they agreed to send for you. I had begged them at first, and then threatened them. . . . Perhaps they were afraid that you would get to hear of their refusal."

"But they must have known that, if they sent for me, I would never let you be left to die alone in the forest!"

"No, not necessarily. . . . you see, those are our customs, and they didn't even imagine that you would look at the question any differently."

Helped by Sister Jeanne, I began to cut away, with a knife and forceps, the plaster encasing Herico's leg. As each successive layer came away, I felt more sickened: there was nothing but pus and decomposition. The calf muscles had become no more than greenish filaments which we stripped away piece by piece. . . . It took three long sessions, spread over two days, to clean the wound thoroughly. In the end, the tibia was left completely bare, and the whole of the fibula could be seen. There was just one healthy muscle that remained attached to it.

The only thing I had in the medicine chest was permanganate of potassium, which I used diluted in boiled water to keep the wound clean. I left the results of the operation to God's grace.

Besides, I had to set off once more on my round of the villages. In my absence my nurse-assistant, Sister Jeanne, continued the same rudimentary treatment, meanwhile building up the patient's strength with large, healthy, regular meals.

This went on for nearly a year. And rarely have I seen such an admirable example of miracles which nature performs, for little by little, the muscles, the nerves, the blood vessels, and flesh built themselves up afresh around the bones, and the leg which had once been almost entirely rotten from foot to knee became normal once more. All except for one detail, that is: the flesh would never grow back over the forward surface of the tibia. On either side of this sterile area, perhaps eight inches long and three wide, the edges of the wound were perfectly healthy, but the bone itself presented a blackish appearance. With improvised instruments, I tried scraping the bone and experimenting with various grafts. But all to no effect. Herico was by now the picture of health, but he was still unable to get about except by edging himself forward on his hind quarters, using his hands for support. It was in this way that he came to the church each day.

A decision had to be made. One day, I said to him:

"Herico, I think I will try taking the bone from your leg. I believe it is the only way to heal it. . . ."

"Do as you think best, *Babe*. . . ."

It took me two days to bring myself to face this operation. Finally, one morning, I came to a decision.

Herico came and lay down on the little lawn of fairly lush, soft grass in front of the "presbytery." That was to be the operating table. For instruments, I had chosen a small carpenter's chisel, a pair of curved dental forceps, and a light hammer. Needless to say, there was no chloroform, or any other sort of anesthetic.

"Herico, I'm afraid this is going to hurt you a lot. . . . You must think of the suffering of your Father, Jesus, when He was nailed to the Cross, and try to join your suffering with His so that your people become converted, and to redeem your sins and mine. . . . Try not to move or cry out. Understood?"

"Yes, *Babe*," he replied calmly.

I asked Sister Jeanne to hold the patient's head to one side so that he would not see the operation, and to look herself in that direction, which was toward the church. Then, placing the chisel against the bone, just below the knee, I gave it a sharp tap with the hammer. The bone broke cleanly in two. Next I performed the same operation just above the ankle. I slid the head of the curved forceps into the wound, seized the bone, and lifted it out. Triumphantly, I brandished it, still held in the forceps.

"Look, Sister Jeanne! . . . . I've got it! . . . ."

Sister Jeanne took one look, and fainted. Fortunately, her fainting fit lasted no more than a moment.

As for Herico, he too looked around; his eyes were wide and staring, and his face was gray which was the Papuan equivalent of going deathly pale. I noticed then that drops of blood were trickling from his lower lip. He had literally bitten his lip until the blood came, to prevent himself moving or uttering a sound. With dry mouth, he managed to say:

"Thank you, *Babe*. . . . I hope that our Father Jesus is content."

One more difficulty remained: from keeping his leg bent for so long, Herico's knee joint had grown completely stiff, and would no longer function. Some time later, when the wound was rapidly closing up, I quite simply grasped the knee, and with brutality that ultimately proved beneficent, forced the articulation to start working again. . . . Once again, Herico bore the pain with heroic fortitude.

Four months later, he accompanied me when I went to Yule for the annual retreat: the journey took six days, and of course had to be made on foot. . . .

Today, twenty years later, Herico has a perfectly sound limb, and can run like a hare!

WIVES FOR COWS

"Polygamy here does not seem to be primarily a case of morals but of labor. Wealth to the African is measured by the number of his cows. And the more cows he has the more wives he acquires. As soon as a man gets a few extra cows he makes a down payment on the dowry for the second wife, who is to become an additional farm hand for him. It is not surprising that we find it hard to convince even our Catholic Action leaders, when they acquire extra cows, that they cannot follow the age-old practice in Africa of using them to buy farm hands, who are also wives."   —JOSEPH M. GLYNN

THE WORKERS OF PEACE VILLAGE

by Edmund T. Shambaris

> The spirit of the pioneer belongs to men of many na-
> tions. Here is an account with a Japanese setting that
> parallels our own American traditions.

"But, Father, we're not like the ordinary Japanese," protested
Nakamura-san. "We work twice as hard as the ordinary Japanese."

This bit of boasting sounded very much like a loud blowing of
one's horn and should, I thought, have been said with tongue
in cheek. To work twice as hard as the ordinary Japanese farmer,
would be a considerable feat. So I put on a "doubting Thomas"
look and asked to be shown the evidence. I was.

Heiwa-mura is a pioneer village. In these days of skyscrapers
and paved roads and TV, it is hard to even imagine a pioneer
establishment outside of a Hollywood movie set. But tucked
away in the mountains north of Kyoto, on the top of Mt. Tai
San Ji, stands the quiet, hidden village of Heiwa-mura. "Peace"
is what it would be called in English—"Peace Village."

After a long, steady climb, the traveler suddenly, and almost
without any warning, emerges on the top of the mountain, and
there drinks in a panorama that would make any travelogue
narrator go into ecstasies. Standing there, one finds it easy to feel
that the people of the mountaintop live close to God.

One might expect to find a desolate hermitage in this mountain fastness. Instead, on the plateau summit the climber sees a
small, cleared settlement of about twenty tiny houses, clustering

together. There, indeed, is a refuge from clutter and confusion—
a refuge literally carved from the wilderness.

It all began five years ago, although the dreaming and planning
goes back much further.

Morita and Nakamura had been buddies for years, visiting one
another and frequently discussing the future—which they saw
only in rosy colors. Those were the days of dreams. But they were
also the days of Japan's imperialism. Morita and Nakamura were
caught up in a machine for which they had no liking—the machine of war. They, along with millions of other young men,
were called into military service. They were parted to serve overseas.

Morita and Nakamura did not meet again until years later,
after the war had been fought and lost. Their paths crossed in
Kyoto, where one worked in a bakery and the other in a bicycle
shop. The war was over but not the dreams. Japan was building
a new nation. Why couldn't they build a new world for themselves and their families?

The two friends heard that the Government was giving out
parcels of abandoned or uninhabited land to returned veterans,
as part of a rehabilitation program. Instantly they knew what
they wanted to do. Years earlier, they had rambled through the
hills and mountains around Kyoto, and they had always been
attracted to the mountaintop of Tai San Ji. There was the place
to build a new world! But would the Government give them the
land?

After many trips to Government bureaus and the unraveling
of miles of red tape, the two friends finally held a paper that
made the top of Tai San Ji theirs. But one condition was attached: in a specified number of years, they must have a definite
amount of land under cultivation. The job was too much for
two to do alone, so they looked around for additional partners.
Few men were interested in such a difficult and backbreaking
venture. But in time Morita and Nakamura found fourteen pioneer spirits like themselves.

To establish a village and make farm land from a remote
mountain fastness, is a challenging undertaking. It is even more

formidable and discouraging when the job must be done "on a shoestring." The start was not propitious. Sun, wind, rain, and wild animals worked against the pioneers. The untamed soil did not respond to plowing. Instead of top grass, matted vegetation with roots a foot deep had to be removed; the patient workers cut it into squares and lifted it out, piece by piece.

About this time, in the town of Aoyagi where they had gone for supplies, Morita and Nakamura met Father Clement Boes-flug. The veterans were immediately attracted to the priest. They had rejected Buddhism years earlier, because it did not answer the problems of life. They listened to the American missioner, and then asked that instructors in religion be sent to the mountaintop.

After working from the crack of dawn, the pioneers would stumble into catechism class at eight or nine o'clock at night. Some fell asleep from fatigue, others stayed until the early hours of morning, asking questions. This went on until the workers and their families had finished their studies and were baptized.

Father Boesflug helped those new Christians in every way he could. Through friends, he procured supplies such as cement, nails, tiles, food, and so on. In return the converts built their own chapel, in the center of the new village.

The big project now is a waterworks. For five years the villagers have hauled water by buckets from the bottom of the mountain. They figure that in about a year they will have water flowing through the long trench they have dug.

The last time I was in Peace Village, Nakamura asked, "Where shall we put the electric outlets in the chapel?" Electricity will follow as soon as the water is flowing.

Yes, things are looking up in Heiwa-mura.

TOUGH HOMBRE

by Peter Petrucci

> Juan Vega lived surrounded by legends of his own deeds
> but Father Petrucci found only another soul hidden in
> the Yucatecan wilderness.

I finally met Juan Vega. When friends heard that I was going to
Chunpom on a mission trip, they told me that I shouldn't fail to
see him. Some spoke of him as "a white man among the Mayan
Indians." Others called him "a bad man who killed a lot of
innocent people." Still others called him "the leader of the Mayan Indians around Chunpom."

For the first time in many, many years, a catechism class had
been organized in Chunpom. The man responsible was my catechist, Juan Arzapalo. He had gone down, rounded up some children of the village, and made them ready for First Communion.
He reported, also, that after some struggle he had prepared a
"bad man" for confession and Communion. The "bad man" was
Juan Vega.

I went down to examine the catechist's work. Chunpom is
one of the most out-of-the-way places in the Quintana Roo jungle.
The road to the village is only a mule trail. I remember thinking
that Chunpom was a good place for any bad man to hide.

The first person I met in the village was Juan Vega himself.
When he came to greet me, I saw a small, bent, and aged man.
In a soft, modulated voice, he asked me to have supper with him
that evening. He didn't look like a bad man.

After Rosary and confessions, I went to Juan Vega's house. It was an old hut, like all the huts of Chunpom, made of wooden poles and topped by a thatched roof. It was quite dark inside. After the customary greetings, I sat down to eat. During the meal, Juan told me his story.

He was born on the island of Cozumel about eighty years ago. His mother was a pious woman, and instructed the boy in his Faith. When he was ten years old, he made a fishing trip to the Yucatan mainland with his father. On the mainland, the islanders met some Mayan Indians who appeared to be friendly—but then something went wrong. The Indians fell upon the boy's father and other members of the party. All were killed except Juan.

The boy was captured and taken to the Mayan village, where he was appointed a scribe because he could read and write. Eventually he married a Mayan woman and raised a fine family.

"They say I killed many people," Juan remarked. "It is not true. The villagers often came to me for advice, and I would tell them not to kill their captives. That is the way my mother taught me. The Mayas usually followed my advice, but sometimes in war bad things happen. The Indian wars have long since ended, but the stories grow bigger every year!"

After Juan Vega finished his story, he made his confession. The next morning he received Holy Communion—for the first time in seventy years. I don't think that the angels found him a very "tough hombre."

GRATITUDE

"One thing we can be grateful for—it is getting hard indeed for a Christian to think that God likes his race better than other races. A Christian may still like his race better than others, but it's getting very hard to think that God agrees with him. And even if he does think that God agrees with him, it is getting very hard, almost impossible, to say it aloud."

—ALAN PATON

WHY LATIN AMERICANS
DON'T LIKE US

by Albert J. Nevins

> It is always a surprise for the average citizen of the
> United States to learn that, despite his aid to other
> peoples and a desire to be liked by all, there are many
> who do not care for him.

The plane had left behind the rich, fertile fields of Sao Paulo
and was heading over the dismal Matto Grosso swamplands. The
flight was an easy one, and the young Brazilian engineer beside
me was inclined to talk.

"You don't seem like an American," he said, interjecting a personal note for the first time. "At least, not like the Americans
I've met."

"Don't you care for Americans?" I asked, gathering an impression from his tone.

"No," he replied frankly. "I don't. Americans are too—too
proud."

For most Americans it usually comes as a shock when they
discover that, as a nation, they are not liked. The average citizen,
who has contributed to the largess that his Government has distributed all over the world, has a firm conviction that, because
of his philanthropies, he must be a very popular fellow indeed.
He is quite convinced that everyone should like him; and when

response is lacking, he is hurt and confused. Now he must be told one more fact: Latin Americans don't like us.

"Americans are like children," an educated Peruvian told me in Lima. "They are very immature. Everything they make must be the biggest or the fastest or some other superlative. They believe that the only end in life is to become rich. They think skyscrapers and jet planes can replace culture."

Any analysis of Latin-American sentiment toward the United States is a complex affair at best. In some instances the Latin American has right on his side; in other cases he is a victim of misunderstanding, and in still others, there is no justification for his attitude.

Latin-American memories are long. Colombians still remember the part the United States played in separating Panama from them. It was the guns of American warships that prevented the Colombian armies from putting down the rebellion that gave Panama independence. Nicaraguans still recall the marching footsteps of American marines, who garrisoned their country into the 1930's. Cubans find it difficult to forget the Platt Amendment, which allowed the United States to intervene in Cuban national affairs, and which was not abandoned until 1934.

Past business practices of United States corporations did little to help the situation. Many American companies pirated the nations of Latin America, extracting huge profits through the exploitation of cheap manpower.

"American corporations robbed the wealth from our soil," declared a Bolivian, "and they did this at the expense of the masses who, despite their work, were left starving."

But all of these things are of the past. There is no historical doubt that we made some mistakes. It is to our credit that we have also attempted to rectify them.

The Charter of the Organization of American States, signed in Bogota in 1948, no longer permits intervention in national affairs. We admitted our Panama blunder to Colombia in 1921, and paid damages. Under President Franklin D. Roosevelt, the U.S. Marines were withdrawn from Haiti, Nicaragua and the Dominican Republic. When just a few years ago the Panamanian Government protested over an airbase that had been granted us on their soil, we pulled out almost overnight, turning the complete base over to the Panamanians—who were surprised and somewhat chagrined at our unexpected action.

Even in the field of business, the picture has changed. There are still some abuses, but today they are exceptions rather than the rule. National Governments in Latin America have expropriated American property in some instances, and in others have passed laws requiring the extensive hiring of national personnel. American investors now take a long-range view and refrain from any action that will kill the goose that lays the golden eggs. In fact, many American companies who once possessed bad labor records have now gone to the opposite extreme and are the leaders in supplying all sorts of labor and social benefits for their workers, largely as a matter of good business.

But if old charges die slowly, new ones are continually being added. Some of them have foundation in fact, others are purely imaginary, and still more come from the subtle promptings of local Communists.

There is a general feeling throughout Latin America that the United States has forgotten its immediate neighbors in favor of the European powers. Latin Americans point out the tremendous sums that have gone to Europe, and the smaller loans and grants that were given to the other Americas.

Another criticism is that we have aided certain Latin-American countries with military equipment and military missions that have the effect of strengthening the dictatorial governments in power against the will of the people. It is also charged that our educational fellowships and student-exchange programs are too often operated on the basis of political expediency rather than on the basis of what is best for the country involved.

There was a case in Chile, for example, where American funds were used to promote communism. An American administrator arrived in this particular city to see if an American grant could be used to further education. The area was almost entirely Catholic, and the Catholic parish in the city was attempting to build a new school. The priests, who also happened to be Americans, applied for aid in their project and were turned down for the reason that such funds could not be used for sectarian purposes. The other school of the city, run by Communists, applied and received aid. To say that the people of the city were perplexed by this action of the United States is an understatement.

But it is in the field of religion that the major cause for Latin-American suspicion arises. And it is in the field of religion that American foreign policy has made some tragic mistakes. The Latin American lives in a Catholic culture that colors all of his thinking and his life. While it is true that, because of lack of priests, vast masses of Latin Americans are without the sacraments, are poorly instructed, and often without the practice of their Faith, they are nevertheless baptized and consider themselves Catholics.

Even the diminishing breed of anticlerical that was nurtured in the secularism of the last century has a Catholic twist to his mind. "Scratch an anticlerical deep enough, and you will find a Catholic," says an old Latin proverb. And there is a great deal of truth in it.

With this Catholic background in Latin America, it is unfortunate that the policy of the United States has never tried to tighten the ties by making known the fact that the largest single religious group in the United States is the Catholic Church. Judging from results, it would seem that the opposite were true.

"There are not many Catholics in the United States, Padre?" inquired a young Argentine. It was a question frequently asked, and like all the other askers, he, too, was surprised when told the actual facts.

One of the greatest divisive causes in recent years has been the influx of fringe Protestant groups that vigorously proselytize, and unfairly attack the religious beliefs of the vast majority of the people. Protestant missionaries have been at work in Latin America for over a century, and many of them have built up firm and loyal followings and hold the respect of the people in general. But since the end of World War II, other groups have come in, not so much to propagate Christianity (if one is to judge by their actions) but to attack the Catholic Church.

The result of their work is reflected in a cartoon that appeared in a large secular daily. Entitled "The Good Neighbor Policy," it showed Uncle Sam with a big stick chasing Latin Americans into a Protestant church. Untrue, of course. Unfortunate, also, because it perpetuates an already mistaken idea.

Many bishops of Latin America have expressed serious concern over the teachings of some Americans who have come down to their countries as agents of one or another U.S. aid program. Birth control, sterilization, and other teachings hostile to Catholic doctrine have been advocated by those people. Because those emissaries are officials of United States agencies, their acts are interpreted as being part and policy of the American Government.

In contrast, consider the wonderful impression created by David McDonald, president of the Steelworkers' Union. He was one of the few prominent Catholics sent down by our Government as a "good-will ambassador." In Latin America, where unionism and communism are almost synonymous, this union official demonstrated that one can be a good Catholic and still be an active union member. Mr. McDonald's example of attendance at Mass and reception of Communion did more to offset Red propaganda than millions of dollars spent in technical aid.

William O'Dwyer was the most popular American Ambassador ever sent to Mexico. He had the respect and admiration of the Mexican people. Why? Because he was *simpatico*. Being a Catholic, he understood the deep religious background of the Mexican peasant.

Finally, the last cause for dislike of Americans can be laid at the door of some American tourists who join the exodus to our neighboring countries every year. Many of them are loud, rowdy, and profligate. They look down on native people.

A WOLOF TAKES A WIFE

by John J. Considine

> Moslems and Christians mingle in Dakar's version of
> something old, something new, something borrowed,
> something blue.

The cocks and the muezzins vied with each other in waking us
this morning. As the sun comes up in Dakar, streams of muffled
figures plod silently toward their work, many wearing the fez or
its local equivalent, for three quarters of the population of Dakar
is Moslem.

Indeed, of the 17 million dwellers in French West Africa (of
which Dakar is the capital) 7 million are sons of the prophet.
Small wonder, then, that the Moslem call to prayer, sounded
by hoarse-voiced Negro muezzins throughout the Medina,
Dakar's native city, fills our ears here in the house of the White
Fathers.

This abundance of Moslems, which has influenced so greatly
Catholic mission work in French West Africa, heightens the joy
at every evidence of Christian advance. Hence, the especially
keen happiness of all thoughtful folk who witnessed today the
wedding of Mark Monet and Angelique Mendy. The ceremony
was a visible triumph for many things that the missioners have
been striving after here for something over a century, and I as
a Maryknoller was very happy to be a participant.

French West Africa consists of eight separate divisions. The
division of Senegal, of which Dakar is local center as well as the

capital of the entire area, is not one of the most flourishing in the Faith. The southern sections of Dahomey and of the Ivory Coast, where the African Mission Society of Lyons carries on, rank highest. Islam rules everywhere in the interior—which includes the French Sudan, the Upper Volta and the Niger Colony —territory commited predominantly to the White Fathers. But there are islets of non-Islamized peoples and among these the White Fathers have made good progress.

The last three of the eight divisions—French Guinea, Senegal and Mauritania—are cared for by the Holy Ghost Fathers; while Guinea and small sectors of Senegal have given them consolation, the great part of their territory has offered them a hard fight.

All the more joy for these missioners, therefore, in such events as today's.

Mark Monet is the youngest son of a large and what is known locally as an old Catholic family. He and his brother have been active in Dakar's Catholic youth movement. Angelique is next to the youngest child of a similarly outstanding Catholic family. Her father was mayor of Dakar and she has followed a pattern set by her elders of being very active in charities and in Catholic societies. Rather reticent and instinctively modest, Angelique gives the impression of being shy and retiring but the fact is that she is remarkable for her initiative. In her quiet way, she organizes not only her fellow Africans but as well great numbers among the 25,000 Europeans in Dakar, all of whom fall under the spell of her charm and her goodness.

When Mark and Angelique announced that they would wed, a wave of enthusiasm touched the entire colony of some 10,000 African Catholics in the city of Dakar. "A perfect pair," many said. "Wonderful promise for a fine Catholic family," remarked others. Many of the Catholics are simple workmen who lead lowly lives. A considerable number, however, are well educated. Few if any are rich; but as Government employees or as officers in European companies, they have the means to possess good homes and to assume the ways of cultivated folk of the Western World. This they do with a measure and modesty that make them one of the maturer of the groups of *evolués* that are developing in so many centers in Africa.

The cynics among the Europeans in Africa poke fun at the *evolués* as disoriented savages who take upon themselves the trappings of civilization yet engage in ridiculous gaucheries that can only bring disdain on them. Such critics forget that our ancestors were once plain men of the forest. The first among our forebears to put on the clothes and follow the habits of the cultured circles of ancient Rome probably made foolish blunders and drew the jibes of the lookers-on. But Christian discipline and shrewd consideration among the more thoughtful quickly set up canons that came to govern the new society.

Before our eyes here in Dakar we have an example of this evolution of Christian society. All these Catholics are of the Wolof people, a tribe of some 600,000 that has lived for unnumbered generations in Senegal. They are large of build, fine of feature, of a handsomely rich black. They have been mediocre farmers who have disdained raising flocks. They have a tradition for careful organizations; like many other tribes in Africa, they trace heredity on the side of the mother.

About a century ago, the French came and willy-nilly the Wolofs were drawn into their orbit. Government officials and the army dwelt on material things, except at times to encourage the Wolofs to become Moslems since so many French administrators felt this was best for the African. The missioners, meanwhile, brought them the Faith and Christian ideals and gave them schools even before the Government built any.

Today in Dakar the farthest advanced among the African Catholics comprise the top rank in African society here. While many Moslem men are well educated and formed to modern culture, as a rule their women are not. This means that the men are ashamed of the women. Moslems do not enter easily into mixed society with the wife coequal companion of the husband.

This morning for the marriage of Mark and Angelique this best of Dakar's African society was on hand in Sacred Heart Church. Besides the grownups there were heavy contingents of teen-agers with the banners of their Catholic youth societies.

As Angelique with modest poise came gracefully down the center aisle, they gave her their formal salute in loud staccato with much deep feeling. She is their leader; they love her as their little queen.

There were, of course, all the trappings of the West. Six maids of honor in exquisite blue followed the bride in her cloud of white. Six charming little flower girls also in blue and two tiny boy attendants in white brought smiles from everybody, with their unpredictable twists and squirms. Bishop Guibert of Dakar celebrated the Nuptial Mass and, quite as he might do for a distinguished couple at the Cathedral of Notre Dame in Paris, he delivered a special sermon as an exhortation to Mark and Angelique. He recited their life histories and must have made them feel uneasy by the high accomplishments with which he taxed them for the future.

After Mass a great concourse of brothers, sisters, fathers, mothers, uncles, aunts and cousins poured into the sacristy to salute His Excellency and to witness the signing of the record. Many of the men were in morning clothes and the women were smartly dressed in finery that in great part had come from Paris.

A large new garage was engaged for the informal wedding breakfast that followed. Hardly a fitting place, one might feel, for fine dresses; but it was appropriately clean and neatly decorated. Great candy ornaments made of peanut brittle (Dakar exports thousands of tons of peanuts annually for their oil) decorated the long tables, at the head of which the newlyweds established themselves for the reception.

Among the hundreds present at the reception were several dozen Moslems and their wives. While the Christians were in Western clothes, as were many of the Moslem men, the Moslem women wore ornate native garb of richly flowing robes, colorful kerchiefs on their heads and a profusion of necklaces and bracelets of hammered gold and silver. There are, it goes without saying, friendly family relations between the Christian minority in Dakar and many of the city's Moslems.

I found it extremely interesting to talk to the guests whom I met through the kindness of my host in Dakar, Father Rummelhardt. There were, for instance, Mr. and Mrs. Faye. Mr. Faye is an instructor in one of Dakar's schools, a thoughtful man from Moslem stock, who entered the Church while in college. He is married to a young lady whose family name is also Faye and who has two brothers Trappist monks—one in the monastery near Yaounde in the French Cameroons and the other in a great Trappist foundation in France.

With Father Rummelhardt, I later visited the Faye home and met little John, aged three, and tiny Marie Regina, six months old. Mr. Faye had just returned from Europe, where he had visited Our Lady's shrine at Lourdes. And on Marie Regina's wrist, as she played with Father Rummelhardt's neck rosary, dangled a tiny bracelet with a medal her dad brought back from Lourdes.

At the lunch, too, was Martha Kpakpo, a young lady from Dahomey who is in her third year in medical college here in Dakar, and is due to go to Paris to secure her degree as doctor of medicine. Martha is of the Fon people, as the practiced eye can ascertain by noting the oval shape of her head. Dahomey is the farthest advanced of the eight divisions of French West Africa and supplies an unusual number of Government employees, many of whom are Catholics. Indeed, Catholic schools help get many Catholics into positions where they can do good. Of the 80 candidates at present in the Dakar Institute of Midwives, 55 are Catholics.

Unfortunately, African priests and Sisters are few in Dakar and Senegal generally, though their development is further advanced in other sections of West Africa. One African priest was on hand for the wedding of Mark and Angelique. We can hope that this highly essential category of African leaders can soon be in better supply.

Mark and Angelique were wreathed in smiles as I added my good wishes to the congratulations of their neighbors and host of friends. How they felt about me I don't know but I can say quite definitely that I felt very close and warm toward these two children of the Wolof people as I shook their hands.

STRANGER IN THE COURT

by Michael J. O'Connor

Here's a cloak and dagger story that we doubt you will figure out until the very end. It proves once again that strange things happen in Red China.

The little man in the baggy, mustard-colored uniform of the Chinese Communist Army stood uncertainly outside the mission gate and looked cautiously at the courtyard within. Facing it on three sides were five doors, all of them shut tight. The whitewash was peeling from the walls. The mission would have looked completely abandoned and deserted, had not a tiny ribbon of smoke curled from the window of a rear room.

The Communist soldier looked warily behind him, up and down the alley. He shifted his snub-nosed machine gun from his right hand to a more comfortable cradle over his left elbow, slowly took a crumpled package of cigarettes from his right pocket, selected one with his mouth and lit it.

Yesterday Wong, his squad leader, had returned from the liberation of this village and had told of the foreigner with the big beard who lived at this Catholic Mission. So early this morning, the soldier had started across the endless rice fields. It had been a three-hour walk in the hot South China sun, and his uniform, so comfortable six months ago in the snow-swept north, absorbed the heat and held it tightly against his body.

As he walked, he had thought. Thought of his home village,

Red Mountain, so far away, and of his family. He thought of his training, the endless marches, the parades, the indoctrination talks by the raspy-voiced section leader. The slogans ran through his mind: "Liberty through labor," "China for the Chinese," "Imperialist aggression." He remembered sweeping through village after village, the curious eyes, the flags, the dancing, the quick execution of the apathetic few who had been branded reactionaries. Each village had been the same.

Now at the Catholic mission, he stepped carefully through the narrow gate and looked in turn at the five doors opening on the small courtyard. Which one led to the chapel? The door near the smoke-blackened window was for the kitchen; the two with screens must be rooms for the cook and the priest. But on his left were two pairs of huge double doors, their wooden hinges set into concrete. He stepped over and looked through the center crack of one pair of doors and saw desks and benches—it was the schoolroom, although now empty of children. He moved slowly, cautiously, towards the other large doors—they *must* be for the chapel.

The soldier wanted to pray. It had been eight months since he had entered a church. The last time had been in Red Mountain Village, far to the north. There his life had centered around the tall-spired church that had dominated the countryside. There he had been known and respected as Kwok the Teacher. Father Thebideux had hired him when he had finished middle school. The priest had fed him well and paid him well and had been his friend.

All that was now ended. The Liberation Army had come in the night and had seized his father. Quickly the story spread that landlords would be given their lives, and perhaps some of their land, if their sons volunteered. Before morning Kwok had scratched his name on the roll, and had been whisked away in a truck with a half dozen equally scared youths of his village. Since then he had heard nothing from home.

Kwok shook his head to clear it of such thoughts. The little mission building, so low and flat, so unlike the tall church at

Red Mountain, would contain, he hoped, a place where he could pray again. He walked softly over to the second set of double doors, behind which, he felt sure, was the chapel. Once again he glanced behind him, and his ears were alert for the sound of anyone approaching.

He remembered Yuan Ning, the raw-boned farmer from Shantung Province. Yuan was in the squad behind his, and Kwok had felt that Yuan, too, was a Lord of Heaven believer, after he had seen him make a quick sign of the cross in the darkness one night. But Yuan had been seen entering a Lord of Heaven church at Lui Fung, and had been reported. Later, after many hours with the section commander and his aides, Yuan had stood before the entire regiment and had confessed his "crime." Since then, he had been a beaten man, unobtrusive, unspeaking and unspoken to. Everyone said that some day he would "disappear."

Kwok, the teacher, opened the door a trifle, exposing a half-inch crack of darkness. He moved closer and put his eye to the slit. The chapel—for such it was—was small. There a red light burned, as he had hoped. He grasped the iron handle of the door tightly.

But he didn't open the door. He stopped suddenly as he heard loud and harsh voices in the alley in front of the mission. He whirled around, and saw framed in the gate five or six soldiers, curiosity plain on their faces as they looked at the mission courtyard and at him. His face went pale, and he knew he looked embarrassed—caught in the act. The first of the soldiers, obviously a platoon leader, stepped into the courtyard and looked intently, suspiciously, at Kwok, in dead silence.

The leader was a tall, thin man with a well-fitted uniform. His sallow skin stretched tightly over high cheekbones. He was, Kwok guessed, a Shansi man, and probably an old soldier. His tight-lipped face seemed to have little kindness in it, as he stared at Kwok with half-closed eyes.

"What are you doing here?" It was less a question than a command. Kwok's hand fell from the doorknob of the chapel. He slowly shuffled across the mission courtyard. He sidled past the platoon leader, past the soldiers. He felt that all of them were watching his retreating back. And he remembered Yuan Ning.

The platoon leader turned to the soldiers behind him and issued crisp commands. They saluted and he saluted. Then they turned and headed down the alley, but in a direction opposite to that Kwok had taken. The tall, thin man watched them go. When the soldiers had disappeared he turned abruptly and re-entered the mission yard. He strode briskly to the first screen door on the right, hesitated, then tapped lightly on the wooden frame.

The screen door opened. In the doorway stood a westerner wearing a cassock. He was a large man, but his cheeks were sunken under a white beard. His blue eyes had a touch of fear in them.

"Yes?" he asked.

"May I come in?" said the soldier.

The priest opened the screen door wide to allow the other to enter. But the platoon leader motioned him aside and closed the screen door himself. Next he shut the heavy wooden doors, and dropped the iron bar in place behind them. He turned to the surprised priest, and to his greater surprise, bowed to him.

"I am a priest, Father," the visitor said simply.

The foreign priest eyed him suspiciously. "But—How—"

"Do not be afraid, Father," said the Chinese soldier in clear, smooth Latin. "I wish to go to confession."

Later the two priests sat with tea bowls in their hands, and talked with the friendliness and warmth of priests who have not seen their own kind in a long while.

When the Chinese rose to leave, he said: "By the way, I chased a soldier from your chapel door before I came in. I suppose you are often troubled with them?"

"Yes. Often," said the missioner. "I think they wander through the village seeking, shall we say, what reminds them of home."

Two miles away, Kwok was hot in his clumsy uniform; the gun was heavy on his arm as he trudged along the road. His head was bent under the intense heat and his mind was dull with fatigue.

He thought: "Red Mountain Village, with the white spire soaring heavenwards . . . I wanted to pray, but . . . that thin-lipped platoon leader, will he report me?"

CANTICLE OF LIGHT

Dedicated to Mother of Light

O Sun, stars, moon—praise you your Light—
Whose rays inflame the cold, stark night.

O stars whose fires kindle skies
I saw you dancing in her eyes
Before the skies were made!

O moon who wears twin lilies white,
I saw her feet pursuing night
Before the flowers were made!

O sun whose flames conceive the days,
I heard her magnify My praise
Before the Day was born!

O lightning spearing East to West,
I saw a sword transpierce her breast
Before lightnings were loosed!

O radiant bridge whose archways glow,
I saw her tears through laughter flow
Before rainbows were spanned!

O sun, stars, moon—praise you the light
Whose Rays Eternal shatter night!

—MARIE FISCHER

SO RED THE ROOD

by Everett F. Briggs

> The early days of Christianity in Japan were marked by extraordinary opportunity and then tragic failure. Father Briggs, long a student of Japanese history and culture, tells the reasons why.

Twenty-four persons—including six Spanish Franciscans, three Japanese Jesuits, and fifteen Catholic laymen, two of whom were mere boys—were condemned to mutilation and crucifixion when the active persecution by Hideyoshi began. In the prison of Kyoto, the lobes of the left ears of the victims were sliced off. Then the condemned men were exposed to the public gaze. Three together, they were forced into rude, cartlike vehicles, in which they were drawn through the streets of the metropolis, while a crier preceded them to attract attention. Subsequently, the martyrs-to-be set out, under heavy guard, on the long journey to Nagasaki, in the southern island—Nagasaki, soon to become the "holy land" of Christianity in Japan.

Not far from modern Kobe, the marchers were allowed a brief rest, and there a young man begged to join their company. The new recruit had been baptized only eight months before. A little farther on, another layman fell in with them. At length, all were carried by boat to the southern island. From Hakata (now Fukuoka) the twenty-six martyrs set out on foot for Nagasaki, arriving there three days later—February 5, 1597.

* From *New Dawn in Japan*, Longmans, Green and Company.

Twenty-six rough-hewn crosses had been erected on the slope of
Mount Tate (pronounced *Tahtay*), looking across the city to the
sea. To the right and left of each cross stood a soldier armed
with a lance. The twenty-six Christians were required to mount
the crosses. With ropes, their wrists and ankles were bound to the
crossbeams. Outstretched, the martyrs waited through hours of
agony, for the glory to come. Toward evening the fateful word
of command rang out, and the alert sentinels plunged their
spears into the hearts of the first martyrs of Japan.

In all their ten centuries in the Island Empire, the Buddhist
priests could point to nothing like the impassioned eloquence of
crucified Paul Miki. That Japanese Jesuit Brother had preached
in very truth "like dying man to dying men." Nor could the
Buddhists boast of heroism like that of little Ludovico, who
looked down from his cross in childish glee, completely oblivious
of his heartbroken mother sobbing outside the bamboo barrier.

Two years after this massacre, Hideyoshi, the Napoleon of
Japan, was gathered to his ancestors, and the Church had another respite—the calm before an impending storm. The new
shogun, Iyeyasu, was not only an able soldier, but also a skill-
full diplomat. Like his predecessors, he was desirous of main-
taining commercial relations with the foreigners, and he tolerated
the presence of the missioners as long as he could use them to
ingratiate himself with the traders. Nevertheless, during the first
ten years of Iyeyasu's rule the Church flourished. Although persecutions were waged by individual daimios in their own fast-
nesses, such was the progress of the Faith that the first decade
of the seventeenth century deservedly has been called the high-
water mark of Catholic missions in Japan. According to one record, the Japanese faithful numbered 600,000 souls during this
period of history, although less than 500,000 may be a more
exact figure.

Simultaneously, however, malign influences were furiously at
work. First of all, suspicion of the foreigner, a suspicion characteristic of pre-war Japanese—characteristic, indeed, of the whole
Orient, inclusive of Siberia—had not abated in the least. True,
the suspicions of the Japanese were not without some founda-

tion in fact. Then as now, the medley of genuine piety, devotion, and self-sacrifice on the part of the missioners, and the shameless, un-Christian tactics of the nations from which they came, presented, at best, an enigma to intelligent Orientals.

Against these suspicions, the missioners were utterly defenceless. To be sure, they made mistakes of their own, mistakes that stemmed from overzealousness, and these did not help their cause. But it is stupid and vicious to contend, as some writers have done, that the persecuted missioners were more to blame for their sorry plight than were the monsters who harried them. Moreover, the fact of a common nationality was sufficient ground for condemning the pioneer missioners together with the unscrupulous foreign traders. The latter, like buccaneers everywhere, kept the port cities of Japan in turmoil, and some went so far, on occasion, as to carry off natives into alien slavery. At that time, as during the author's years in Nippon, the Japanese people hardly could be blamed for suggesting that the missioners would do better to go home and preach the Gospel to their own benighted countrymen.

The arrival of mission helpers of other nationalities, men who were less circumspect than the pioneer apostles, served to heighten the prevailing tension. Finally, the activities of most of these foreigners were staged in sections of the country that were far from the capital, and that enjoyed a greater measure of autonomy. Consequently, the allegiance of local rulers in the southern island, the stronghold of Christianity, was a burning question in the mind of the usurping shogun. The possibility that daimios of the south might unite against him had become a nightmare to Iyeyasu.

To make matters worse, at this uncertain juncture English and Dutch traders arrived on the scene, and took up with gusto a campaign of vilification against the Portuguese and Spaniards, in order to supplant the traders of those nationalities. In particular, Will Adams, a shipwrecked English mariner forced into the employ of Iyeyasu, was no friend to the Latin competitors of his own countrymen. Although Adams does not seem to have cherished any particular animus towards Catholicism and the

Catholic missioners, he did much to unsettle the shogun's mind against all Portuguese and Spanish nationals.

Be it said to the credit of the Portuguese and Spanish adventurers, they never were prejudiced against the spread of the Faith. If missioners wished to follow them to new lands, in order to preach the Gospel of Christ, that was agreeable to the traders. Their galleons were not closed to God, if God did not disdain to walk their irreligious decks. Doubtless, the rulers of the missioners' homelands were not always single-minded. Doubtless, too, the compatriots of the missioners often saw, in the prospect of association with them, advantages of mutual support. Nevertheless, there was no intent on the part of any of the Portuguese or Spanish, positively to exclude the diffusion of the Gospel.

The late comers—the English and Dutch traders—offered the shogun the benefits of foreign trade without the drawbacks of a "foreign" religion. They were solely and brutally on business bent, even to the exclusion of religion. Indeed, the Dutch traders owed much of the singular toleration that they came to enjoy, to the part they played in the annihilation of the Christians of Shimabaru. At any rate, the new arrivals were able to convince the shogun that toleration of the foreign religion was a price he did not need to pay for the benefits of foreign trade.

Principally, therefore, for political reasons, Iyeyasu was persuaded to proscribe Christianity. He issued an edict in 1614, ordering that all Christian churches were to be destroyed, and that all Christians were to recant or be exiled. Actually, many sterling Christians were deported to the inhospitable northern islands, while others found their way as far south as Macao and the Philippines. (In Macao one may still see the ruins of a church that was erected by some of those exiled Japanese Catholics.) All missioners were commanded to bid farewell to the land of their adoption. Over thirty succeeded in escaping deportation; and of those who were expelled, not a few managed to return. It is recorded that, during the ensuing thirty years, at least a dozen groups of missioners were smuggled in. Those who thus succeeded in penetrating Japan—probably one hundred—were eventually put to death for the sake of Christ.

Still, the full fury of the storm waited on Iyeyasu's death. That shogun had realized that the feudal chiefs, among whom not a few were Christians, sympathized with the common people, whose only crime had been to embrace a "foreign" religion that they believed to be true. It remained for the shoguns Hidetada (1605–23) and Iemitsu (1623–51) to initiate a persecution of Christianity as systematic and dreadful as any in the history of the world. On this point both foreign and Japanese writers agree.

A new department of government, called the "Christian Inquiry," was inaugurated under Hidetada. It was the business of this service to hunt down like wild beasts both foreign missioners and their converts, compelling them to renounce Christianity, on pain of torture and death. The "Inquiry" offered monetary rewards for the betrayal of the faithful; and these sums were successively increased, through the years up to 1711. In the extirpation of the "foreign" religion, modes of torture and execution proceeded from horror to horror. With an excess of sadistic cruelty, the persecutors actually vied with one another in perpetrating prolonged and frightful barbarities; they would not permit the dispatching of their victims at one blow. The persecution was one of the most savage of all history.

In the systematic development of this scientific sadism, two refinements were outstanding. First, there was the fiendish technique of lacerating the bodies of the victims with bamboo saws, and thereafter plunging them, red and raw with wounds, into the boiling *solfataras* on Unzen. That "terrible mountain" seemed to steam to the very skies with its bubbling sulphur wells, which the Japanese even today describe as "hells."

The ultimate refinement was known as the "torment of the fosse." In this the hapless victim, completely swathed except for one hand left free to make the sign of recantation, was suspended head downwards in a pit five or six feet deep. The pits were often partly filled with offal. There in those black holes, many of our brothers and sisters in the Faith hung for as long as a week, exuding blood from mouth and nostrils, maddened by fearful pressure on the brain, until death mercifully released them from almost insupportable anguish. Often the persecutors prolonged the victims' agony by letting blood from veins that bulged black at their temples. It takes a steady nerve and a strong stomach even to contemplate such sickening tortures; but it ill behooves us to shrink from facts, in an age when Christians are again being persecuted in many parts of the world.

Some Japanese who had recanted under the "torture of the fosse," later declared that "neither the pain caused by burning with fire, nor that caused by any other torture, deserves to be compared with the agony produced in this way." Yet Japanese history records the heroic martyrdom of a young girl who endured the anguish for fifteen days!

Lest any Christian escape the dragnet, the whole country was divided into units of five families, each of which was held responsible for the conduct of the others, under pain of punishment affecting the whole group. In practice, this meant that each family became the watchdog of the orthodoxy of four other families, in order to insure its own immunity from the rigors of the law. But the persecutors did not entrust the matter completely to the zeal of these "neighborhood groups," as they were called. Whenever suspicion attached to the beliefs of people in any community, the government conducted its own inquisition. During this process, which was known as "Image trampling," the entire population of the suspected quarter was compelled publicly to tread upon a plaque depicting the Crucified Christ or the Mother of God. Even babes in arms were obliged to place their tiny feet upon the sacred emblems.

Once the nation had been combed of Christians, the preservation of Buddhism, which had been recognized in the meantime as the state religion, was left to the bonzes. The latter required the Japanese people to appear annually at their local temples, in order to take a prescribed oath. This oath forswore all connection with the "wicked religion"—a term that the bonzes began to use for the Christian Faith. The registers of the temples are extant in many places in Japan; they are monuments to the persecuting zeal of the Tokugawa dynasty, a great family of politicians.

How many Catholics were put to death during those bleak centuries, it is difficult to say. According to one Japanese record, 200,000 persons were punished for the "crime" of being Christian. Whether or not this punishment entailed death, is not certainly known; but there is good reason to believe that as many Christians sacrificed their lives in the course of these Japanese persecutions, as were martyred during the ten persecutions of ancient Rome. If, then, faith like this—and for their faith, contempt of life like this—is the stuff of the soul of Japan, who would not wish to have that nation saved for Christ?

We may not follow the long series of events that led to the extirpation of the Christian religion in Japan. But the final act of that great tragedy—the Shimabara Rebellion—is deserving of special mention. This revolt broke out on Kyushu, during the autumn of 1637. It did not originate with the persecuted Christians, but they were involved in it inevitably.

The uprising is traceable directly to the discontent of the general population of the fiefs of Arima and Amakusa Island, which long had suffered under the needless and senseless cruelty of their respective daimios. After the transfer of the daimio of Arima, the new governor dispossessed all the retainers of his predecessors. He reduced those samurai worthies to the humbler status of tillers of the soil, an occupation for which they had no training and little liking. The degraded and dispossessed soldiers, of course, made unsuccessful farmers. As such, they soon were unable to meet the impossible exactions of their new overlord, who demanded more and more taxes.

This monster, in order to spur the clumsy efforts of the samurai-farmers, subjected them to the ordeal of the *"mino* dance" in which the unfortunate victim was dressed in a peasant raincoat of straw, and set afire. What was only a diversion to the tyrannical overlord, often resulted in the fatal burning of the poor wretch condemned to undergo the torture.

When human nature could endure no more, the samurai-farmers of Arima rose in revolt. They were joined by the downtrodden, non-Christian peasants of near-by Amakusa Island; and also, by the persecuted Christians of both fiefs, who for years had been groaning under a tyranny too terrible for words. The insurgents probably numbered about forty thousand men, women, and children. They all took refuge in Hara Castle, an almost-impregnable, moated stronghold situated by the sea, in the district of Shimabara. There, on that rallying ground of the oppressed, where the first defenders of the people's rights in Japan rose against a villainous slavery, Christianity made its last public stand in feudal Nippon.

The besieged Christians fought under banners inscribed with the names of "Iezusu," "Maria," and "Santo Iago" (the latter the patron saint of Spain). In vain did the enemy, 160,000 strong, attack the castle. Time and time again they stormed the outer ramparts, only to be thrown back by the desperate men behind the walls. During three months the embattled peasants held the flower of the shogun's armies at bay. The courage of the besieged struck terror into the hearts of the Tokugawa generals, who became so frantic that they unashamedly enlisted the services of the Dutch in Hirado. Those good people from Europe bombed Hara Castle from February 24 to March 12, but without making any appreciable breach in the fortifications.

In the course of the siege, a message was dispatched from the fortress, on the wings of an arrow. It explained to the attackers the motives of the entrenched Christians, and this testimonial will ever remain as a refutation of those who would question the sincerity of the early Japanese converts to Catholicism.

"We have done this," said the missive, "not with the hope of obtaining lands and houses, but simply because the Christian religion has been forbidden by the shogun. If we should continue to live as Christians, and these laws be not repealed, our bodies being weak and sensitive, we might sin against the Lord of Heaven. These things fill us with grief beyond endurance; hence our present condition."

At the height of the siege, the enemy commander promised amnesty to all non-Christians, as well as to all Christians who would abjure their Faith. When the outlook became desperate, the entire non-Christian element went over to their oppressors. For the Christians, however, there was no escape: after their epic struggle, they could hardly expect the leniency that they had been denied while they suffered unresistingly under the yoke of their persecutors. When at last the castle was taken by assault, on April 12, 1638, more than thirty thousand starved farmers, who had lived on grass during the last weeks of the siege, were put to the sword. The number included men, women, and children. Hara Castle was leveled to the ground, and a forest of human heads were impaled outside the city of Nagasaki.

Onlookers agreed that Christianity existed no longer in Japan. But the inhabitants of Shimabara could never be sure of that. For on summer nights, curious pinpoints of light, like many tiny stars twinkling through a distant cloudbank, ride the wavelets lapping at the ruins of Hara Castle. In vain have scientists explained that this seeming phenomenon is due to the phosphorescent emissions of a certain fish. To the people of Shimabara (among whom the author once sojourned), those twinkling lights on the restless sea will always be the souls of the besieged Christians, who chose to perish in Hara Castle lest they "sin against the Lord of Heaven."

OUT OF HOCK

When Widow Perez in Santiago, Chile, learned that her deceased husband had won the national lottery, she searched the house for the winning ticket. Then she exhumed his body—only to find that grave robbers had stolen his clothes. Detectives tracked down the thieves and learned they had pawned the suit. Finally, the widow found the suit in a pawnshop and in a pocket was the ticket—insuring comfort for the rest of her life.

THE LOTUS MOON FESTIVAL

by *Albert J. Nevins*

> Here's a picture of the tranquil life found in pre-war Korea. Simple pleasures bring great joys as Francis and Wu Han emerge triumphant from the games of the lovely Lotus Moon Festival.

Cold winds from the north blew down over White Head Mountain no longer. The ice had disappeared from the river. Although a few patches of snow remained in the hollows, the breath of spring had come to the air. The Month of the Sleepy Moon was almost at an end. Mr. Paik's school was still open, but the approach of spring made farm chores multiply for Francis and Wu Han. Both Francis and Wu Han passed their thirteenth birthdays working in the rice fields which were being prepared for planting.

What spare time the boys could find was used in the construction of a kite. This was being built for the competitions to take place in Yengwon two months later, at the great festival that would be held on the first day of the Month of the Lotus Moon. In the average Korean's life, there are two big feasts to break the ordinary monotony of the year. These are the New Year celebration, and the festival on the first day of the Lotus Moon.

In the beginning, the boys planned to build two kites, one for

* From *The Adventures of Wu Han*, Dodd Mead and Company. Copyright, The Maryknoll Fathers.

Wu Han and one for Francis. But after talking over the contests, they decided that only one kite would be made. Francis was to fly the kite in the competition, which would take place on Dragon Lantern Hill in Yengwon. He had had more kite-flying experience, anyway. Wu Han, who had grown stronger than Francis although they were both the same age, would enter the boys' wrestling competition. For centuries, wrestling had been one of Korea's most popular sports, and the annual wrestling matches were eagerly anticipated.

The girls would not be overlooked, either. Part of each year's festival was a swing contest, and the girl whose swing went the highest was declared the winner. In every free moment, Mary was over at the Ri farm. There was a swing there, on which the girls practiced.

The building of the kite was a long-drawn-out task. For many weeks the boys had been collecting all the broken pieces of bowls and jars that they could find. Those discarded bits of crockery were to play an important part in the kite contest.

Finally, actual work on the kite began. First, the boys made the reel from which the kite would be flown. They found four rounded sticks of hard wood. The sticks were cut into eight-inch lengths, and then rubbed as smooth as glass. These four sticks were joined together by a pair of wooden crosspieces, each crosspiece resembling an X. The result was a square framework, each side of which measured about eight inches. A hole was drilled in the center of each X; then another rounded stick, about eighteen inches long, was passed through the hole of each X and fastened tightly to the framework. This last stick formed the handle of the reel. Later, string would be wound on the reel, and by turning this handle, the string could be let out or taken in. After the reel was put together, it was again polished smooth, and then set aside to be painted.

Next, the boys went to work on the kite itself. The framework was built somewhat on the style of the framework of the reel. The wood for the framework was bamboo. The strips of bamboo were tied together with heavy, silken thread. Two diagonal cross-pieces were used to give the frame added strength. The result was a rectangular frame a foot wide and fifteen inches long, joined at the corners by an X. The joints were then smoothed down, so that no rough edges would stick out. Lastly, the joints and thread were glued for added strength.

It might be asked why so much time and effort were put into making the framework so strong. But Korean kite contests are rough sport, particularly for the kites. It takes a strong kite to survive!

After the framework was thoroughly dry, a special kite paper was stretched tightly over the bamboo, and glued. When the gluing was finished, none of the bamboo showed. The kite was allowed to dry during the night. Next day a circular hole was cut in the kite paper, about an inch and a half in diameter. The center of the circle fell exactly over the junction of the two diagonals.

"We must try the kite out now, to make sure it is balanced properly," Francis told Wu Han.

A temporary piece of string was attached to the junction of the diagonals. Three inches along this string, two small pieces of string were tied. The free end of each string was fastened to the upper corners of the kite, one string going to the right, the other string going to the left.

"The length of these strings is important. They give the kite the proper angle to take advantage of the wind," Francis told Wu Han, who never had a kite of his own. "If the strings are too long, some of the wind escapes over the top of the kite. If they are too short, some wind escapes under the bottom."

After the strings were attached, the boys took the kite outside for a trial. It was immediately caught up by the breeze. They did not let it out too far, but merely checked it for balance, and the manner in which it rode before the wind.

"It flies like a bird!" Wu Han exclaimed.

"Yeh! This is a good kite," Francis agreed.

The kite was taken back indoors. The temporary string was carefully cut off. The boys had obtained some paint from Mok Sin Poo at the mission, and now they made the face of the kite a brilliant Chinese red. When that dried, Francis painted a decorative border around the edge of the kite. He also painted a design around the center circle, which had been cut out. These decorations were put on in bright yellow. The finished kite was quite handsome!

The string that was to go on the kite reel was the next problem to be worked on. A small jar of glue was heated, and the string was passed through the glue. Then, before the glue had time to harden, the string was quickly passed through a pile of pulverized glass and crockery. This glass-and-china powder adhered to the glue, and soon the boys had the equivalent of a long, slender piece of sandpaper. The treated string was hung outdoors to dry. Several days were needed to treat the entire length, and dry it. Finally the string was wound on the reel and attached to the kite. Everything was then in readiness—and just in time! The day was the last of the Month of the Dragon Moon; on the next day, the Festival of the Lotus Moon would take place.

Early the following morning, everyone was bustling about the Kim farmhouse. It was the big day! Even Mr. Kim had arranged his schedule so that he would not have to make oil deliveries on this day. By the time breakfast was ready, all the farm chores were done. Breakfast was hurriedly eaten, the tables were put away, and the dishes cleaned. The women went to get dressed up for their holiday, while Mr. Kim went out to hitch the pony to the cart. Francis and Wu Han brought out the kite. They could hardly wait to get started.

Mr. Kim wore his long, white coat, and black horsehair hat. It was only for very special occasions that he put on the horsehair hat. Grandmother was dressed in her best silk dress; her skirt was gray, and her blouse was white. She looked very dignified. Wu Han noticed with great pleasure that she was wearing the silver bracelet he had given her for her hankap. Omani wore a blue skirt, but her blouse was of yellow. Mary was dressed in her most colorful clothes, and her braids were tied with wide, bright red ribbons. Little Joseph was clad in embroidered garments; he had on a wide belt that was bright and cheerful because of its many colors.

"Halmani, Omani, and Joseph will ride in the cart," Mr. Kim told the children. "The rest of us will have to walk alongside. There is not room enough for all of us."

Omani sat on the front seat of the cart holding Joseph in her lap. Grandmother sat in the rear of the cart, where she guarded the basket of lunch and the kite. The children walked alongside with Mr. Kim, who held a line by which he led the pony. Francis and Wu Han spent the time making plans for the day. Wu Han, who had had to shift for himself in Pyongyang, was very good at planning. As Francis described the action of the kite contest, Wu Han made suggestions.

"From what you tell me," said Wu Han, "it would be best for you to remain on the defensive in the early part of the kite contest. Let the other boys do all the fighting."

As the family neared the village, they found the road more and more crowded with people. When they reached Yengwon, they stopped to make a short visit at the mission church, and then continued on to the park where the festival was being held. At the entrance to the park, the pony was hitched to a post near other bulls, horses and ponies, and the family went into the park on foot.

"Find a nice, shady tree," Grandmother Kim told the children.

"There's one up ahead, Halmani. No one is under it, either," Mary said excitedly.

They went to the shady tree, where Omani spread blankets on the ground. Then she and Grandmother Kim sat down. Joseph was allowed to crawl about on the blankets. The rest of the party disappeared in different directions. Mr. Kim and Wu Han went to the field where the wrestling was to take place. Francis ran through the park to Dragon Lantern Hill, so that he wouldn't be late for the kite contest. Mary scampered off to the grove where the swings had been set up. She had promised to meet her friend, Teresa Ri, there.

At the wrestling field, Mr. Kim and Wu Han found that the men had already started to wrestle. Pairs of men were grunting and straining all about. Over at one end of the field, boys were lined up, waiting for their turn.

"It's over there, Apagee. I hope I'm not too late."

"You are not late," said Mr. Kim. "Now, remember what I have told you. There will be so many boys in the contest that the winner may have to wrestle ten or twelve times before the day is over. Therefore, it is wise to go slowly so that you will have strength for the end of the day. To win, you must use your head as well as your muscles! Watch for a chance to take your opponent by surprise, and then try to end the match quickly."

"Say a prayer that I win, Apagee," cried Wu Han as he ran over to join the line of boys. He passed Dong One who was standing in the line.

"Am I late, Dong One?" asked Wu Han.

"No. They have not given the numbers out yet. Where is Francis?"

"He has gone up to Dragon Lantern Hill."

"My brothers are up there, too."

Then, as Wu Han took his place at the end of the line, Dong One called, "Good luck!"

"Good luck to you!" answered Wu Han. "I hope we don't meet at the start."

In a short time, a man came and distributed numbers to the boys. Two of each number were given out. The two boys who drew the same numbers were to be opponents. Wu Han's opponent was a husky farm boy he had never seen before. Both boys took off their jackets and sandals. They circled each other cautiously. Because only one fall was allowed in the preliminary rounds, Wu Han did not want to take unnecessary chances. Suddenly the farm boy made a quick lunge at Wu Han, who quickly sidestepped, and stuck out his foot. The farm boy, carried forward by his own momentum, tripped over Wu Han's foot and fell forward to the ground. That round ended almost as soon as it had begun! According to the rules, whenever a person's two knees or any part of his shoulders touched the ground, he was defeated. In the case of an accidental slip, the judge could allow the match to continue. The farm boy's fall had not been accidental. It had been caused by Wu Han's foot, so the judge gave

Wu Han a slip of paper that entitled him to get into the next round.

An old man standing near by spoke to a companion and said, "I'm going to stay here and watch this boy. He uses his head!"

Wu Han overheard the remark and felt very much encouraged.

Mr. Kim, who had been watching at a distance, came up. "That was very good, but you have a long way to go yet," he said.

Wu Han and Mr. Kim sat down in the grass to watch the other wrestlers and wait for the first round to end. They were very interested in a match where an exceptionally well developed boy seemed to be only playing with his opponent.

"Who is that down there, Grandfather?" Mr. Kim asked an old man sitting near by.

"That is Ryang Il Tuk. He was the champion last year."

Just then Tuk made a sudden move and held his opponent's head in his arm. The muscles of his back stood out as he applied pressure. Tuk brought his knee up against his opponent's head, and the boy collapsed to the ground.

"If anyone is to win the matches here today, he will first have to defeat Tuk," Mr. Kim said to Wu Han.

"That doesn't look easy to do," replied Wu Han, his enthusiasm somewhat dimmed.

Meanwhile, up on Dragon Lantern Hill, the contest of the kites had begun. At a given signal, the boys had sent their kites into the air. From that moment, once a kite broke loose or touched the ground, its owner was eliminated. The beginning of the kite contest seemed a kind of wild confusion. Boys jostled one another, sent kites crashing into each other, or tangled them up. Within the first ten minutes of the contest, half the boys were already eliminated. All the boys had treated their kite strings with bits of broken glass as Francis had, so they could force string against string, hoping to cut through their opponents' lines. Many of the kite strings appeared to be razor-sharp, so easily did they cut kites free.

Francis had been in the contest in previous years, but he had never won a prize. Each year he had been eliminated in the first few minutes. Now following Wu Han's advice, he played a defensive game. He did not attack any other kite. When he was attacked, he would not give battle, but ran away by letting his kite out. This plan worked very well—after an hour he was one of five boys who still had kites in the air. Then he altered his strategy slightly. He no longer ran away when attacked, but fought back. However, he would not attack first.

"I'll let the others fight it out," he told Dong Two, who had been eliminated earlier. "Then I'll be around to fight the winner!"

Down at the swing contest, Mary and Teresa Ri had been eliminated almost at the start. They were off at one side watching the preparations for the final round. Girls were standing on each of the gaily decorated swings, their feet strapped to the seats for safety. There were ten contestants left. On a pole hung a cone-shaped, glass vial. A man began to pour red-colored water into the vial. The water escaped through a hole in the bottom, drop by drop. When the vial was empty, the girl whose swing was going the highest at the time was declared the winner. When the man began to pour the colored water, the girls starting from a standstill began to pump frantically. Each girl dreamed of making the perfect swing maneuver—turning over in a complete circle.

It was exciting to watch the brightly clad girls flashing through the air. From a distance it looked as though great colored birds were flying in and out of the trees. After about five minutes, the vial was empty, and the champion received her prize. It was a large bolt of bright red cloth that had been made in China.

When the sun stood in the center of the sky, a recess was called for all the games except the kite contest. Mr. Kim and Wu Han walked back to the tree where Halmani and Omani were sitting. Mary was already there.

"Only three boys are left in the kite contest," Mary called to Wu Han when she saw him approaching, "and Francis is one of them."

"How is Wu Han doing in the wrestling?" Omani asked.

"Wu Han is doing well," answered her husband. "He has downed four boys already."

Grandmother Kim's face beamed with pleasure. "I have fine grandsons!" she boasted.

"I wish I had won the swing contest," Mary said.

"Do not be downhearted," consoled Grandmother Kim. "You are only a small girl. The other girls are larger and older. There will be other years."

"Teresa and I are going in the double contest this afternoon," continued Mary hopefully. "Perhaps we'll win that one."

"We shall see. Now let us eat some of this good lunch we brought with us."

Since the wrestling would not be resumed for a half hour, Apagee, Wu Han, Omani and Mary walked up to Dragon Lantern Hill after lunch. Grandmother remained behind with Joseph.

As the little group reached the top of the hill, Wu Han cried excitedly, "Only Francis and another boy are flying kites! I hope he wins."

Francis saw his family and smiled at them. His kite was soaring high in the sky. His tactics had changed once again. Now he was on the offensive. He would work his kite in against his opponent's. Since it is necessary to cut in one spot, his opponent would reel in or reel out his string each time.

Francis thought to himself, "I must be careful. In rubbing against his string, I'm weakening my own. For if I cut his, his cuts mine. I'll work on his line about halfway down. Meanwhile, I'll keep reeling my kite in."

He began this new way of attack. He was happy to see that his opponent did not realize what was happening. Time and time again, the string of Francis' kite brushed against the other. Always hitting in the same general area, Francis was slowly reeling in his own string, so that it was a different spot that struck his opponent's line each time.

Once again Francis worked his kite over so that his string met his opponent's. This time the two lines seemed to hold together as if tangled. Then one line drifted free.

"A kite is loose!" the crowd shouted.

Francis' kite straightened out. His string grew taut. His opponent's string dropped to the ground, while the kite, now free, began to disappear on the wind.

"You won, Francis! You won!" shouted Wu Han.

"I'm going to tell Halmani," cried Mary, running down the hill.

"Ai, my son won the kite contest," said the beaming Mr. Kim, to some men standing near him.

"It was a good fight," answered one man.

"This is a proud day for you," said another.

Meanwhile, Francis, flushed with victory, reeled in his kite. His only reply to the loud cheers that sounded about him was a deep blush. He had never been happier on any festival day. After his kite was reeled in, the judge presented him with two large bolts of the best cotton cloth.

"Wait until Halmani sees this!" said Omani as she fingered the cloth her son had given her. "Ai, but she will be very proud of you, Francis."

Arm in arm, Francis and Wu Han strode down the hill to the wrestling field.

"Now, if I can win, it will be a perfect, perfect day," Wu Han said.

"How many more must you wrestle to win?" asked Francis.

"Four. But it's the last one I worry about."

"The last one?"

"Yeh!" said Wu Han. "His name is Ryang Il Tuk."

"Oh, he's good!" exclaimed Francis. "I saw him win last year."

"Yeh! But I've been watching him closely. I think I've learned a few things."

"What have you learned, Wu Han?"

"Watch and see," said Wu Han mysteriously, as the boys reached the wrestling field.

It was not time to resume the wrestling contest, so the two boys sat down in the field to wait. The Dong brothers came over.

"I hear you won the kite contest, Francis. Congratulations!" said Dong One.

"Thank you," said Francis. "How did you make out?"

"I had the bad luck to meet Tuk in the second round," answered Dong One.

"Look at his face and you'll know," added Dong Three.

Dong One's eye and nose were swollen from contact with Tuk's elbow.

"He had a bloody nose, too," said Dong Two, "but our omani stopped it."

"I have no envy of you, Wu Han," said Dong One. "You're liable to meet Tuk at any time now. He's like a tiger."

"Did you ever wrestle a tiger?" asked Dong Two, teasing his brother. "How do you know how it is to wrestle a tiger?"

"Yeh! I wrestled a tiger. I wrestled Tuk," retorted Dong One, feeling his nose.

Just then the head judge called the young wrestlers to the side of the field for the drawing of opponents.

"Good luck, Wu Han!" called Francis.

"Good luck," cried the Dong Boys in unison.

Wu Han did not draw Tuk as an opponent. Nor after he had won, did he draw him on the next round. Wu Han won the quarter-final match, and then the semi-final. Now only he and Tuk were left for the final contest. The old man who had been watching Wu Han in the forenoon spoke to a companion. "This promises to be an excellent match. I have been watching the young man on the right all morning. He uses his intellect. Now, I am a scholar, and I prize intelligence. Here we shall see brain against muscle. But even I cannot predict the outcome. Tuk is as strong as a bull."

The wrestling field was crowded with spectators, gathered to see the final match of the boys' contest. There were few in the crowd who gave Wu Han even an outside chance of winning. The final match differed from the preliminaries in that two falls were necessary to win. The judge called the two boys into the center of the wrestling field and gave them their instructions. Then the contestants stepped several paces back, waiting for the signal to begin.

Tuk strutted around, confident of the outcome. He was many

pounds heavier than Wu Han, and several inches taller. His body was hard and muscular. He had a large following of fans, many of whom were now spreading predictions of certain success.

"When you tear his head off, Tuk, do it gently," cried one.

"It is almost time to eat rice," called another. "Don't keep us here too long."

Wu Han stood in silence. His few friends in the crowd remained silent, too, because they did not wish to get into an argument with Tuk's admirers.

Then the judge gave the command to start the match. Tuk rushed at Wu Han as if anxious to get the business finished. Wu Han stood until Tuk was almost upon him—then quickly jumped aside, while Tuk's momentum carried the attacker beyond. Tuk turned and rushed Wu Han again. Again Wu Han eluded Tuk's grasp. Tuk was beginning to get angry. The laughter of the crowd at his misses was causing him to lose face. The third time he approached Wu Han slowly.

Once more the two boys circled, each looking for an opening. Slowly the circle closed. Tuk made a sudden lunge and caught Wu Han about the head. Wu Han was not taken by surprise, however, because he gave a sudden twist and was free. Tuk, caught off balance, started to take a step back to reorganize himself but Wu Han bent low and seized his leg. There was a jerk, a twist—and Tuk was on his back.

For a moment the crowd stood in stunned silence. Then a great cheer rose. This wrestling match was beginning to prove interesting. The mighty Tuk had lost a fall.

Tuk sat on the ground, red-faced and angry. "It was an accident," he muttered to himself. "I was off balance. It will not happen again!"

The two wrestlers prepared for the second fall. Cheers were now coming from the crowd for Wu Han. There was great excitement. Wu Han saw Francis jumping up and down, urging him on. Mr. Kim made a gesture to indicate that Wu Han shouldn't get overconfident. The cries were suddenly silenced when the judge gave the signal to commence the second round.

This time Tuk did not rush out. Evidently he planned to take no chances. He knew that, in a battle of real strength, he could defeat Wu Han. His strategy called for Wu Han to make the openings. Again the two boys circled each other. They caught hold of each other's wrists and began grappling for closer holds. Tuk clamped an arm lock on Wu Han but was unable to hold it. Back and forth over the grass they struggled. One boy or the other would be forced to one knee, but never to two. Both boys were breathing heavily, and the sweat ran down Tuk's back in little rivulets.

"Hold still and wrestle!" Tuk said to the ever-moving Wu Han.

"Wrestle? Do you know how to wrestle?" Wu Han taunted in return.

Tuk grappled with his opponent carefully. He caught Wu Han's wrist, and suddenly worked into a hammer lock. Deliberately he twisted Wu Han's arm, as if he would snap it in two at the elbow. Flashes of pain shot through Wu Han and he struggled to be free. The hold had forced him to turn his back to Tuk. Suddenly, the arm was free, but it was so numb that it hung limply behind his back.

Tuk had released it on purpose, and as he did so he enfolded Wu Han in his own arms. Tuk's two hands locked across Wu Han's chest; he pulled Wu Han tightly against his body, and started to turn. The spin gathered momentum, and the two boys whirled around. Centrifugal force pulled Wu Han's legs outward. At the moment it did, Tuk released his hands—and Wu Han went flying through the air, landing with a hard jolt. He had lost the second fall.

Now Tuk received the cheers of the crowd. Wu Han sat on the grass, rubbing his numb arm, attempting to restore the circulation. He was breathing in great gasps. He took full advantage of the rest period, and when the judge signaled to commence wrestling again, he felt more like himself. Both he and Tuk were tired, however. There had been many opponents, and both energy and strength were less than when the day started. Both boys began the last round cautiously. The winner of this one would be the champion. Tuk's confidence had been restored, and he taunted Wu Han to stand still. But Wu Han moved in and out as quickly as his weary legs could carry him.

Tuk caught Wu Han's head between his arm and his body. He tightened the head lock, at the same time shoving his shoulder down towards Wu Han's body in an attempt to force Wu Han to both knees. Wu Han put one of his feet on Tuk's left foot and grasped Tuk's other leg. Fearing he would be thrown off balance, Tuk lurched free but in so doing he released his hold sufficiently for Wu Han to escape.

Once again the two opponents circled each other. Again they grappled, and again Tuk emerged with a head lock. Again Wu Han put one foot on Tuk's, and grasped his other leg. Once more Tuk was forced to free himself and release Wu Han.

The next time the two boys caught hold of each other, Wu Han emerged from the struggle with a head lock on Tuk. He put every bit of strength remaining into the pressure he was applying on Tuk's head. Since Wu Han had escaped from the same hold twice before, Tuk decided to follow his opponent's method. He lifted his foot to place it on Wu Han's, and at the same time reached out for Wu Han's other leg. At that instant, Wu Han sank down on one knee. Tuk, groping blindly and still in the head lock, was confused and off balance. Using his knee as a lever, Wu Han threw Tuk to the ground.

A great cheer went up from the crowd. Some of the men who had been watching ran out and lifted Wu Han to their shoulders. Amidst the ringing cries of the spectators, the winner was carried around the field. Tuk, alone and forgotten in defeat, sat dejectedly on the grass. Wu Han was carried back to the judges' platform, to be awarded his prize. The men let him slide to the ground. The head judge came forward, leading a young bullock, or ox, and presented it to Wu Han. Proudly, Wu Han led the ox out through the crowd. The Dong boys and Francis caught up with him.

"You were wonderful!" cried Francis. "Wait until Halmani and Omani see your prize!"

"How I'd have liked to win that!" said Dong One, rubbing

one swollen eye and looking at the ox out of the other. "You certainly repaid Tuk for my eye."

"What did you mean by what you said when we came down from the kite contest?" Francis asked.

"By what I said?" asked Wu Han, puzzled.

"Yeh. You said you thought you had learned something that would help you against Tuk."

"Oh, yeh, I remember now," answered Wu Han. "Every time I had the chance, I watched Tuk this morning. I noticed that, whenever he tried to get a really important hold, he took little, short steps forward, with his right foot always in front. So when I saw him taking those steps this afternoon, I was always prepared. I knew that he did not think quickly, and I thought I might have the chance to trick him."

"Trick him?" asked Dong Two.

"How?" asked Dong One.

"Well, I knew he was stronger than I was. Therefore, I had to get him off balance if I wanted to get a fall. So in the last fall, I allowed him to get two headlocks on me."

"But why?" asked Francis quickly.

"I hoped I could get out of them by attempting to throw him off balance. Probably I couldn't have if Tuk was clever, but losing that first fall frightened him and made him think I might get him off balance. So when I put a headlock on him, I reasoned that he would try to get out of it in the same way. Especially since I had just done that twice previously."

"And he did!" said Dong One.

"Yeh," continued Wu Han. "He did what I expected. And I was ready to catch him unawares. In trying to get me off balance, he forgot he was off balance himself."

It was a happy family that went through Yengwon late that afternoon, on the way back to their farmhouse. Even Mary, who had not won anything, was happy at the success of her brothers. Wu Han had tied the ox to the back of the wagon. Grandmother Kim sat in her usual place. She held the bolts of cloth in her lap.

Proudly, she called to every acquaintance, "See what we are

bringing home from the games. See! This beautiful cloth from China and this strong, young ox!"

Wu Han and Francis, walking beside the wagon, smiled each time she made her little speech. For Grandmother Kim sounded as if she had won the cloth and the ox all by herself.

A PLEA TO THE PRINCE

A score of centuries, O Prince
  Of Peace, has lapsed since,
Within Thy virgin Mother's womb,
  Thou sought 'midst men to come.

The rich, the strong, the fair, the gay,
  Their Saviour sent away;
And only cattle stood beside
  The manger glorified.

And ever since that first Noel,
  The rich are poor, the well
Are ill, the fair are tainted deep,
  And singers needs must weep.

But we, but we, O Infant Christ,
  Have we not sacrificed,
Have we not burned and burned away
  Our pride of yesterday?

Are we not poor and sad and ill?
  Are we not lone and chill?
Oh, come into our midst again,
  So purified by pain!

—AMBROSE NAKAO

FIVE LITTLE SISTERS

by John J. Considine

A poignant stop-off at a leper colony during a trip
through the African continent leaves Father Considine
with never-to-be-forgotten memories.

We crossed the parade, Sister Peter Mary saluting the passers-by
along the way. The Baganda greeting is a very beautiful one,
though unusually complex, and there was a lovely pathos in its
soft and slightly sad lilt as the lepers made the exchange with
the Sister. Each time both parties made a momentary halt and
slight bow.

"Even though we meet a dozen times a day, we must repeat
most faithfully that little litany," Sister explained. "I must confess," she added with a rueful smile, "that as an impatient American I find it trying at times, in the midst of heavy work, to go
through the formality. It is a fine test for one of my temperament
to adapt my ways to the leisurely pace of these people."

We entered the huts of some of the graver cases and found
men and women with flesh lesions that no longer would heal,
and with putrefaction that produced a repellent stench.

"This advanced state of the disease is due to neglect or to the
attempt to hide its existence. In days gone by, there was no hope
of cure; hence, on discovering that they were victims, people

* From *Africa, World of New Men*. Dodd Mead and Company. Copyright,
The Maryknoll Fathers.

sought madly to fight off a revelation of their dread condition. With the disease so common, there is a general knowledge throughout the countryside of tricks of concealment, which can be practiced for a while. There is a local plant that provides a black juice that can be painted over the initial sores quite effectively. Finally when it is too late, the poor creatures are dragged in to us by their relatives."

"The reports of the new medicines must be changing this attitude," I commented.

"Yes, but too late for many folk. Here is Bertha, a lovely old lady who is a burned-out case. As you can see, the disease did great havoc before it was halted. Until infirmity made it impossible for her to move any more, the old dear hobbled to Mass every morning."

Bertha was an aged woman, sitting placidly outside her hut, in the sun. She would hobble no more, for she was handless, footless, and blind.

"Are all these patients from among the peasant farmers?" I asked.

"Father, leprosy knows no boundaries. Some of these patients belong to families that are in comfortable circumstances. The most unique hut on the property is one that harbors five young women who were already professed as Sisters, or part way through their religious training in a novitiate, when they were discovered to have the disease."

"Five religious who are lepers!" I cried. "May we visit them?"

"By all means! Naturally, they do not wear their religious habits. And among the residents of the camp, not all of the five are known for what they are, since some of the young women prefer to live unnoticed."

Raphael Brown in his survey of leprosy reports that 109 Catholic missionaries (64 priests, 6 Brothers, 39 Sisters) contracted leprosy in modern times, and that 42 of them were still living in 1951. The heavy incidence of leprosy in East Africa is high-lighted by this concentration of five religious victims at Nyenga.

The house reserved for the religious was better constructed than the standard huts, but still very simple. As we approached, two of the residents were sitting at the door, chatting.

"I have two American priests who wish to pay you a visit," said Sister Peter Mary in the vernacular. "How many are at home?"

"Modesta is inside, but Perpetua and Francesca are not present," came the reply.

"Please call them for a moment. Fathers, this is Sister Bertha, who was a professed religious for a number of years in Tanganyika before her illness was discovered."

Sister Bertha was spare and hardy. She gave us the impression that she could take care of herself.

"What was her assignment before she came here?" I asked.

"She was a schoolteacher. Now she acts somewhat as the mother of the group, since she is the oldest. Nobody is completely reconciled to being a leper, but from the start she has been very sensible in accepting her lot."

By this time, a gentle little miss had come out of the house and now stood with us."

"This is Modesta," said our guide. "She is from Uganda. She speaks English, Father, so you must give her some good advice. She was a second-year novice in her community, and she made a grand little candidate. She is extremely homesick for her convent; and because she yearns so to go back, she takes her plight badly."

"Modesta," I said, "you must remember that, before we can give anything worth while to God, we must love it so dearly that being deprived of it will break our heart. Isn't that true? You've loved dearly the beautiful life that God gave you, particularly the happy years in the novitiate. Thus you possess the perfect gift to offer Him with the Biblical prayer. 'The Lord giveth and the Lord taketh away; blessed be the name of the Lord.' You really do say that prayer, don't you, Modesta?"

"Father," Modesta replied falteringly, her eyes hauntingly sad, "with my lips and with my heart I sing that prayer a hundred times a day, but with my eyes I cry it all away again."

I felt that if I attempted to say any more I'd be shedding tears myself. Fortunately, Teresa returned at this juncture with Perpetua.

"Perpetua was a postulant in Uganda," came the next report. "She is wonderfully helpful in teaching the children." Perpetua smiled.

"Have you many brothers and sisters at home, Perpetua?" I asked.

The smile turned to stone. I tried similar questions but evoked not a monosyllable of reply.

"Perpetua never talks about home, Father," said Sister apologetically. "You have not yet met Teresa. Teresa is a postulant from Kenya."

Teresa was a pleasant person who wanted to talk. "I dream every day of going back to the Sisters, Father," she said. "It will not be long now."

"The saddest days of all lie ahead for girls like Teresa," explained the Sister as we walked away from the group. "There is such a popular horror of leprosy that it is practically impossible for one known among the people as a victim of leprosy to be effective thereafter as a religious."

Francesca then appeared, large of build and easily the most vital of the five. "Francesca," the Sister said, "is a member of the Luo tribe in Tanganyika and was a postulant at the novitiate of the Maryknoll Sisters in Musoma. She is a fine, sensitive person who feels her affliction dreadfully."

"Francesca," Sister said in the vernacular of the girl, "these two Fathers are from Musoma."

"Oh, I must go back with you!" Francesca cried excitedly. "I must go back with you!" Then she put her face in her hands, and with a great sob cried, "But I am not yet ready."

"Three weeks ago," Sister Peter Mary told us, "the doctor pronounced Francesca negative, and she was walking on air. Yesterday, however, the doctor found her positive again. She went to Mother and wept as if her heart would break. Two Maryknoll Sisters visited her recently from Musoma and made her immensely happy, but the reaction after they left was sad to see."

"Sister," I said, "lepers are very much people, aren't they?"

"Very much, Fathers! One of the most horrible things in all history is the spectacle of the suffering leper driven out by men and cursed as unclean. There are other diseases equally as terrible but none carry the social stigma of leprosy."

"Sister," I commented, "more people should meet lepers. More people should witness the pathetic sight of these five religious, suffering from the disease itself, surely, but suffering especially from what to them is the dreadful catastrophe of being outcasts as unclean."

Raphael Brown quotes advice from the chaplain of a leprosarium in the Philippine Islands: "The worst thing about leprosy is not the disease, but the shame of having it. All too often, victims of leprosy are branded as outcasts, living dead, smitten by God . . . Leprosy is not a crime or a disgrace, but just another ailment of the human body, and should be treated as such. Let us not stigmatize these unfortunate patients."

Sister Catherine Sullivan, a veteran of Carville, gave some good advice in a conference to seminarians in Louisiana: "In your sermons, do not use the word leper as a synonym for sin . . . adding to the burden of misrepresentation and tragic misunderstanding already much too heavy for those who are its victims."

The Fifth International Congress on Leprosy, held at Havana in 1948, recommended that preachers and writers avoid altogether the use of the terms leprosy and leper. It recommended the employment of the term Hansen's Disease. The suggestion has merit, since it is true that the very appellation evokes horror. However, the impracticalness of the suggestion is evident in the fact that the Congress itself, when it met in Madrid 1953, still found it necessary to employ the word Leprosy in its title.

Father Paul and I bade good-by to our five new-made friends in the leper camp at Nyenga. When we drove away, they followed us to the gate. I looked back and saw Modesta and Francesca waving after us disconsolately.

THE MOTHER OF A MARTYR

by James Anthony Walsh

The co-founder of Maryknoll visits the simple home of a widowed French woman and gets a clearer insight into the motives that led her son to give his life for Christ in far-off Indochina.

One day toward the close of May, 1885, a telegram arrived at the Paris Seminary, containing these words, *"Béchet decapité"*— (Béchet beheaded). Five weeks later a communication was received from the Bishop of West Tongking, Indochina, stating that Father Béchet, an alumnus of the Seminary, had indeed been put to death, with three of his catechists and four other native Christians.

Gaspard Claude Béchet belonged to the city of Lyons, France, and was ordained in 1881, in which year he left Paris for his mission. After two years he was threatened with serious lung trouble and was sent out for a change of air to visit at leisure the principal Catholic settlements in the province known as Nam-dinh.

A newly appointed general of this province had just issued a circular promising thirty bars of silver to anyone bringing to him a Frenchman, and Father Béchet was evidently unaware of his danger, when, after Mass on Trinity Sunday, he set out with his companions to walk to a village some miles distant. Just before noon as they were passing through a considerable settlement (Ké Hou) the priest was seized, with his friends, by a group of soldiers who took him to their captain, a sworn enemy of the Christian faith. A short interrogatory was made by the local mandarin, in reply to which Father Béchet answered that he was a missionary-priest, whose duty was simply to preach religion.

It was decided that all should be beheaded, the priest first; but the faithful group of native Christians threw themselves on Father Béchet at the moment of execution, to embrace and protect him. The young priest asked for a few moments' respite, which he used to excite his followers to perfect dispositions. Together the little group recited in loud voice the act of contrition, and Father Béchet gave absolution to his companions. The soldiers then immediately dispatched the native Christians, reserving to the last the death of the priest. They wished to bind his hands, but he asked to be left free to present his neck to the sabre-blows of his executioners. This was done and so numerous were the strokes before the final severance that the neck was literally hacked to pieces.

Such was the martyrdom of Gaspard Béchet, whose "life" I happened to find in an old paper-covered volume at St. John's Seminary in Brighton (Massachusetts). I was attracted to the chapter by the fact that the subject of this biography was a comparatively recent martyr, and also by a "newsy" reference to a street and its number. The article proved indeed a "find," for the author had actually visited the mother of this Gaspard Béchet and had conversed with her on the subject of her son's heroic oblation. I read the sketch eagerly and wrote in my notebook the street address, which, by a singular coincidence, was the *Rue des Machabées*, Lyons.

I was glad, afterwards, to have done so, for unexpectedly, at the end of July in the same year, I found myself in Lyons, where by a stroke of good luck I met the priest who had first called my attention to Gaspard Béchet. My stay in the city was to be very short, but I had made up my mind to look up the *Rue des Machabées*, 17, and learn what I could about Mme. Béchet. Father shook his head, reminding me that the account which I had read was not at all recent and that many years had passed since Gaspard Béchet's death.

We decided, nevertheless, that a visit to the house indicated might prove fruitful, and the next morning three Boston priests said their Masses at Notre Dame, a beautiful votive basilica that from the heights of Fourvière looks down upon the lower city like a mighty sentinel. When we had inspected the marvelous interior, over which Mary presides as Queen, we went out for the customary "little breakfast" at one of the open air cafés bordering the cliff, and planned a busy morning which I had determined should start with a search for Mme. Béchet, if she were still among the living in this great silk city.

I had my way, and we found the street, *Rue des Machabées*, after a short walk. We passed along quickly until we came to No. 17. It was a new apartment house, and the rough brick, fresh from the kiln, had not yet been covered with cement, although several families were evidently installed. There was no answer to our knock, but after some skirmishing in dark courts, which, had I been alone, would have made me feel like a book agent or a thief, we managed to draw a head from one of the lower windows. *"Does Mme. Béchet live here?"* we asked.

And the reply came quickly, accompanied by a suspicious look: *"There is no one of that name in this neighborhood."* By this time other windows were occupied with interested auditors, from whose eyes the final vestiges of sleep were just disappearing, and an impromptu council of the court was held. No one had ever heard of the lady. And no one had ever heard of her son, the martyr. A prophet certainly seems to be without honor in his own country, I reflected. My companions urged me to give up further search, as the old lady was evidently dead and forgotten, but I pleaded for one more try, this time at the parish church, near-by.

It was not difficult to find the church, but the parochial residence—a dignified name for it—was another problem. Finally, after passing under arches centuries old, we stumbled into a court-yard littered with rubbish, and discovered a door, which had the appearance of constant use and suggested an ancient respectability that still lingered on its escutcheon. It proved to be an entrance to the Curé's home and we were admitted without delay. The Curé was not in but his assistant, a young priest, was pleased to give us all the information he possessed, which was little enough. He had heard something of Gaspard Béchet, but could not recollect anyone speaking of his mother as still alive. However, there was, he told us, an old woman around the corner, who had covered the *quartier* for three-quarters of a century and was a veritable directory of persons and happenings in *Saint Just*, as this neighborhood is called. The young priest would run down immediately and interview her, which he did, returning in a few moments with the news, quite commonplace to him, that Mme. Béchet had moved up to *Point du Jour* and was living not far from the house of the Curé there, who would certainly give us more precise directions.

Point du Jour! Was it several miles away? I asked, fearing the prospect of an impossible distance; and I was relieved to learn that ten minutes on the electric cars would take me to the object of my search. But it was time then to leave the heights and my pilgrimage to a martyr's mother must wait.

The sun was not high the next morning as I crossed the Rhone. I passed the Palace of Justice to the foot of Fourvière, and mounted the impressive hillside, just as the city below was stirring into full activity.

At the top as I left the funicular railway, that iron conqueror of rocky heights, I found an electric car marked *Point du Jour*, and entered it in accidental company with a cassocked priest to whom I told the object of my errand. *Gaspard Béchet*—it was a new name to him but he would show me the Curé's house, and within a quarter of an hour I found myself in the presence of an ascetic-looking priest, with long gray hair, whose kindly expression of countenance indicated a beautiful and simple character.

Yes, he could direct me to Mme. Béchet. "Poor woman," he added, "she will be glad to see you and to speak of her son. She lives quite alone across the street and has few friends or acquaintances." The good Curé would have talked at length, but I was pressed for time, so he searched his treasures and drew forth a photograph of Gaspard Béchet's class, which he graciously let me have. Then together we went out into the white light of the hot sun, the old priest walking bare-headed until we had reached a point directly opposite Mme. Béchet's apartment, when he bade me adieu and hastened back to his home.

I found myself before a new building not unlike that which we had visited on the previous day in the *Rue des Machabées* —a typical French apartment house arranged for the poorer classes. I jangled the bell and the face of an old lady appeared at a window on the first floor, a few feet above the street and quite near me. *It was Mme. Béchet.* She looked at me inquiringly, anxiously I thought, and I realized the difficulty which I might have in establishing my identity. Certainly, the sidewalk and a first-story window with gathering spectators did not appeal to me as the proper setting for my inquiry, so I pronounced the good Curé's name, referred to him as my guide, and immediately Mme. Béchet drew in the shutters and the gatebolt clicked its invitation to enter the court, where I found the object of my search ready to listen to my story.

I followed her into her simple apartment, which, so far as I could make out, consisted of a kitchen and one other room, the kitchen serving as a reception room, at least on this occasion. It was still early and Mme. Béchet felt obliged to apologize for some disorder which I took for granted existed, but which, as so often happens, a man would hardly have noticed had not his attention been called to it. I stated the object of my visit—to congratulate her as the mother of a son who had died gloriously in his battle for souls, and to secure further information about her boy with a view, when opportunity should offer, of making his life known as an inspiration to our American youth.

The poor mother's eyes filled with tears. She could not speak at first, but, rising, called my attention to several photographs of Gaspard which hung on the walls of the little room. One taken before his departure from the Paris Seminary, another in the group which the Curé had just given me, and a third in Oriental dress. "Oh, it was hard to lose him," she said at length, "so hard to be old and alone without him!" He was her only child, she told me. She knew that God was good, that she should rejoice in her son's noble example and in the thought of his eternal glory. She was conscious of his help in heaven and that he was waiting to greet her, but time passed *"oh, so slowly!"*—and his bright, cheerful disposition had been such a comfort. Even when he had left her for Tongking, his letters were always looked for so eagerly.

I asked if I might be privileged to see a few of his letters. *"Ah, his letters!"* she replied sadly. She had passed them to friends who wished to read them, and many of those precious letters had never been returned. *"Photographs?"* I could see what she had, and she would look for others, but my visit was so unexpected that she could not think, and if I would call again she would have her house in order and souvenirs at her hand. It seemed to please Mme. Béchet to be told that American Catholics are interested to know more about the Church's modern martyrs, and that her son's letters would doubtless be welcome reading and would do much good for souls.

I promised to try to visit her on my return to Lyons, and as she accompanied me to the door I requested a photograph. Mechanically, she took off her apron and stood in the passage-way, silent and sad, with just the shadow of a friendly and trusting smile, which I felt would be more marked when I should return; and with an *au revoir*, I left this mother of a martyr to think about her unusual visitor.

Later I went back to Lyons, only to find a letter that called me immediately to the north of France, and I was disappointed not to be able to call on Mme. Béchet. Fortunately, however, interested friends, priests well known in Lyons, visited Mme. Béchet on different occasions and secured a large collection of original letters.

Not long after my visit, Mme. Béchet gave up her two rooms and retired to a Home in charge of some Sisters in Lyons. A report reached us soon after that this good soul had already taken its flight to heaven, but later we learned that Mme. Béchet was still living, looking eagerly for the day when God should bring about the reunion for which she had waited so patiently.

THE DEATH OF FATHER PRICE

by John C. Murrett

> Father Price was a missioner in North Carolina when
> he joined Father Walsh to found Maryknoll. Already
> an old man, he led the first mission band to China and
> died a year later.

Father Price found a happy augury in the fact that his operation
had been scheduled for September 8, the Feast of the Nativity
of Our Blessed Mother, and accordingly he noted in the Diary:
"Today, Mother, the doctor decided to have the operation on
Monday, your feast. I shall offer myself to you as a birthday gift.
I wrote letters today, making what preparations I could for the
operation. I do not feel strong, Mother, and my rheumatism
hurts. Help me, Mother. Praise, Mother, to you and Jesus for ever
and ever!"

This is the final entry of the Diary, which had been begun
more than eleven years previously. Faithfully, almost daily, a
"letter," as he called it, had been written to Our Lady! Surely,
then, with entire confidence he could place his hope in her, as he
faced the ordeal that in his case might prove especially trying.
But of far more importance than his own recovery of health was
the desire that, come what might, he would fulfill her wishes.
And if he were to be called home, those prayerful letters had
already prepared the way.

There was yet a last letter to his own sister, which was written
on the day before the operation, but it contained no allusion to

* From *Tar Heel Apostle*. Longmans Green and Co. Copyright, The Maryknoll Fathers.

the impending event. In fact, the reader might think that the missioner was writing from Yeungkong, though he did mention the fact he had been traveling.

He wrote of future plans for the mission in the usual strain, and then went on to say: "I am building a house here—or rather extending the present one—so that we shall be much better situated in the future. Be sure God takes good care of me, and I never lack what is best for me."

One would like to play with the thought that possibly in this instance, when Father Price was actually writing of the construction work on the house at Yeungkong, there was flitting through his mind a thought that the inspired words of Saint Paul might have suggested—"the abode of this earthly habitation being dissolved, an eternal dwelling is prepared in heaven." Certainly he had spent long years in the building for himself of such an eternal dwelling.

But he continued in the letter to express his eagerness for news from home: "Keep me informed about all. Be sure I do not forget any. . . . Write as often as you can. We welcome every little scrap from home. I will write again as soon as I can find time."

On the evening of September 7, the doctor prepared Father Price for the operation, but on the morning of the feast, he offered the Holy Sacrifice of the Mass in the hospital chapel. It was the last time on earth that the Tar Heel apostle would stand at the altar—for his own immolation was at hand, and he was ready.

Later in the morning, the operating-room Sister noticed that Father Price had small chains on his legs and on his arms. She wanted to remove them, fearing that the Protestant doctors in attendance would not understand, but he would not permit her to do so. As a matter of fact, those chains were fastened with little padlocks, and they had no keys to open them. Long since, Father Price had dispensed with the keys!

Sister Eusebé, who was in attendance and to whom we are indebted for much information of these last days, related that, when Father Price was taken to the operating room at nine o'clock, he remembered that it was Our Blessed Mother's feast, and observed, "Today is a nice day to go to heaven."

But the Sister immediately rejoined: "Yes, it is a nice day to go to heaven, but I don't want you to go to heaven today. I should lose my own courage if you were to die."

Evidently the Sister reasoned that, if Father Price could not have a successful operation on Our Blessed Mother's nativity day, then the way would be hard for anyone! The missioner, however, really had a better inkling of his own condition than had the doctors. The Sister whose office it was to prepare Father Price's room for his return from the operation, found a sealed envelope on the little service table. She read the message thereon: "To be opened after my death."

Happenings in the operating room indicated that Father Price had not been far wrong in his view of the possibilities. Sister Eusebé reported: "When the three doctors who operated, opened Father Price's stomach, a great deal of pus came out. The whole stomach was gangrenous. Although the doctors used antiseptics and gave serum to save him, they knew it was useless."

Coming back again to the world of reality, as the effect of the ether left him, Father Price asked, "Is the operation finished?"

In answer the Sister said simply, "Yes, all finished."

Quietly then, and somewhat regretfully, the missioner observed, "I thought I should go to heaven instead of coming back to this bed."

To this the Sister replied, somewhat chidingly: "You mustn't go to heaven just yet! Remember, you have just come to China, and there are many pagan souls waiting here to be converted."

But Father Price had his own view of the situation. "I like to work," he answered, "but I am old—too old to work. All I can do is pray, and surely I can pray better in heaven!" There could be no reply to that.

Then followed three days of patient suffering. The outlook was desperate, since his actual condition was made so clearly known in the operating room; but the Sisters continued to have hope. However, about seven o'clock that third evening (September 11), he grew quite definitely worse, and his doctor was summoned for a special visit. On seeing the condition of Father Price, the doctor made an incision in the abdomen and, finding the patient in such great pain, gave an injection of morphine. Hitherto the sufferer had stoutly refused any such method of relief; but at the earnest insistence of the doctor, he yielded.

Father Price then began to feel somewhat better, but he himself realized that it was at best only a short respite. About eight o'clock he observed to the Sister in attendance, "I feel better, but tomorrow morning I should like to have Father Tour give me Extreme Unction."

To this request, the Sister answered, "Father, you just said that you felt better, and now you want to die!"

In surprise, he asked, "Don't you think I am very sick?" Then with conviction, he affirmed, "My body is dead."

When the Sister kindly reproached him about his anxiety to go to heaven so soon, he answered, with a smile, that it would be a splendid day for the trip to heaven, since the morrow would be the Feast of the Holy Name of Mary.

Rest came during the night, and the patient was able to take some nourishment—in all, three glasses of milk. Through the long vigil, one of the Sisters remained at the bedside. When she took the sufferer's pulse at five o'clock the following morning, she noted that he was very weak. But he remained asleep until seven o'clock, at which time Sister asked him if he wished to receive Holy Communion. He expressed a desire to wait for Father Tour, to whom he was much devoted, but the Sister reminded him that that priest was quite a distance away, and would not arrive until later in the morning. Accordingly, Father Price received Holy Communion at once from Father Lemaire, who was then convalescing in the hospital.

The Sister observed simply, "He received Holy Communion devoutly and prayed like a saint."

As the early morning advanced, Father Price grew weaker and kept asking for Father Tour. Finally the Sister asked him if he would receive Extreme Unction from Father Lemaire. He answered, "Yes, Sister—we have to be ready."

After the anointing, the dying priest grew weaker, and asked the Mother Superior and the Sister who were about the bed to say the Rosary for him. He suffered much—so much that it wrung a cry from him, "Oh, how I suffer!"

"Yes, Father," said the Mother Superior, "you are suffering much, but soon you will be with the Blessed Virgin and Bernadette, whom you so love."

"You think so?" he replied. "Oh, what happiness!"

Truly he was looking forward eagerly to the meeting with the "Holy Mother," as the Chinese affectionately call the Mother whom Our Lord bequeathed from the Cross to mankind.

At nine o'clock, Father Tour, unaware until then of the crisis, arrived at the hospital and hastened at once to the bedside of his sick friend. Father Price greeted him joyfully—overjoyed to see his friend, who had been also his director since his arrival in China the previous year. The two priests were alone for a quarter of an hour. Of this period of Father Price's last day on earth, Father Tour has written:

"His hands and forehead were cold. Had it not been for that, we should have felt no anxiety for the day. He was very quiet and even somewhat hopeful. Still, there was no doubt but that he was sinking. I spoke to him of all things dear to him: of Jesus, Mary, Joseph, of Our Lady of Lourdes, of Bernadette—and he was smiling and giving his assent all the while.

"Then I spoke of Father Walsh and of all the beloved Maryknollers. At each name he lifted his head heavenward and prayed according to the thoughts and intentions I suggested . . . Maryknoll proper, Scranton, San Francisco, Yeungkong."

After about fifteen minutes with Father Tour, the dying priest began to grow painfully weak. He himself knew that it was the end—or rather, the beginning.

"Now," he said quietly, "the time is coming. I am finished. I am going."

"At about nine-thirty," continued Father Tour in his narrative, "I understood that he was sinking more speedily. 'Dear Father Price,' I said, 'you will kindly bless your friend, Father Tour, and in his person, dear Father Walsh and all beloved Maryknollers, won't you?'

The Death of Father Price 435

" 'Most willingly and from the depth of my heart,' he replied.

" 'You offer now your sufferings, and even your life, for the prosperity of your beloved Society, and you pray and will ever pray that they all may do the work of God in a truly apostolic spirit, don't you?'

" 'Most certainly,' he answered.

"And as I bowed before him by the side of his bed, he placed his weak hand on my head and blessed me, making the Sign of the Cross on me."

The end of an apostolate on earth had reached its term. The heroic missioner had gone forth as the laborer in the morning of his youth. Through more than thirty years in the ministry, he had toiled faithfully, enduring "the burden and the heats thereof." Now he had come to the evening. He was going home with the day well spent, ready and eager to render his account to the most loving and understanding of Masters.

"Up to nine-forty-five," continued Father Tour, "he repeated the ejaculations after me, but his tongue was no more free. Until then he always gently smiled at the Holy Name and the name of Maryknoll. I started the prayers for the commendation of the soul—in English—which he seemed to follow throughout.

"When these prayers were over, he could see no more. Then he felt very distressing pain in his wound and moved pitifully to the right and to the left a dozen times, while his breath was more and more hard and scarce. At ten o'clock, he opened wide his eyes and was shaken most painfully. The good Sister on one side and I on the other helped him as best we could—until he breathed his last quite peacefully, after some five minutes of rest."

Thus in far-off China, far from the fields of his youth and earlier priesthood, separated even from the few Maryknoll confreres who had accompanied him, the veteran missioner yielded his heroic soul to his Creator. He died on the day, perhaps the day above all days, which he would have wished, for it was the Feast of the Holy Name of Mary (September 12, 1919), and by the same token, Maryknoll's name day as well! It was the festal day also on which, eight years earlier, he had taken the name "Mary Bernadette" to himself.

Father Price had spent his life in mission work: he had ended it in mission sacrifice. In his own person he had exemplified the complete sacrifice incumbent on the missioner. In China he had not accomplished mission work, so much as he had exemplified the spirit in which mission work must be accomplished: he had gone the whole way in striving to perform it. He had indeed desired and had prayed that this sacrifice might mean the shedding of his own blood, but God had His own plan for the victim.

How fitting that his sacrifice was completed on Mary's name day! He had been one of her favored knights. To her cause—to Maryknoll and to Lourdes—he had given a full measure of devotion. That was his task, and he had striven to fulfill it. Indeed, of only One could it ever be said, "His destined task was completed in His day." But as Father Price lay dying on that far-off field, he could turn lovingly to her—Our Lady of Lourdes—Our Lady of Maryknoll—as she waited to present him to her Divine Son. And gallantly this dying soldier could salute her Son, his own great Captain, with the announcement, *"Mission terminée."*

ONLY A VEIL

Only a veil between me and Thee,
*   Jesus, my Lord;*
A veil of bread it appears to me,
Yet seemeth such that I may not see
*   Jesus, my God.*

Lift not the veil between me and Thee,
*   Jesus, my Lord!*
These eyes of earth can never see
The glory of Thy Divinity,
*   Jesus, my God.*

Keep then the veil between me and Thee,
*   Jesus, my Lord!*
Some day 'twill fall when my soul is free
To gaze on Thee for Eternity,
*   Jesus, my God.*

—JAMES ANTHONY WALSH

CHRIST SPEAKS TO YOU

Selected by James Keller

Nothing could be more fitting than that Our Lord should have the last word in this anthology. So here Christ speaks to you in His own words.

His Claim to Be Heard

1. "I and the Father are one." (John 10, 30)
2. "Amen, amen I say to you, before Abraham was made, I am." (John 8, 58)
3. "I am the way, and the truth, and the life. No man cometh to the Father, but by me." (John 14, 6)
4. "Heaven and earth shall pass, but my words shall not pass." (Matt. 24, 35)
5. "For this was I born, and for this came I into the world, that I should give testimony to the truth. Every one that is of the truth, heareth my voice." (John 18, 37)
6. "I am the light of the world; he that followeth me, walketh not in darkness, but shall have the light of life." (John 8, 12)
7. "Now this is eternal life; that they may know thee, the only true God, and Jesus Christ, whom thou hast sent." (John 17, 3)
8. "I am the resurrection and the life; he that believeth in me, although he be dead, shall live." (John 11, 25)

* From *You Can Change the World*, selected by Father James Keller.

9.   "I am the vine; you the branches: he that abideth in me, and I in him, the same beareth much fruit: for without me you can do nothing." (John 15, 5)

10. "Every plant which my heavenly Father hath not planted, shall be rooted up." (Matt. 15, 13)

11. "Blessed art thou, Simon Bar-Jona: because flesh and blood hath not revealed it to thee, but my Father who is in heaven. And I say to thee: That thou art Peter; and upon this rock I will build my church, and the gates of hell shall not prevail against it. And I will give to thee the keys of the kingdom of heaven. And whatsoever thou shalt bind upon earth, it shall be bound also in heaven: and whatsoever thou shalt loose on earth, it shall be loosed also in heaven." (Matt. 16, 17-19)

12. "And whosoever shall fall on this stone, shall be broken; but on whomsoever it shall fall, it shall grind him to powder." (Matt. 21, 44)

13. "I am the door. By me, if any man enter in, he shall be saved." (John 10, 9)

14. "I am the bread of life; he that cometh to me shall not hunger: and he that believeth in me shall never thirst." (John 6, 35)

15. "Amen, amen I say unto you, Except you eat the flesh of the son of man, and drink his blood, you shall not have life in you. He that eateth my flesh, and drinketh my blood, hath everlasting life; and I will raise him up in the last day. For my flesh is meat indeed: and my blood is drink indeed. He that eateth my flesh, and drinketh my blood, abideth in me, and I in him. As the living Father hath sent me, and I live by the Father; so he that eateth me, the same also shall live by me." (John 6, 54-58)

The Commission to Go

16. "All power is given to me in heaven and earth. Going therefore teach ye all nations: baptizing them in the name of the Father, and of the Son, and of the Holy Ghost. Teaching

them to observe all things whatsoever I have commanded you: and behold I am with you all days even to the consummation of the world." (Matt. 28, 18-20)

17. "Go ye into the whole world, and preach the gospel to every creature. He that believeth and is baptized, shall be saved: but he that believeth not shall be condemned." (Mark 16, 15-16)

18. "As the Father hath sent me, I also send you." (John 20, 21)

19. "You have not chosen me: but I have chosen you; and have appointed you, that you should go and should bring forth fruit, and your fruit should remain." (John 15, 16)

20. "The harvest indeed is great, but the laborers are few. Pray ye therefore the Lord of the harvest, that he send forth laborers into his harvest." (Matt. 9, 37-38)

21. "And other sheep I have, that are not of this fold: them also I must bring, and they shall hear my voice, and there shall be one fold and one shepherd." (John 10, 16)

22. "Come ye after me, and I will make you to be fishers of men." (Matt. 4, 19)

23. "Launch out into the deep, and let down your nets for a draught." (Luke 5, 4)

24. "Fear not: from henceforth thou shalt catch men." (Luke 5, 10)

25. "Behold I send you as sheep in the midst of wolves. Be ye therefore wise as serpents and simple as doves." (Matt. 10, 16)

26. "Let us go into the neighboring towns and cities, that I may preach there also: for to this purpose am I come." (Mark 1, 38)

27. "In this is my Father glorified; that you bring forth very much fruit, and become my disciples." (John 15, 8)

28. "You are the light of the world. A city seated on a mountain cannot be hid. Neither do men light a candle and put it under a bushel, but upon a candlestick, that it may shine to all that are in the house. So let your light shine before men, that they may see your good works and glorify your Father who is in heaven." (Matt. 5, 14-16)

29. "And every one that hath left house, or brethren, or sisters, or father, or mother, or wife, or children, or lands for my name's sake, shall receive a hundred fold, and shall possess life everlasting." (Matt. 19, 29)

By Means of Love

30. "Thou shalt love the Lord thy God with thy whole heart, and with thy whole soul, and with thy whole mind. This is the greatest and the first commandment. And the second is like to this: Thou shalt love thy neighbor as thyself. On these two commandments dependeth the whole law and the prophets." (Matt. 22, 37-40)
31. "A new commandment I give unto you; that you love one another, as I have loved you." (John 13, 34)
32. "This is my commandment, that you love one another, as I have loved you." (John 15, 12)
33. "By this shall all men know that you are my disciples, if you have love one for another." (John 15, 13)
34. "Greater love than this no man hath, that a man lay down his life for his friends." (John 15, 13)
35. "You are my friends, if you do the things that I command you." (John 15, 14)
36. "For the Son of man also is not come to be ministered unto, but to minister, and to give his life a redemption for many." (Mark 10, 45)
37. "You have heard that it hath been said: Thou shalt love thy neighbor, and hate thy enemy. But I say to you: Love your enemies: do good to them that hate you: and pray for them that persecute you and calumniate you. That you may be the children of your Father who is in heaven, who maketh his sun to rise upon the good and bad, and raineth upon the just and the unjust." (Matt. 5, 43-45)
38. "If you love them that love you, what reward shall you have? Do not even the publicans this? And if you salute your

brethren only, what do you more? Do not also the heathens this?" (Matt. 5, 46-47)

39. "As long as you did it to one of these my least brethren, you did it to me." (Matt. 25, 40)

40. "Dost thou see this woman? I entered into thy house, thou gavest me no water for my feet; but she with tears hath washed my feet, and with her hairs hath wiped them. Thou gavest me no kiss; but she, since she came in, hath not ceased to kiss my feet. My head with oil thou didst not anoint; but she with ointment hath anointed my feet. Wherefore I say to thee: Many sins are forgiven her, because she hath loved much. But to whom less is forgiven, he loveth less." (Luke 7, 44-47)

41. "Amen, I say to you, this poor widow hath cast in more than all they who have cast into the treasury: For all they did cast in of their abundance; but she of her want cast in all she had, even her whole living." (Mark 12, 43-44)

42. "Father, forgive them, for they know not what they do." (Luke 23, 34)

43. "They that are in health need not a physician, but they that are ill. Go then and learn what this meaneth: I will have mercy and not sacrifice. For I am not come to call the just, but sinners." (Matt. 9, 12-13)

44. "The son of man is come to save that which was lost." (Matt. 18, 11)

45. "The son of man came not to destroy souls, but to save." (Luke 9, 56)

46. "So I say to you, there shall be joy before the angels of God upon one sinner doing penance." (Luke 15, 10)

47. "Even so it is not the will of your Father, who is in heaven, that one of these little ones should perish." (Matt. 18, 14)

48. "The bruised reed he shall not break; and smoking flax he shall not extinguish: till he send forth judgment unto victory." (Matt. 12, 20)

49. "John the Baptist came neither eating bread nor drinking wine; and you say: He hath a devil. The Son of man is come

eating and drinking; and you say: Behold a man that is a glutton and drinker of wine, a friend of publicans and sinners." (Luke 7, 33-34)

50. "Woman, where are they that accused thee? Hath no man condemned thee?" Who said: "No man, Lord." And Jesus said: "Neither will I condemn thee. Go, and sin no more." (John 8, 10-11)

51   "Bring forth quickly the first robe, and put it on him and put a ring on his hand, and shoes on his feet; And bring hither the fatted calf, and kill it, and let us eat and make merry: Because this my son was dead, and is come to life again: was lost, and is found. And they began to be merry." (Luke 15, 22-24)

The Gain of Suffering

52. "Remember my word that I said to you: The servant is not greater than his master. If they have persecuted me, they will also persecute you: if they have kept my word, they will keep yours also." (John 15, 20)

53. "If the world hate you, know ye that it hath hated me before you." (John 15, 18)

54. "I have given them thy word, and the world hath hated them, because they are not of the world; as I also am not of the world. I pray not that thou shouldst take them out of the world, but that thou shouldst keep them from evil." (John 17, 14-15)

55. "Amen, amen I say to you, that you shall lament and weep, but the world shall rejoice; and you shall be made sorrowful, but your sorrow shall be turned into joy. A woman when she is in labor, hath sorrow, because her hour is come; but when she hath brought forth the child, she remembereth no more the anguish, for joy that a man is born into the world. So also you now indeed have sorrow; but I will see you again, and your heart shall rejoice; and your joy no man shall take from you." (John 16, 20-22)

56. "Then shall they deliver you up to be afflicted, and shall put you to death: and you shall be hated by all nations for my name's sake. And then shall many be scandalized: and shall betray one another: and shall hate one another." (Matt. 24, 9-10)

57. "These things I have spoken to you, that in me you may have peace. In the world you shall have distress: but have confidence, I have overcome the world." (John 16, 33)

58. "He that loveth his life shall lose it; and he that hateth his life in this world, keepeth it unto life eternal." (John 12, 25)

59. "If any man will come after me, let him deny himself, and take up his cross daily, and follow me." (Luke 9, 23)

60. "He that findeth his life, shall lose it: and he that shall lose his life for me, shall find it." (Matt. 10, 39)

61. "Amen, amen I say to you, unless the grain of wheat falling into the ground die, itself remaineth alone; but if it die, it bringeth forth much fruit." (John 12, 24-25)

62. "And if thy right eye scandalize thee, pluck it out and cast it from thee. For it is expedient for thee that one of thy members should perish, rather than thy whole body be cast into hell." (Matt. 5, 29)

63. "The kingdom of heaven suffereth violence and the violent bear it away." (Matt. 11, 12)

64. "You have heard that it was said to them of old: Thou shalt not commit adultery. But I say to you, that whosoever shall look on a woman to lust after her, hath already committed adultery with her in his heart." (Matt. 5, 27-28)

65. "Blessed are the clean of heart: for they shall see God." (Matt. 5, 8)

66. "Blessed are the poor in spirit: for theirs is the kingdom of heaven." (Matt. 5, 3)

67. "Blessed are they that hunger and thirst after justice: for they shall have their fill." (Matt. 5, 6)

68. "Blessed are they that suffer persecution for justice' sake: for theirs is the kingdom of heaven." (Matt. 5, 10)

69. "Blessed are ye when they shall revile you, and persecute you, and speak all that is evil against you, untruly, for my

sake: Be glad and rejoice, for your reward is very great in heaven. For so they persecuted the prophets that were before you." (Matt. 5, 11-12)

70. "And fear ye not them that kill the body, and are not able to kill the soul: but rather fear him that can destroy both soul and body in hell. (Matt. 10, 28)

71. "But he that shall persevere to the end, he shall be saved." (Matt. 24, 13)

THE MARYKNOLL HYMN

To raise up sterling men for God,
  Maryknoll, our Maryknoll,
Whose blood may stain the heathen sod,
  Maryknoll, fair Maryknoll,
This is thy aim, thy sacred call,
To bring Christ's name and grace to all.
  God speed thee on to save man's soul,
  O House of God, our Maryknoll!

O Mary, the Apostles' Queen,
  For Maryknoll, thy Maryknoll,
Throughout this country do thou glean
  For Maryknoll, thy Maryknoll,
Vocations to the darkened East,—
Who need the offering hand of priest
  To bless them, ere Death sounds its toll,—
  From Maryknoll, thy Maryknoll.

—FRANCIS X. FORD